Mathematics 3

Strategic Intervention Guide

 Macmillan/McGraw-Hill Glencoe

The McGraw·Hill Companies

**Macmillan
McGraw-Hill**

Send all inquiries to:
Macmillan/McGraw-Hill
8787 Orion Place
Columbus, OH 43240-4027

ISBN: 978-0-02-106156-3
MHID: 0-02-106156-4

Printed in the United States of America.

5 6 7 8 9 10 021 10 09 08

GRADE 3
Contents

Strand Assessment
Each strand assessment has a student activity page and a teacher page with instruction and skills chart.

Measurement and Geometry

Skill Builder Lessons and Activities

Number Sense

Patterns

Operations

Place Value

Measurement and Geometry

Data Collecting and Probability

To the Teacher

Welcome to the *Macmillan/McGraw-Hill Strategic Intervention Guide.* The goal of these materials is to provide assessment and instruction in the prerequisite skills that some of your students need to be successful in math at this grade level.

For each topic in the student text, there is an inventory test. You will find these inventory tests as blackline masters on the "A" pages in this Guide. The results of these assessments will help you diagnose any gaps in student knowledge. You can then provide students with materials needed to reteach as appropriate.

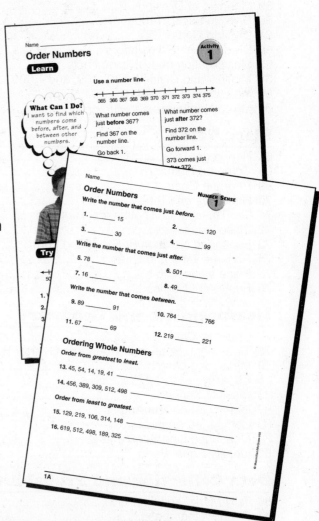

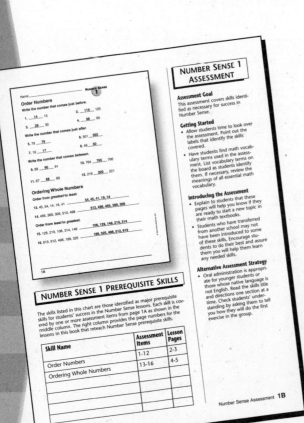

The charts found on the "B" pages following the blackline masters will prescribe a special *Skill Builder* lesson in the handbook for each test item that a student answers incorrectly.

The *Skill Builder* lessons, in blackline format, are presented in language that is simple and direct. The lessons are highly visual and have been designed to keep reading to a minimum. The blackline masters are in the last section of this book, pages 2–145.

The *Learn* section begins with a student asking *What Can I Do?* This section provides stepped-out models and one or more strategies to help bridge any gaps in the student's knowledge. Following this is *Try It*, a section of guided practice, and *Power Practice*, a section containing exercises to ensure that your students acquire the math power they need to be successful in each chapter of their math textbook.

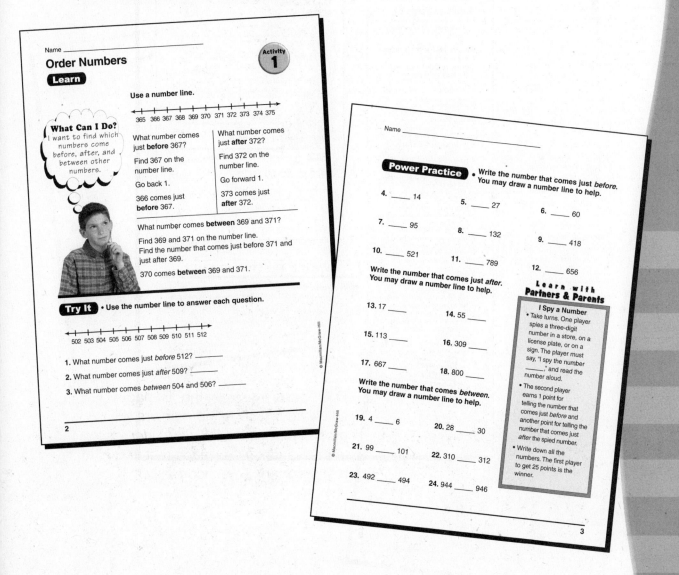

The Teacher Guide, found on the "T" pages, provides a complete lesson plan for each *Skill Builder*. Each *Skill Builder* lesson plan includes a lesson objective, *Getting Started* activities, teaching suggestions, and questions to check the student's understanding. There is also a section called *What If the Student Can't*, which offers additional activities in case a student needs more support in mastering an essential prerequisite skill or lacks the understanding needed to complete the *Skill Builder* exercises successfully.

Many of the *Skill Builder* lessons plans have a feature called *Learn with Partners & Parents*. This activity is intended for students to use at home with parents or siblings or at school with a classmate-partner to practice a math skill in a game-like setting.

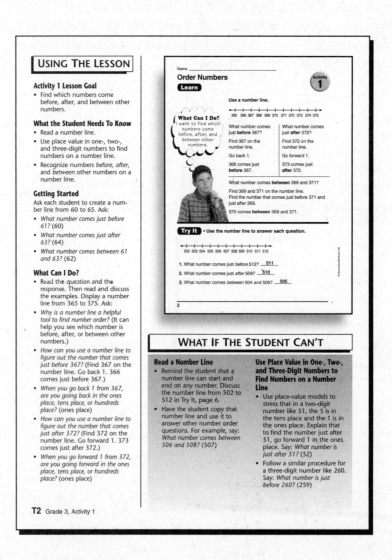

STRAND ASSESSMENT

Order Numbers

Write the number that comes just _before_.

1. _____ 15   **2.** _____ 120

3. _____ 30   **4.** _____ 99

Write the number that comes just _after_.

5. 78 _____   **6.** 501 _____

7. 16 _____   **8.** 49 _____

Write the number that comes _between_.

9. 89 _____ 91   **10.** 764 _____ 766

11. 67 _____ 69   **12.** 219 _____ 221

Ordering Whole Numbers

Order from _greatest_ to _least_.

13. 45, 54, 14, 19, 41 _____

14. 456, 389, 309, 512, 498 _____

Order from _least_ to _greatest_.

15. 129, 219, 106, 314, 148 _____

16. 619, 512, 498, 189, 325 _____

Name_____

Order Numbers

Write the number that comes just *before*.

1. _____ 15   2. _____ 120

3. _____ 30   4. _____ 99

Write the number that comes just *after*.

5. 78 _____   6. 501_____

7. 16 _____   8. 49_____

Write the number that comes *between*.

9. 89 _____ 91   10. 764 _____ 766

11. 67 _____ 69   12. 219 _____ 221

Ordering Whole Numbers

Order from *greatest* to *least*.

13. 45, 54, 14, 19, 41 _____

14. 456, 389, 309, 512, 498 _____

Order from *least* to *greatest*.

15. 129, 219, 106, 314, 148 _____

16. 619, 512, 498, 189, 325 _____

© Macmillan/McGraw-Hill

1A

NUMBER SENSE 1 PREREQUISITE SKILLS

The skills listed in this chart are those identified as major prerequisite skills for students' success in the Number Sense lessons. Each skill is covered by one or more assessment items from page 1A as shown in the middle column. The right column provides the page numbers for the lessons in this book that reteach Number Sense prerequisite skills.

Skill Name	Assessment Items	Lesson Pages
Order Numbers	1-12	T2-T3
Ordering Whole Numbers	13-16	T4-T5

Assessment Goal

This assessment covers skills identified as necessary for success in Number Sense.

Getting Started

- Allow students time to look over the assessment. Point out the labels that identify the skills covered.

- Have students find math vocabulary terms used in the assessment. List vocabulary terms on the board as students identify them. If necessary, review the meanings of all essential math vocabulary.

Introducing the Assessment

- Explain to students that these pages will help you know if they are ready to start a new topic in their math textbooks.

- Students who have transferred from another school may not have been introduced to some of these skills. Encourage students to do their best and assure them you will help them learn any needed skills.

Alternative Assessment Strategy

- Oral administration is appropriate for younger students or those whose native language is not English. Read the skills title and directions one section at a time. Check students' understanding by asking them to tell you how they will do the first exercise in the group.

Name _____

Rounding

Choose the number that correctly completes each sentence.

1. When _____ is rounded to the nearest ten, it rounds to 70.

| 57 | 67 | 76 | 79 |

2. When _____ is rounded to the nearest hundred, it rounds to 400.

| 349 | 286 | 394 | 451 |

3. When _____ is rounded to the nearest thousand, it rounds to 6,000.

| 5,137 | 6,477 | 4,985 | 5,324 |

Round to Tens, Hundreds, and Thousands

Round to the nearest *ten*.

4. 68 _____   **5.** 24 _____   **6.** 76 _____

7. 32 _____   **8.** 89 _____   **9.** 11 _____

Round to the nearest *hundred*.

10. 135 _____   **11.** 819 _____   **12.** 462 _____

13. 210 _____   **14.** 786 _____   **15.** 365 _____

Round to the nearest *thousand*.

16. 3,901 _____   **17.** 5,537 _____   **18.** 4,444 _____

19. 1,121 _____   **20.** 3,289 _____   **21.** 6,731 _____

Rounding

Choose the number that correctly completes each sentence.

1. When _____ is rounded to the nearest ten, it rounds to 70.

    57   67   76   79

2. When _____ is rounded to the nearest hundred, it rounds to 400.

    349   286   394   451

3. When _____ is rounded to the nearest thousand, it rounds to 6,000.

    5,137   6,477   4,985   5,324

Round to Tens, Hundreds, and Thousands

Round to the nearest *ten*.

4. 68 _____   **5.** 24 _____   **6.** 76 _____

7. 32 _____   **8.** 89 _____   **9.** 11 _____

Round to the nearest *hundred*.

10. 135 _____   **11.** 819 _____   **12.** 462 _____

13. 210 _____   **14.** 786 _____   **15.** 365 _____

Round to the nearest *thousand*.

16. 3,901 _____   **17.** 5,537 _____   **18.** 4,444 _____

19. 1,121 _____   **20.** 3,289 _____   **21.** 6,731 _____

© Macmillan/McGraw-Hill

2A

NUMBER SENSE 2 PREREQUISITE SKILLS

The skills listed in this chart are those identified as major prerequisite skills for students' success in the Number Sense lessons. Each skill is covered by one or more assessment items from page 2A as shown in the middle column. The right column provides the page numbers for the lessons in this book that reteach the Number Sense prerequisite skills.

Skill Name	Assessment Items	Lesson Pages
Rounding	1-3	T10-T11
Round to the Nearest Ten	4-9	T6-T7
Round to Tens, Hundreds, and Thousands	4-21	T8-T9

NUMBER SENSE 2 ASSESSMENT

Assessment Goal

This assessment covers skills identified as necessary for success in Number Sense.

Getting Started

- Allow students time to look over the assessment. Point out the labels that identify the skills covered.

- Have students find math vocabulary terms used in the assessment. List vocabulary terms on the board as students identify them. If necessary, review the meanings of all essential math vocabulary.

Introducing the Assessment

- Explain to students that these pages will help you know if they are ready to start a new topic in their math textbooks.

- Students who have transferred from another school may not have been introduced to some of these skills. Encourage students to do their best and assure them you will help them learn any needed skills.

Alternative Assessment Strategy

- Oral administration is appropriate for younger students or those whose native language is not English. Read the skills title and directions one section at a time. Check students' understanding by asking them to tell you how they will do the first exercise in the group.

Name_____

Round to the Nearest Ten, Hundred, or Thousand

Write which two tens the number is between.
Round to the nearest *ten*.

1. 72 is between _____ and _____.   72 rounds to _____.

2. 16 is between _____ and _____.   16 rounds to _____.

Write which two hundreds the number is between.
Round to the nearest *hundred*.

3. 159 is between _____ and _____.   159 rounds to _____.

4. 546 is between _____ and _____.   546 rounds to _____.

Write which two thousands the number is between.
Round to the nearest *thousand*.

5. 5,399 is between _____ and _____.   5,399 rounds to _____.

6. 8,601 is between _____ and _____.   8,601 rounds to _____.

Comparing Numbers

Use the number line to compare each pair of numbers.
Write > or <.

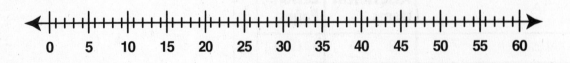

7. 47 ◯ 39   **8.** 15 ◯ 51   **9.** 53 ◯ 35

Round to the Nearest Ten, Hundred, or Thousand

Write which two tens the number is between.
Round to the nearest _ten_.

1. 72 is between _____ and _____.   72 rounds to _____.

2. 16 is between _____ and _____.   16 rounds to _____.

Write which two hundreds the number is between.
Round to the nearest _hundred_.

3. 159 is between _____ and _____.   159 rounds to _____.

4. 546 is between _____ and _____.   546 rounds to _____.

Write which two thousands the number is between.
Round to the nearest _thousand_.

5. 5,399 is between _____ and _____.   5,399 rounds to _____.

6. 8,601 is between _____ and _____.   8,601 rounds to _____.

Comparing Numbers

Use the number line to compare each pair of numbers.
Write > or <.

0 5 10 15 20 25 30 35 40 45 50 55 60

© Macmillan/McGraw-Hill

7. 47 ◯ 39   **8.** 15 ◯ 51   **9.** 53 ◯ 35

3A

NUMBER SENSE 3 PREREQUISITE SKILLS

The skills listed in this chart are those identified as major prerequisite skills for students' success in the Number Sense lessons. Each skill is covered by one or more assessment items from page 3A as shown in the middle column. The right column provides the page numbers for the lessons in this book that reteach the Number Sense prerequisite skills.

Skill Name	Assessment Items	Lesson Pages
Round to the Nearest Ten	1-2	T6-T7
Round to the Nearest Ten, Hundred, or Thousand	1-6	T8-T9
Compare Numbers	7-9	T12-T13

Assessment Goal

This assessment covers skills identified as necessary for success in Number Sense.

Getting Started

• Allow students time to look over the assessment. Point out the labels that identify the skills covered.

• Have students find math vocabulary terms used in the assessment. List vocabulary terms on the board as students identify them. If necessary, review the meanings of all essential math vocabulary.

Introducing the Assessment

• Explain to students that these pages will help you know if they are ready to start a new topic in their math textbooks.

• Students who have transferred from another school may not have been introduced to some of these skills. Encourage students to do their best and assure them you will help them learn any needed skills.

Alternative Assessment Strategy

• Oral administration is appropriate for younger students or those whose native language is not English. Read the skills title and directions one section at a time. Check students' understanding by asking them to tell you how they will do the first exercise in the group.

Count On

Complete each addition pattern.

1. 3, 4, 5, 6, _____, _____

2. 236, 237, 238, 239, _____, _____

3. 10, 20, 30, 40, _____, _____

4. 34, 36, 38, 40, _____, _____

5. 15, 20, 25, 30, _____, _____

6. 40, 50, 60, 70, _____, _____

Skip Count

**Each pattern is a skip counting pattern.
Write the missing number in each pattern.**

7. 2, 4, _____, 8, 10

8. 3, _____, 9, 12, 15

9. 5, 10, 15, _____, 25

10. _____, 8, 12, 16, 20

11. 10, 20, 30, _____, 50

12. 14, 16, 18, _____, 22

Count Back

Complete each subtraction pattern.

13. 10, 9, 8, 7, _____, _____

14. 35, 34, 33, 32, _____, _____

15. 403, 402, 401, 400, _____, _____

16. 29, 28, 27, 26, _____, _____

17. 41, 40, 39, 38, _____, _____

Count On

Complete each addition pattern.

1. 3, 4, 5, 6, _____, _____   **2.** 236, 237, 238, 239, _____, _____

3. 10, 20, 30, 40, _____, _____   **4.** 34, 36, 38, 40, _____, _____

5. 15, 20, 25, 30, _____, _____   **6.** 40, 50, 60, 70, _____, _____

Skip Count

Each pattern is a skip counting pattern.
Write the missing number in each pattern.

7. 2, 4, _____, 8, 10   **8.** 3, _____, 9, 12, 15

9. 5, 10, 15, _____, 25   **10.** _____, 8, 12, 16, 20

11. 10, 20, 30, _____, 50   **12.** 14, 16, 18, _____, 22

Count Back

Complete each subtraction pattern.

13. 10, 9, 8, 7, _____, _____

14. 35, 34, 33, 32, _____, _____

15. 403, 402, 401, 400, _____, _____

16. 29, 28, 27, 26, _____, _____

17. 41, 40, 39, 38, _____, _____

4A

PATTERNS 1 PREREQUISITE SKILLS

The skills listed in this chart are those identified as major prerequisite skills for students' success in the Patterns lessons. Each skill is covered by one or more assessment items from page 4A as shown in the middle column. The right column provides the page numbers for the lessons in this book that reteach Patterns prerequisite skills.

Skill Name	Assessment Items	Lesson Pages
Count On	1-6	T14-T15
Skip Count	7-12	T18-T19
Count Back	13-17	T16-T17

PATTERNS 1 ASSESSMENT

Assessment Goal

This assessment covers skills identified as necessary for success in Patterns.

Getting Started

- Allow students time to look over the assessment. Point out the labels that identify the skills covered.

- Have students find math vocabulary terms used in the assessment. List vocabulary terms on the board as students identify them. If necessary, review the meanings of all essential math vocabulary.

Introducing the Assessment

- Explain to students that these pages will help you know if they are ready to start a new topic in their math textbooks.

- Students who have transferred from another school may not have been introduced to some of these skills. Encourage students to do their best and assure them you will help them learn any needed skills.

Alternative Assessment Strategy

- Oral administration is appropriate for younger students or those whose native language is not English. Read the skills title and directions one section at a time. Check students' understanding by asking them to tell you how they will do the first exercise in the group.

Skip Count by 5s

Skip count by 5s. Write the next two numbers in each pattern.

1. 5, 10, 15, 20, _____, _____   **2.** 15, 20, 25, 30, _____, _____

3. 30, 35, 40, 45, _____, _____   **4.** 25, 30, 35, 40, _____, _____

5. 20, 25, 30, 35, _____, _____   **6.** 45, 50, 55, 60, _____, _____

Skip Count Backward

Complete each skip counting pattern.

7. 56, 49, 42, ___, ___, ___   **8.** 72, 63, ___, 45, ___

Each pattern is a skip counting pattern. Write the next number in each pattern.

9. 36, 30, 24, 18, _____   **10.** 40, 36, 32, 28, _____

Ordinal Numbers

Start from the left. Name the correct place of the shaded object. Circle a, b, c, or d.

11.

a. first

b. second

c. third

d. fourth

12.

a. fifth

b. sixth

c. seventh

d. eighth

Name_____

Skip Count by 5s

Skip count by 5s. Write the next two numbers in each pattern.

1. 5, 10, 15, 20, ____, ____   **2.** 15, 20, 25, 30, ____, ____

3. 30, 35, 40, 45, ____, ____   **4.** 25, 30, 35, 40, ____, ____

5. 20, 25, 30, 35, ____, ____   **6.** 45, 50, 55, 60, ____, ____

Skip Count Backward

Complete each skip counting pattern.

7. 56, 49, 42, ___, ___, ___   **8.** 72, 63, ___, 45, ___

Each pattern is a skip counting pattern. Write the next number in each pattern.

9. 36, 30, 24, 18, ____   **10.** 40, 36, 32, 28, ____

Ordinal Numbers

Start from the left. Name the correct place of the shaded object. Circle a, b, c, or d.

11.

12.

© Macmillan/McGraw-Hill

a. first   **a.** fifth

b. second   **b.** sixth

c. third   **c.** seventh

d. fourth   **d.** eighth

5A

PATTERNS 2 PREREQUISITE SKILLS

The skills listed in this chart are those identified as major prerequisite skills for students' success in the Patterns lessons. Each skill is covered by one or more assessment items from page 5A as shown in the middle column. The right column provides the page numbers for the lessons in this book that reteach Patterns prerequisite skills.

Skill Name	Assessment Items	Lesson Pages
Skip Count by 5s	1-6	T18
Skip Count Backward	7-10	T20-T21
Ordinal Numbers	11-12	T19

PATTERNS 2 ASSESSMENT

Assessment Goal

This assessment covers skills identified as necessary for success in Patterns.

Getting Started

- Allow students time to look over the assessment. Point out the labels that identify the skills covered.

- Have students find math vocabulary terms used in the assessment. List vocabulary terms on the board as students identify them. If necessary, review the meanings of all essential math vocabulary.

Introducing the Assessment

- Explain to students that these pages will help you know if they are ready to start a new topic in their math textbooks.

- Students who have transferred from another school may not have been introduced to some of these skills. Encourage students to do their best and assure them you will help them learn any needed skills.

Alternative Assessment Strategy

- Oral administration is appropriate for younger students or those whose native language is not English. Read the skills title and directions one section at a time. Check students' understanding by asking them to tell you how they will do the first exercise in the group.

Name ________________________________

PATTERNS 3

Patterns

Complete each pattern.

1. 20, 40, 60, 80, _____

2. 50, 100, 150, 200, _____

3. 10, 20, 30, _____

4. 2, 4, 6, 8, _____

5. 3, 6, 9, 12, _____

6. 4, 8, 12, 16, _____

7. 30, 60, 90, _____

8. 5, 10, 15, 20, _____

9. 300, 600, 900, 1,200, _____

10. 700, 1,400, 2,100, 2,800, _____

Draw what the next figure in the pattern could be.

11. ○○○○○●,

○○○○●●,

○○○●●●,

○○○○○○

____

12. ▲▲▲▲▲▲▲△,

▲▲▲▲▲▲△△,

▲▲▲▲▲△△△,

△△△△△△△△

Name _____

Patterns

Complete each pattern.

1. 20, 40, 60, 80, _____   2. 50, 100, 150, 200, _____

3. 10, 20, 30, _____   4. 2, 4, 6, 8, _____

5. 3, 6, 9, 12, _____   6. 4, 8, 12, 16, _____

7. 30, 60, 90, _____   8. 5, 10, 15, 20, _____

9. 300, 600, 900, 1,200, _____

10. 700, 1,400, 2,100, 2,800, _____

Draw what the next figure in the pattern could be.

11. ○○○○○● ,

○○○○●● ,

○○○●●● ,

○○○○○○

_____

12. ▲▲▲▲▲▲▲△ ,

▲▲▲▲▲▲△△ ,

▲▲▲▲▲△△△ ,

△△△△△△△△

_____

© Macmillan/McGraw-Hill

6A

PATTERNS 3 PREREQUISITE SKILLS

The skills listed in this chart are those identified as major prerequisite skills for students' success in the Patterns lessons. Each skill is covered by one or more assessment items from page 6A as shown in the middle column. The right column provides the page numbers for the lessons in this book that reteach the Pattterns prerequisite skills.

Skill Name	Assessment Items	Lesson Pages
Patterns	1-12	T22-T23

PATTERNS 3 ASSESSMENT

Assessment Goal

This assessment covers skills identified as necessary for success in Patterns.

Getting Started

- Allow students time to look over the assessment. Point out the labels that identify the skills covered.

- Have students find math vocabulary terms used in the assessment. List vocabulary terms on the board as students identify them. If necessary, review the meanings of all essential math vocabulary.

Introducing the Assessment

- Explain to students that these pages will help you know if they are ready to start a new topic in their math textbooks.

- Students who have transferred from another school may not have been introduced to some of these skills. Encourage students to do their best and assure them you will help them learn any needed skills.

Alternative Assessment Strategy

- Oral administration is appropriate for younger students or those whose native language is not English. Read the skills title and directions one section at a time. Check students' understanding by asking them to tell you how they will do the first exercise in the group.

Addition Facts to 20

Add.

1. 7 + 4 = _____   **2.** 4 + 5 = _____   **3.** 8 + 6 = _____

4. 15 + 4 = _____   **5.** 9 + 8 = _____   **6.** 10 + 7 = _____

Add Two-Digit Numbers

Add.

7. 25   **8.** 57   **9.** 64
    + 31   + 42   + 14

10. 76   **11.** 44   **12.** 27
    + 18   + 37   + 51

Add 2 or More One- or Two- Digit Numbers

Add.

13. 4 + 7 + 8 + 5 = _____

14. 22 + 6 + 31 = _____

15. 35 + 29 + 18 = _____

16. 13 + 20 + 28 + 31 = _____

17. 14   **18.** 15
    25   22
    19   8
    + 31   + 13

Name _____

Addition Facts to 20

**OPERATIONS
1**

Add.

1. $7 + 4 =$ _____ **2.** $4 + 5 =$ _____ **3.** $8 + 6 =$ _____

4. $15 + 4 =$ _____ **5.** $9 + 8 =$ _____ **6.** $10 + 7 =$ _____

Add Two-Digit Numbers

Add.

7. 25
       + 31

8. 57
       + 42

9. 64
       + 14

10. 76
        + 18

11. 44
        + 37

12. 27
        + 51

Add 2 or More One- or Two- Digit Numbers

Add.

13. $4 + 7 + 8 + 5 =$ _____

14. $22 + 6 + 31 =$ _____

15. $35 + 29 + 18 =$ _____

16. $13 + 20 + 28 + 31 =$ _____

17. 14
         25
         19
        + 31

18. 15
         22
          8
        + 13

© Macmillan/McGraw-Hill

7A

OPERATIONS 1 PREREQUISITE SKILLS

The skills listed in this chart are those identified as major prerequisite skills for students' success in the Operations lessons. Each skill is covered by one or more assessment items from page 7A as shown in the middle column. The right column provides the page numbers for the lessons in this book that reteach the Operations prerequisite skills.

Skill Name	Assessment Items	Lesson Pages
Addition Facts to 20	1-6	T24-T25
Add Two-Digit Numbers	7-12	T26-T27
Add 2 or More One- or Two-Digit Numbers	13-18	T28-T29

OPERATIONS 1 ASSESSMENT

Assessment Goal

This assessment covers skills identified as necessary for success in Operations.

Getting Started

- Allow students time to look over the assessment. Point out the labels that identify the skills covered.

- Have students find math vocabulary terms used in the assessment. List vocabulary terms on the board as students identify them. If necessary, review the meanings of all essential math vocabulary.

Introducing the Assessment

- Explain to students that these pages will help you know if they are ready to start a new topic in their math textbooks.

- Students who have transferred from another school may not have been introduced to some of these skills. Encourage students to do their best and assure them you will help them learn any needed skills.

Alternative Assessment Strategy

- Oral administration is appropriate for younger students or those whose native language is not English. Read the skills title and directions one section at a time. Check students' understanding by asking them to tell you how they will do the first exercise in the group.

OPERATIONS 2

Basic Addition Facts

Find each sum.

1. $5 + 0 =$ _____

2. $\quad 4$
$\quad \underline{+\ 7}$

3. $12 + 7 =$ _____

4. $\quad 9$
$\quad \underline{+\ 6}$

Addition Patterns

Add. Use mental math.

5. $40 + 30 =$ _____

6. $600 + 500 =$ _____

7. $50 + 90 =$ _____

Using an Addition Table

Find each sum using the addition table.

+	0	1	2	3	4	5	6	7	8	9
0	0	1	2	3	4	5	6	7	8	9
1	1	2	3	4	5	6	7	8	9	10
2	2	3	4	5	6	7	8	9	10	11
3	3	4	5	6	7	8	9	10	11	12
4	4	5	6	7	8	9	10	11	12	13
5	5	6	7	8	9	10	11	12	13	14
6	6	7	8	9	10	11	12	13	14	15
7	7	8	9	10	11	12	13	14	15	16
8	8	9	10	11	12	13	14	15	16	17
9	9	10	11	12	13	14	15	16	17	18

8. $8 + 7 =$ _____   **9.** $15 + 3 =$ _____   **10.** $9 + 6 =$ _____

Basic Addition Facts

Find each sum.

1. 5 + 0 = _____

2. 　4
　+ 7

3. 12 + 7 = _____

4. 　9
　+ 6

Addition Patterns

Add. Use mental math.

5. 40 + 30 = _____

6. 600 + 500 = _____

7. 50 + 90 = _____

Using an Addition Table

Find each sum using the addition table.

+	0	1	2	3	4	5	6	7	8	9
0	0	1	2	3	4	5	6	7	8	9
1	1	2	3	4	5	6	7	8	9	10
2	2	3	4	5	6	7	8	9	10	11
3	3	4	5	6	7	8	9	10	11	12
4	4	5	6	7	8	9	10	11	12	13
5	5	6	7	8	9	10	11	12	13	14
6	6	7	8	9	10	11	12	13	14	15
7	7	8	9	10	11	12	13	14	15	16
8	8	9	10	11	12	13	14	15	16	17
9	9	10	11	12	13	14	15	16	17	18

© Macmillan/McGraw-Hill

8. 8 + 7 = _____　　9. 15 + 3 = _____　　10. 9 + 6 = _____

8A

Assessment Goal

This assessment covers skills identified as necessary for success in Operations.

Getting Started

- Allow students time to look over the assessment. Point out the labels that identify the skills covered.

- Have students find math vocabulary terms used in the assessment. List vocabulary terms on the board as students identify them. If necessary, review the meanings of all essential math vocabulary.

Introducing the Assessment

- Explain to students that these pages will help you know if they are ready to start a new topic in their math textbooks.

- Students who have transferred from another school may not have been introduced to some of these skills. Encourage students to do their best and assure them you will help them learn any needed skills.

Alternative Assessment Strategy

- Oral administration is appropriate for younger students or those whose native language is not English. Read the skills title and directions one section at a time. Check students' understanding by asking them to tell you how they will do the first exercise in the group.

OPERATIONS 2 PREREQUISITE SKILLS

The skills listed in this chart are those identified as major prerequisite skills for students' success in the Operations lessons. Each skill is covered by one or more assessment items from page 8A as shown in the middle column. The right column provides the page numbers for the lessons in this book that reteach Operations prerequisite skills.

Skill Name	Assessment Items	Lesson Pages
Basic Addition Facts	1-4	T24-T25
Addition Patterns	5-7	T34-T35
Using an Addition Table	8-10	T30-T31

Commutative Property of Addition

Complete.

1. $2 + 3 = 3 +$ _____

2. $5 + 4 =$ _____ $+ 5$

3. $7 +$ _____ $= 6 + 7$

4. _____ $+ 2 = 2 + 9$

Doubles to Add

Find each sum.

5. $2 + 2 =$ _____

6. $5 + 5 =$ _____

7. $8 + 8 =$ _____

8.
$$\begin{array}{r} 4 \\ + 4 \\ \hline \end{array}$$

9.
$$\begin{array}{r} 9 \\ + 9 \\ \hline \end{array}$$

10.
$$\begin{array}{r} 6 \\ + 6 \\ \hline \end{array}$$

Addition

Find each sum.

11.
$$\begin{array}{r} 56 \\ + 19 \\ \hline \end{array}$$

12.
$$\begin{array}{r} 148 \\ + 209 \\ \hline \end{array}$$

13.
$$\begin{array}{r} \$3.67 \\ + 1.93 \\ \hline \end{array}$$

14. $45 + 38 =$ _____

15. $59 + 61 =$ _____

16. $\$6.13 + \$1.97 + \$0.67 =$ _____

17. $125 + 50 + 30 =$ _____

Name _____

**Commutative Property
of Addition**

Complete.

1. $2 + 3 = 3 +$ _____   2. $5 + 4 =$ _____ $+ 5$

3. $7 +$ _____ $= 6 + 7$ 4. _____ $+ 2 = 2 + 9$

Doubles to Add

Find each sum.

5. $2 + 2 =$ _____   6. $5 + 5 =$ _____   7. $8 + 8 =$ _____

8.   4
  $+ 4$

9.   9
  $+ 9$

10.   6
  $+ 6$

Addition

Find each sum.

11.   56
  $+ 19$

12.   148
  $+ 209$

13. $3.67
  $+ 1.93$

14. $45 + 38 =$ _____   15. $59 + 61 =$ _____

16. $6.13 + $1.97 + $0.67 =$ _____

17. $125 + 50 + 30 =$ _____

© Macmillan/McGraw-Hill

9A

OPERATIONS 3 PREREQUISITE SKILLS

The skills listed in this chart are those identified as major prerequisite skills for students' success in the Operations lessons. Each skill is covered by one or more assessment items from page 9A as shown in the middle column. The right column provides the page numbers for the lessons in this book that reteach Operations prerequisite skills.

Skill Name	Assessment Items	Lesson Pages
Commutative Property of Addition	1-4	T36-T37
Doubles to Add	5-10	T32-T33
Addition	11-17	T24-T25

OPERATIONS 3 ASSESSMENT

Assessment Goal

This assessment covers skills identified as necessary for success in Operations.

Getting Started

- Allow students time to look over the assessment. Point out the labels that identify the skills covered.

- Have students find math vocabulary terms used in the assessment. List vocabulary terms on the board as students identify them. If necessary, review the meanings of all essential math vocabulary.

Introducing the Assessment

- Explain to students that these pages will help you know if they are ready to start a new topic in their math textbooks.

- Students who have transferred from another school may not have been introduced to some of these skills. Encourage students to do their best and assure them you will help them learn any needed skills.

Alternative Assessment Strategy

- Oral administration is appropriate for younger students or those whose native language is not English. Read the skills title and directions one section at a time. Check students' understanding by asking them to tell you how they will do the first exercise in the group.

Subtraction Facts to 20

Subtract.

1. $16 - 8 =$ _____

2. $\begin{array}{r} 15 \\ -\ 7 \\ \hline \end{array}$

3. $19 - 6 =$ _____

Subtraction

Find each difference.

4. $\begin{array}{r} 51 \\ -\ 14 \\ \hline \end{array}$

5. $\begin{array}{r} 321 \\ -\ 162 \\ \hline \end{array}$

6. $\begin{array}{r} \$8.04 \\ -\ 5.36 \\ \hline \end{array}$

7. $80 - 65 =$ _____

8. $\$5.49 - \$0.89 =$ _____

9. $213 - 75 =$ _____

Subtract Two-Digit Numbers

Subtract.

10. $\begin{array}{r} 98 \\ -\ 54 \\ \hline \end{array}$

11. $\begin{array}{r} 79 \\ -\ 22 \\ \hline \end{array}$

12. $\begin{array}{r} 56 \\ -\ 18 \\ \hline \end{array}$

13. $41 - 23 =$ _____

14. $64 - 36 =$ _____

Name _____

Subtraction Facts to 20

Subtract.

1. 16 − 8 = _____   **2.** 15
                                         − 7

3. 19 − 6 = _____

Subtraction

Find each difference.

4.   51   **5.**   321   **6.** $8.04
       − 14   − 162   − 5.36

7. 80 − 65 = _____

8. $5.49 − $0.89 = _____

9. 213 − 75 = _____

Subtract Two-Digit Numbers

Subtract.

10.   98   **11.**   79   **12.**   56
        − 54   − 22   − 18

13. 41 − 23 = _____   **14.** 64 − 36 = _____

© Macmillan/McGraw-Hill

10A

OPERATIONS 4 PREREQUISITE SKILLS

The skills listed in this chart are those identified as major prerequisite skills for students' success in the Operations lessons. Each skill is covered by one or more assessment items from page 10A as shown in the middle column. The right column provides the page numbers for the lessons in this book that reteach Operations prerequisite skills.

Skill Name	Assessment Items	Lesson Pages
Subtraction Facts to 20	1-3	T38-T39
Subtraction	4-9	T40-T41
Subtract Two-Digit Numbers	10-14	T42-T43

Assessment Goal

This assessment covers skills identified as necessary for success in Operations.

Getting Started

- Allow students time to look over the assessment. Point out the labels that identify the skills covered.

- Have students find math vocabulary terms used in the assessment. List vocabulary terms on the board as students identify them. If necessary, review the meanings of all essential math vocabulary.

Introducing the Assessment

- Explain to students that these pages will help you know if they are ready to start a new topic in their math textbooks.

- Students who have transferred from another school may not have been introduced to some of these skills. Encourage students to do their best and assure them you will help them learn any needed skills.

Alternative Assessment Strategy

- Oral administration is appropriate for younger students or those whose native language is not English. Read the skills title and directions one section at a time. Check students' understanding by asking them to tell you how they will do the first exercise in the group.

Addition and Subtraction Facts

Find each sum or difference.

1. $6 + 9 =$ _____

2. $15 - 9 =$ _____

3. $14 - 7 =$ _____

4. $5 + 8 =$ _____

5. $8 + 4 =$ _____

6. $17 - 8 =$ _____

7. $7 + 6 =$ _____

8. $19 - 6 =$ _____

Fact Families

Write the pair of related subtraction facts for each pair of addition facts.

9. $7 + 4 = 11$
$4 + 7 = 11$

_____

_____

10. $6 + 9 = 15$
$9 + 6 = 15$

_____

_____

11. $9 + 8 = 17$
$8 + 9 = 17$

_____

_____

12. $6 + 7 = 13$
$7 + 6 = 13$

_____

_____

13. $7 + 9 = 16$
$9 + 7 = 16$

_____

_____

14. $8 + 6 = 14$
$6 + 8 = 14$

_____

_____

15. $8 + 3 = 11$
$3 + 8 = 11$

_____

_____

16. $7 + 8 = 15$
$8 + 7 = 15$

_____

_____

OPERATIONS
5

Addition and Subtraction Facts

Find each sum or difference.

1. 6 + 9 = _____   2. 15 − 9 = _____

3. 14 − 7 = _____   4. 5 + 8 = _____

5. 8 + 4 = _____   6. 17 − 8 = _____

7. 7 + 6 = _____   8. 19 − 6 = _____

Fact Families

Write the pair of related subtraction facts for each pair
of addition facts.

9. 7 + 4 = 11   10. 6 + 9 = 15
   4 + 7 = 11   9 + 6 = 15

   _____   _____

   _____   _____

11. 9 + 8 = 17   12. 6 + 7 = 13
    8 + 9 = 17   7 + 6 = 13

    _____   _____

    _____   _____

13. 7 + 9 = 16   14. 8 + 6 = 14
    9 + 7 = 16   6 + 8 = 14

    _____   _____

    _____   _____

15. 8 + 3 = 11   16. 7 + 8 = 15
    3 + 8 = 11   8 + 7 = 15

    _____   _____

    _____   _____

© Macmillan/McGraw-Hill

11A

OPERATIONS 5 PREREQUISITE SKILLS

The skills listed in this chart are those identified as major prerequisite
skills for students' success in the Operations lessons. Each skill is covered
by one or more assessment items from page 11A as shown in the middle column. The right column provides the page numbers for the
lessons in this book that reteach Operations prerequisite skills.

Skill Name	Assessment Items	Lesson Pages
Addition and Subtraction Facts	1-8	T46-T47
Fact Families	9-16	T44-T45

OPERATIONS 5 ASSESSMENT

Assessment Goal

This assessment covers skills identified as necessary for success in
Operations.

Getting Started

- Allow students time to look over
  the assessment. Point out the
  labels that identify the skills
  covered.

- Have students find math vocabulary terms used in the assessment. List vocabulary terms on
  the board as students identify
  them. If necessary, review the
  meanings of all essential math
  vocabulary.

Introducing the Assessment

- Explain to students that these
  pages will help you know if they
  are ready to start a new topic in
  their math textbooks.

- Students who have transferred
  from another school may not
  have been introduced to some
  of these skills. Encourage students to do their best and assure
  them you will help them learn
  any needed skills.

Alternative Assessment Strategy

- Oral administration is appropriate for younger students or
  those whose native language is
  not English. Read the skills title
  and directions one section at a
  time. Check students' understanding by asking them to tell
  you how they will do the first
  exercise in the group.

Add 3 or More Numbers

Add.

1. $4 + 3 + 0 + 4 =$ _____

2.
$$
\begin{array}{r}
7 \\
4 \\
2 \\
+\ 5 \\
\hline
\end{array}
$$

Repeated Addition

Find each sum.

3. $2 + 2 + 2 + 2 + 2 + 2 =$ _____   **4.** $5 + 5 + 5 + 5 + 5 =$ _____

3 or More Addends

Find each sum.

5. $8 + 15 + 8 + 15 =$ _____

6. $16 + 16 + 16 + 16 =$ _____

7. $45 + 25 + 45 + 25 + 45 =$ _____

8. $300 + 600 + 300 + 500 + 200 =$ _____

Associative Property of Addition

Find each sum. Add the grouped addends first.

9. $(3 + 7) + 4$

_____ $+ 4 =$ _____

10. $6 + (2 + 9)$

$6 +$ _____ $=$ _____

Name _____

Add 3 or More Numbers

Add.

1. $4 + 3 + 0 + 4 =$ _____

2. $\begin{array}{r} 7 \\ 4 \\ 2 \\ +5 \\ \hline \end{array}$

Repeated Addition

Find each sum.

3. $2 + 2 + 2 + 2 + 2 + 2 =$ _____

4. $5 + 5 + 5 + 5 + 5 =$ _____

3 or More Addends

Find each sum.

5. $8 + 15 + 8 + 15 =$ _____

6. $16 + 16 + 16 + 16 =$ _____

7. $45 + 25 + 45 + 25 + 45 =$ _____

8. $300 + 600 + 300 + 500 + 200 =$ _____

Associative Property of Addition

Find each sum. Add the grouped addends first.

9. $(3 + 7) + 4$

_____ + 4 = _____

10. $6 + (2 + 9)$

$6 +$ _____ = _____

© Macmillan/McGraw-Hill

12A

OPERATIONS 6 PREREQUISITE SKILLS

The skills listed in this chart are those identified as major prerequisite skills for students' success in the Operations lessons. Each skill is covered by one or more assessment items from page 12A as shown in the middle column. The right column provides the page numbers for the lessons in this book that reteach Operations prerequisite skills.

Skill Name	Assessment Items	Lesson Pages
Add 3 or More Numbers	1-2	T48
Repeated Addition	3-4	T49
3 or More Addends	5-8	T50-T51
Associative Property of Addition	9-10	T76-T77

OPERATIONS 6 ASSESSMENT

Assessment Goal

This assessment covers skills identified as necessary for success in Operations.

Getting Started

- Allow students time to look over the assessment. Point out the labels that identify the skills covered.

- Have students find math vocabulary terms used in the assessment. List vocabulary terms on the board as students identify them. If necessary, review the meanings of all essential math vocabulary.

Introducing the Assessment

- Explain to students that these pages will help you know if they are ready to start a new topic in their math textbooks.

- Students who have transferred from another school may not have been introduced to some of these skills. Encourage students to do their best and assure them you will help them learn any needed skills.

Alternative Assessment Strategy

- Oral administration is appropriate for younger students or those whose native language is not English. Read the skills title and directions one section at a time. Check students' understanding by asking them to tell you how they will do the first exercise in the group.

Name _____

Use Arrays to Multiply

Write the multiplication sentence that each array shows.

1.

_____ × _____ = _____

2.

_____ × _____ = _____

Equal Groups

Write the multiplication sentence that each picture shows.

3.

_____ × _____ = _____

4.

_____ × _____ = _____

Draw a picture showing the total amount.

5. 3 groups of 6 squares

6. 7 groups of 5 circles

Multiplication Facts Through 5s

Multiply.

7. $2 \times 3 =$ _____

8. $6 \times 5 =$ _____

9. 8
     × 2
     ———

10. 3
      × 7
     ———

Name _____

Use Arrays to Multiply

Write the multiplication sentence that each array shows.

1. ○ ○ ○ ○
   ○ ○ ○ ○

____ × ____ = ____

2. ○ ○ ○ ○ ○
   ○ ○ ○ ○ ○
   ○ ○ ○ ○ ○

____ × ____ = ____

Equal Groups

Write the multiplication sentence that each picture shows.

3. |||| |||| ||||

____ × ____ = ____

4. ⭐⭐⭐ ⭐⭐
   ⭐⭐   ⭐⭐⭐

____ × ____ = ____

Draw a picture showing the total amount.

5. 3 groups of 6 squares

6. 7 groups of 5 circles

Multiplication Facts Through 5s

Multiply.

7. $2 \times 3 =$ _____

8. $6 \times 5 =$ _____

9. $\begin{array}{r} 8 \\ \times 2 \\ \hline \end{array}$

10. $\begin{array}{r} 3 \\ \times 7 \\ \hline \end{array}$

13A

OPERATIONS 7 PREREQUISITE SKILLS

The skills listed in this chart are those identified as major prerequisite skills for students' success in the Operations lessons. Each skill is covered by one or more assessment items from page 13A as shown in the middle column. The right column provides the page numbers for the lessons in this book that reteach Operations prerequisite skills.

Skill Name	Assessment Items	Lesson Pages
Use Arrays to Multiply	1-2	T64-T65
Equal Groups	3-6	T58-T63
Multiplication Facts Through 5s	7-10	T66

OPERATIONS 7 ASSESSMENT

Assessment Goal

This assessment covers skills identified as necessary for success in Operations.

Getting Started

• Allow students time to look over the assessment. Point out the labels that identify the skills covered.

• Have students find math vocabulary terms used in the assessment. List vocabulary terms on the board as students identify them. If necessary, review the meanings of all essential math vocabulary.

Introducing the Assessment

• Explain to students that these pages will help you know if they are ready to start a new topics in their math textbooks.

• Students who have transferred from another school may not have been introduced to some of these skills. Encourage students to do their best and assure them you will help them learn any needed skills.

Alternative Assessment Strategy

• Oral administration is appropriate for younger students or those whose native language is not English. Read the skills title and directions one section at a time. Check students' understanding by asking them to tell you how they will do the first exercise in the group.

Multiplication Facts Through 9s

Find each product.

1. $4 \times 7 =$ _____

2. $6 \times 6 =$ _____

3. 5
$\times\,8$

4. 7
$\times\,3$

5. 8
$\times\,9$

Multiply with 0 and 1

Multiply.

6. $5 \times 0 =$ _____

7. $0 \times 9 =$ _____

8. 4
$\times\,1$

9. 6
$\times\,0$

10. 1
$\times\,8$

Multiplication Table

Use the multiplication table.

11. Draw a line through the **rows** that have both odd and even numbers.

12. Circle the **columns** that have only even numbers.

13. Write the numbers that are the products of 7. _____

_____

_____

	0	1	2	3	4	5	6	7	8	9	10
0	0	0	0	0	0	0	0	0	0	0	0
1	0	1	2	3	4	5	6	7	8	9	10
2	0	2	4	6	8	10	12	14	16	18	20
3	0	3	6	9	12	15	18	21	24	27	30
4	0	4	8	12	16	20	24	28	32	36	40
5	0	5	10	15	20	25	30	35	40	45	50
6	0	6	12	18	24	30	36	42	48	54	60
7	0	7	14	21	28	35	42	49	56	63	70
8	0	8	16	24	32	40	48	56	64	72	80
9	0	9	18	27	36	45	54	63	72	81	90
10	0	10	20	30	40	50	60	70	80	90	100

Multiplication Facts Through 9s

Find each product.

1. $4 \times 7 =$ _____   2. $6 \times 6 =$ _____

3. $\begin{array}{r} 5 \\ \times 8 \\ \hline \end{array}$ 4. $\begin{array}{r} 7 \\ \times 3 \\ \hline \end{array}$ 5. $\begin{array}{r} 8 \\ \times 9 \\ \hline \end{array}$

Multiply with 0 and 1

Multiply.

6. $5 \times 0 =$ _____   7. $0 \times 9 =$ _____

8. $\begin{array}{r} 4 \\ \times 1 \\ \hline \end{array}$ 9. $\begin{array}{r} 6 \\ \times 0 \\ \hline \end{array}$ 10. $\begin{array}{r} 1 \\ \times 8 \\ \hline \end{array}$

Multiplication Table

Use the multiplication table.

11. Draw a line through the **rows** that have both odd and even numbers.

12. Circle the **columns** that have only even numbers.

13. Write the numbers that are the products of 7. _____

_____

_____

	0	1	2	3	4	5	6	7	8	9	10
0	0	0	0	0	0	0	0	0	0	0	0
1	0	1	2	3	4	5	6	7	8	9	10
2	0	2	4	6	8	10	12	14	16	18	20
3	0	3	6	9	12	15	18	21	24	27	30
4	0	4	8	12	16	20	24	28	32	36	40
5	0	5	10	15	20	25	30	35	40	45	50
6	0	6	12	18	24	30	36	42	48	54	60
7	0	7	14	21	28	35	42	49	56	63	70
8	0	8	16	24	32	40	48	56	64	72	80
9	0	9	18	27	36	45	54	63	72	81	90
10	0	10	20	30	40	50	60	70	80	90	100

© Macmillan/McGraw-Hill

14A

OPERATIONS 8 PREREQUISITE SKILLS

The skills listed in this chart are those identified as major prerequisite skills for students' success in the Operations lessons. Each skill is covered by one or more assessment items from page 14A as shown in the middle column. The right column provides the page numbers for the lessons in this book that reteach Operations prerequisite skills.

Skill Name	Assessment Items	Lesson Pages
Multiplication Facts Through 9s	1-5	T68-T69
Multiply with 0 and 1	6-10	T72-T73
Multiplication Table	11-13	T74-T75

OPERATIONS 8 ASSESSMENT

Assessment Goal

This assessment covers skills identified as necessary for success in Operations.

Getting Started

- Allow students time to look over the assessment. Point out the labels that identify the skills covered.

- Have students find math vocabulary terms used in the assessment. List vocabulary terms on the board as students identify them. If necessary, review the meanings of all essential math vocabulary.

Introducing the Assessment

- Explain to students that these pages will help you know if they are ready to start a new topic in their math textbooks.

- Students who have transferred from another school may not have been introduced to some of these skills. Encourage students to do their best and assure them you will help them learn any needed skills.

Alternative Assessment Strategy

- Oral administration is appropriate for younger students or those whose native language is not English. Read the skills title and directions one section at a time. Check students' understanding by asking them to tell you how they will do the first exercise in the group.

Name _____

Multiplying with Multiples
of 10, 100, or 1,000

Find each product.

1. 40
   × 6

2. 6,000
   ×   5

3. 300
   ×   4

Multiplication Properties

Complete by writing the missing number.
Tell which property you used.

4. 4 × 5 = 5 × _____

5. 7 × 0 = _____

_____ Property

_____ Property

6. 4 × 12 = (4 × _____) + (4 × _____)

_____ Property

Multiplying a Three- Digit Number by a
One- Digit Number

Find each product.

7. 508
   × 5

8. 274
   × 8

9. 6 × $9.34 = _____

10. 7 × 315 = _____

11. 3 × 212 = _____

12. 2 × 419 = _____

Name _____ OPERATIONS **9**

Multiplying with Multiples of 10, 100, or 1,000

Find each product.

| 1. | 40 | 2. | 6,000 | 3. | 300 |
| | × 6 | | × 5 | | × 4 |

Multiplication Properties

Complete by writing the missing number.
Tell which property you used.

4. $4 \times 5 = 5 \times$ _____

_____ Property

5. $7 \times 0 =$ _____

_____ Property

6. $4 \times 12 = (4 \times$ _____ $) + (4 \times$ _____ $)$

_____ Property

Multiplying a Three- Digit Number by a One- Digit Number

Find each product.

| 7. | 508 | 8. | 274 |
| | × 5 | | × 8 |

9. $6 \times \$9.34 =$ _____

10. $7 \times 315 =$ _____

11. $3 \times 212 =$ _____

12. $2 \times 419 =$ _____

© Macmillan/McGraw-Hill

15A

OPERATIONS 9 PREREQUISITE SKILLS

The skills listed in this chart are those identified as major prerequisite skills for students' success in the Operations lessons. Each skill is covered by one or more assessment items from page 15A as shown in the middle column. The right column provides the page numbers for the lessons in this book that reteach Operations prerequisite skills.

Skill Name	Assessment Items	Lesson Pages
Multiplying with Multiples of 10,100, or 1,000	1-3	T78-T79
Multiplication Properties	4-6	T77
Multiplying a Three-Digit Number by a One-Digit Number	7-12	T82-T83

Assessment Goal

This assessment covers skills identified as necessary for success in Operations.

Getting Started

- Allow students time to look over the assessment. Point out the labels that identify the skills covered.

- Have students find math vocabulary terms used in the assessment. List vocabulary terms on the board as students identify them. If necessary, review the meanings of all essential math vocabulary.

Introducing the Assessment

- Explain to students that these pages will help you know if they are ready to start a new topic in their math textbooks.

- Students who have transferred from another school may not have been introduced to some of these skills. Encourage students to do their best and assure them you will help them learn any needed skills.

Alternative Assessment Strategy

- Oral administration is appropriate for younger students or those whose native language is not English. Read the skills title and directions one section at a time. Check students' understanding by asking them to tell you how they will do the first exercise in the group.

Closest (3-Digit) Multiple

Find the closest multiple of 6 and 10 that is greater than each number. Complete.

1. 325 _____ So the quotient of 325 ÷ 6 is about _____.

2. 471 _____ So the quotient of 471 ÷ 6 is about _____.

Find the closest multiple of 7 and 10 that is greater than each number. Complete.

3. 505 _____ So the quotient of 505 ÷ 7 is about _____.

4. 216 _____ So the quotient of 216 ÷ 7 is about _____.

Find the closest multiple of 9 and 10 that is greater than each number. Complete.

5. 536 _____ So the quotient of 536 ÷ 9 is about _____.

6. 800 _____ So the quotient of 800 ÷ 9 is about _____.

Function Table

Complete each table. Then identify the rule.

7.

Input	4	5	7	9
Output	24	30	42	

Rule: _____

Missing Factors

Write each missing factor.

8. 2 × _____ = 8

9. 3 × _____ = 18

10. 5 × _____ = 45

11. 4 × _____ = 32

Name _____

Closest (3-Digit) Multiple

Find the closest multiple of 6 and 10 that is greater than each number. Complete.

1. 325 _____ So the quotient of 325 ÷ 6 is about _____.

2. 471 _____ So the quotient of 471 ÷ 6 is about _____.

Find the closest multiple of 7 and 10 that is greater than each number. Complete.

3. 505 _____ So the quotient of 505 ÷ 7 is about _____.

4. 216 _____ So the quotient of 216 ÷ 7 is about _____.

Find the closest multiple of 9 and 10 that is greater than each number. Complete.

5. 536 _____ So the quotient of 536 ÷ 9 is about _____.

6. 800 _____ So the quotient of 800 ÷ 9 is about _____.

Function Table

Complete each table. Then identify the rule.

7.

Input	4	5	7	9
Output	24	30	42	

Rule: _____

Missing Factors

Write each missing factor.

8. 2 × _____ = 8

9. 3 × _____ = 18

10. 5 × _____ = 45

11. 4 × _____ = 32

© Macmillan/McGraw-Hill

16A

OPERATIONS 10 PREREQUISITE SKILLS

The skills listed in this chart are those identified as major prerequisite skills for students' success in the Operations lessons. Each skill is covered by one or more assessment items from page 16A as shown in the middle column. The right column provides the page numbers for the lessons in this book that reteach Operations prerequisite skills.

Skill Name	Assessment Items	Lesson Pages
Closest (3-Digit) Multiple	1-6	T88-T89
Function Table	7	T84-T85
Missing Factors	8-11	T86

OPERATIONS 10 ASSESSMENT

Assessment Goal

This assessment covers skills identified as necessary for success in Operations.

Getting Started

- Allow students time to look over the assessment. Point out the labels that identify the skills covered.

- Have students find math vocabulary terms used in the assessment. List vocabulary terms on the board as students identify them. If necessary, review the meanings of all essential math vocabulary.

Introducing the Assessment

- Explain to students that these pages will help you know if they are ready to start a new topic in their math textbooks.

- Students who have transferred from another school may not have been introduced to some of these skills. Encourage students to do their best and assure them you will help them learn any needed skills.

Alternative Assessment Strategy

- Oral administration is appropriate for younger students or those whose native language is not English. Read the skills title and directions one section at a time. Check students' understanding by asking them to tell you how they will do the first exercise in the group.

Name _____

Meaning of Division

Draw each picture. Then tell how many equal groups, or how many are in each group.

1. 24 circles
3 circles
in each group

_____ groups of circles

2. 15 triangles
5 equal groups
of triangles

_____ triangles in each group

Division Facts

Find each quotient.

3. $56 \div 7 =$ _____ **4.** $45 \div 9 =$ _____ **5.** $63 \div 7 =$ _____

6. $8\overline{)64}$ **7.** $9\overline{)72}$ **8.** $7\overline{)42}$

Multiply and Divide by 10, 100, and 1,000

Find each product or quotient.

9. $6 \times 100 =$ _____ **10.** $7 \times 1,000 =$ _____

11. $40 \div 10 =$ _____ **12.** $800 \div 100 =$ _____

Multiplication and Division Facts

Multiply.

13. $\begin{array}{r} 6 \\ \times 4 \\ \hline \end{array}$ **14.** $\begin{array}{r} 9 \\ \times 3 \\ \hline \end{array}$

Divide.

15. $5\overline{)25}$ **16.** $6\overline{)42}$

Meaning of Division

Draw each picture. Then tell how many equal groups, or how many are in each group.

1. 24 circles
3 circles
in each group   _____ groups of circles

2. 15 triangles
5 equal groups
of triangles   _____ triangles in each group

Division Facts

Find each quotient.

3. $56 \div 7 =$ _____   **4.** $45 \div 9 =$ _____   **5.** $63 \div 7 =$ _____

6. $8\overline{)64}$ **7.** $9\overline{)72}$ **8.** $7\overline{)42}$

Multiply and Divide by 10, 100, and 1,000

Find each product or quotient.

9. $6 \times 100 =$ _____   **10.** $7 \times 1,000 =$ _____

11. $40 \div 10 =$ _____   **12.** $800 \div 100 =$ _____

Multiplication and Division Facts

Multiply.		Divide.	
13. $\begin{array}{r} 6 \\ \times 4 \end{array}$	**14.** $\begin{array}{r} 9 \\ \times 3 \end{array}$	**15.** $5\overline{)25}$	**16.** $6\overline{)42}$

17A

OPERATIONS 11 PREREQUISITE SKILLS

The skills listed in this chart are those identified as major prerequisite skills for students' success in the Operations lessons. Each skill is covered by one or more assessment items from page 17A as shown in the middle column. The right column provides the page numbers for the lessons in this book that reteach Operations prerequisite skills.

Skill Name	Assessment Items	Lesson Pages
Meaning of Division	1-2	T90-T91
Division Facts	3-8	T94-T95
Multiply and Divide by 10, 100, and 1,000	9-12	T100-T101
Multiplication and Division Facts	13-16	T98-T99

OPERATIONS 11 ASSESSMENT

Assessment Goal

This assessment covers skills identified as necessary for success in Operations.

Getting Started

- Allow students time to look over the assessment. Point out the labels that identify the skills covered.

- Have students find math vocabulary terms used in the assessment. List vocabulary terms on the board as students identify them. If necessary, review the meanings of all essential math vocabulary.

Introducing the Assessment

- Explain to students that these pages will help you know if they are ready to start a new topic in their math textbooks.

- Students who have transferred from another school may not have been introduced to some of these skills. Encourage students to do their best and assure them you will help them learn any needed skills.

Alternative Assessment Strategy

- Oral administration is appropriate for younger students or those whose native language is not English. Read the skills title and directions one section at a time. Check students' understanding by asking them to tell you how they will do the first exercise in the group.

Name _____

Meaning of Fractions

Show a fraction.

1. Color $\frac{3}{4}$ of the rectangle.

2. Color $\frac{5}{16}$ of the square.

3. Color $\frac{7}{8}$ of the circle.

4. Color $\frac{2}{3}$ of the square.

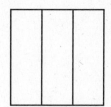

5. Color $\frac{3}{8}$ of the rectangle.

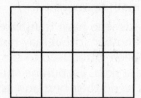

6. Color $\frac{9}{10}$ of the circle.

Mixed Numbers

Write each mixed number.

7. 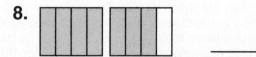 _____

8. 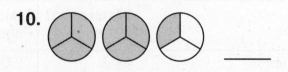 _____

9. _____

10. _____

Name _____

Meaning of Fractions

Show a fraction.

1. Color $\frac{3}{4}$ of the rectangle.

2. Color $\frac{5}{16}$ of the square.

3. Color $\frac{7}{8}$ of the circle.

4. Color $\frac{2}{3}$ of the square.

5. Color $\frac{3}{8}$ of the rectangle.

6. Color $\frac{9}{10}$ of the circle.

Mixed Numbers

Write each mixed number.

7. _____

8. _____

9. _____

10. _____

© Macmillan/McGraw-Hill

18A

OPERATIONS 12 PREREQUISITE SKILLS

he skills listed in this chart are those identified as major prerequisite
kills for students' success in the Operations lessons. Each skill is covered
y one or more assessment items from page 18A as shown in the mid-
le column. The right column provides the page numbers for the
ssons in this book that reteach Operations prerequisite skills.

Skill Name	Assessment Items	Lesson Pages
Meaning of Fractions	1-6	T102-T103
Mixed Numbers	7-10	T104-T105

OPERATIONS 12 ASSESSMENT

Assessment Goal

This assessment covers skills identified as necessary for success in
Operations.

Getting Started

- Allow students time to look over
  the assessment. Point out the
  labels that identify the skills
  covered.

- Have students find math vocabulary terms used in the assessment. List vocabulary terms on
  the board as students identify
  them. If necessary, review the
  meanings of all essential math
  vocabulary.

Introducing the Assessment

- Explain to students that these
  pages will help you know if they
  are ready to start a new topic in
  their math textbooks.

- Students who have transferred
  from another school may not
  have been introduced to some
  of these skills. Encourage students to do their best and assure
  them you will help them learn
  any needed skills.

Alternative Assessment Strategy

- Oral administration is appropriate for younger students or
  those whose native language is
  not English. Read the skills title
  and directions one section at a
  time. Check students' understanding by asking them to tell
  you how they will do the first
  exercise in the group.

Hundreds, Tens, and Ones

Write each missing number.

1. 8 = _____ ones   **2.** 30 = _____ tens   **3.** 200 = _____ hundreds

4. 7 = _____ ones   **5.** 40 = _____ tens   **6.** 600 = _____ hundreds

7. 3 = _____ ones   **8.** 70 = _____ tens   **9.** 900 = _____ hundreds

Regroup Ones

Write the number of tens and ones.

10. 25 = _____ tens _____ ones   **11.** 68 = _____ tens _____ ones

12. 49 = _____ tens _____ ones   **13.** 72 = _____ tens _____ ones

14. 39 = _____ tens _____ ones   **15.** 20 = _____ tens _____ ones

16. 96 = _____ tens _____ ones   **17.** 15 = _____ tens _____ ones

Name _____

PLACE VALUE
1

Hundreds, Tens, and Ones
Write each missing number.

1. 8 = _____ ones
2. 30 = _____ tens
3. 200 = _____ hundreds

4. 7 = _____ ones
5. 40 = _____ tens
6. 600 = _____ hundreds

7. 3 = _____ ones
8. 70 = _____ tens
9. 900 = _____ hundreds

Regroup Ones
Write the number of tens and ones.

10. 25 = _____ tens _____ ones
11. 68 = _____ tens _____ ones

12. 49 = _____ tens _____ ones
13. 72 = _____ tens _____ ones

14. 39 = _____ tens _____ ones
15. 20 = _____ tens _____ ones

16. 96 = _____ tens _____ ones
17. 15 = _____ tens _____ ones

© Macmillan/McGraw-Hill

19A

PLACE VALUE 1 PREREQUISITE SKILLS

he skills listed in this chart are those identified as major prerequisite
ills for students' success in the Place Value lessons. Each skill is covered
y one or more assessment items from page 19A as shown in the mid-
e column. The right column provides the page numbers for the
ssons in this book that reteach Place Value prerequisite skills.

Skill Name	Assessment Items	Lesson Pages
Hundreds, Tens, and Ones	1-9	T106-T107
Regroup Ones	10-17	T110-T111

PLACE VALUE 1 ASSESSMENT

Assessment Goal
This assessment covers skills identi-
fied as necessary for success in
Place Value.

Getting Started
- Allow students time to look over
  the assessment. Point out the
  labels that identify the skills
  covered.
- Have students find math vocabulary terms used in the assessment. List vocabulary terms on
  the board as students identify
  them. If necessary, review the
  meanings of all essential math
  vocabulary.

Introducing the Assessment
- Explain to students that these
  pages will help you know if they
  are ready to start a new topic in
  their math textbooks.
- Students who have transferred
  from another school may not
  have been introduced to some
  of these skills. Encourage students to do their best and assure
  them you will help them learn
  any needed skills.

Alternative Assessment Strategy
- Oral administration is appropriate for younger students or
  those whose native language is
  not English. Read the skills title
  and directions one section at a
  time. Check students' understanding by asking them to tell
  you how they will do the first
  exercise in the group.

Name _____

Place Value

Write each number.

1.  _____

2. _____

3. _____

Expanded Form

Write each number in expanded form.

4. 4,512 = 4,000 + _____ + _____ + _____

5. 7,360 = _____ + _____ + _____ + _____

Rename Tens and Ones

Write each missing number.

6. 1 ten 9 ones = _____ ones   **7.** 8 tens 4 ones = _____ ones

Ten Thousands, Thousands, and Hundreds

Write each number.

8. 9 ten thousands _____   **9.** 1 ten thousands _____

10. 3 thousands _____   **11.** 5 thousands _____

12. 6 hundreds _____   **13.** 7 hundreds _____

14. 7 ten thousands _____   **15.** 2 hundreds _____

Name _____

Place Value

Write each number.

1.

2.

3.

_____ _____ _____

Expanded Form

Write each number in expanded form.

4. 4,512 = 4,000 + _____ + _____ + _____

5. 7,360 = _____ + _____ + _____ + _____

Rename Tens and Ones

Write each missing number.

6. 1 ten 9 ones = _____ ones   7. 8 tens 4 ones = _____ ones

Ten Thousands, Thousands, and Hundreds

Write each number.

8. 9 ten thousands _____   9. 1 ten thousands _____

10. 3 thousands _____   11. 5 thousands _____

12. 6 hundreds _____   13. 7 hundreds _____

14. 7 ten thousands _____   14. 2 hundreds _____

© Macmillan/McGraw-Hill

20A

PLACE VALUE 2 PREREQUISITE SKILLS

The skills listed in this chart are those identified as major prerequisite skills for students' success in the Place Value lessons. Each skill is covered by one or more assessment items from page 20A as shown in the middle column. The right column provides the page numbers for the lessons in this book that reteach Place Value prerequisite skills.

Skill Name	Assessment Items	Lesson Pages
Place Value	1-3	T116, T119
Expanded Form	4-5	T117
Rename Tens and Ones	6-7	T118
Ten Thousands, Thousands, and Hundreds	8-15	T114-T115

Assessment Goal

This assessment covers skills identified as necessary for success in Place Value.

Getting Started

- Allow students time to look over the assessment. Point out the labels that identify the skills covered.
- Have students find math vocabulary terms used in the assessment. List vocabulary terms on the board as students identify them. If necessary, review the meanings of all essential math vocabulary.

Introducing the Assessment

- Explain to students that these pages will help you know if they are ready to start a new topic in their math textbooks.
- Students who have transferred from another school may not have been introduced to some of these skills. Encourage students to do their best and assure them you will help them learn any needed skills.

Alternative Assessment Strategy

- Oral administration is appropriate for younger students or those whose native language is not English. Read the skills title and directions one section at a time. Check students' understanding by asking them to tell you how they will do the first exercise in the group.

Name _____

Equivalent Names

Match a number in Column A with a number in Column B that names the same number.

Column A

1. 2,509 _____

2. 259 _____

3. 2,059 _____

4. 2,590 _____

Column B

a. 25 hundreds 9 tens

b. 2 thousands 5 tens 9 ones

c. 25 hundreds 9 ones

d. 200 + 50 + 9

e. 2 thousands 5 hundreds 9 tens

---

5. 3,303 _____

6. 3,003 _____

7. 333 _____

8. 3,300 _____

a. 3 hundred 3 tens 3 ones

b. 3 thousand 3 hundred 3 ones

c. 3,000 + 3

d. 3 thousand 3 hundred 3 tens 3 ones

e. 3 thousand 3 hundred

Name _____

PLACE VALUE
3

Equivalent Names

Match a number in Column A with a number in Column B
that names the same number.

Column A

1. 2,509 _____

2. 259 _____

3. 2,059 _____

4. 2,590 _____

Column B

a. 25 hundreds 9 tens

b. 2 thousands 5 tens 9 ones

c. 25 hundreds 9 ones

d. 200 + 50 + 9

e. 2 thousands 5 hundreds 9 tens

5. 3,303 _____

6. 3,003 _____

7. 333 _____

8. 3,300 _____

a. 3 hundred 3 tens 3 ones

b. 3 thousand 3 hundred 3 ones

c. 3,000 + 3

d. 3 thousand 3 hundred 3 tens 3 ones

e. 3 thousand 3 hundred

© Macmillan/McGraw-Hill

21A

PLACE VALUE 3 PREREQUISITE SKILLS

The skills listed in this chart are those identified as major prerequisite skills for students' success in the Place Value lessons. Each skill is covered by one or more assessment items from page 21A as shown in the middle column. The right column provides the page numbers for the lessons in this book that reteach Place Value prerequisite skills.

Skill Name	Assessment Items	Lesson Pages
Equivalent Names	1-8	T120-T121

PLACE VALUE 3 ASSESSMENT

Assessment Goal
This assessment covers skills identified as necessary for success in Place Value.

Getting Started
- Allow students time to look over the assessment. Point out the labels that identify the skills covered.
- Have students find math vocabulary terms used in the assessment. List vocabulary terms on the board as students identify them. If necessary, review the meanings of all essential math vocabulary.

Introducing the Assessment
- Explain to students that these pages will help you know if they are ready to start a new topic in their math textbooks.
- Students who have transferred from another school may not have been introduced to some of these skills. Encourage students to do their best and assure them you will help them learn any needed skills.

Alternative Assessment Strategy
- Oral administration is appropriate for younger students or those whose native language is not English. Read the skills title and directions one section at a time. Check students' understanding by asking them to tell you how they will do the first exercise in the group.

Name_____

Counting Coins

Write each amount.

1.

_____ ¢

2.

_____ ¢

3.

_____ ¢

4.

_____ ¢

Name_____

Counting Coins

Write each amount.

1.

_____ ¢

2.

_____ ¢

3.

_____ ¢

4.

_____ ¢

© Macmillan/McGraw-Hill

22A

MEASUREMENT AND GEOMETRY 1
PREREQUISITE SKILLS

The skills listed in this chart are those identified as major prerequisite skills for students' success in the Measurement and Geometry lessons. Each skill is covered by one or more assessment items from page 22A as shown in the middle column. The right column provides the page numbers for the lessons in this book that reteach Measurement and Geometry prerequisite skills.

Skill Name	Assessment Items	Lesson Pages
Counting Coins	1-4	T122-T123

MEASUREMENT AND GEOMETRY 1 ASSESSMENT

Assessment Goal

This assessment covers skills identified as necessary for success in Measurement and Geometry.

Getting Started

- Allow students time to look over the assessment. Point out the labels that identify the skills covered.
- Have students find math vocabulary terms used in the assessment. List vocabulary terms on the board as students identify them. If necessary, review the meanings of all essential math vocabulary.

Introducing the Assessment

- Explain to students that these pages will help you know if they are ready to start a new topic in their math textbooks.
- Students who have transferred from another school may not have been introduced to some of these skills. Encourage students to do their best and assure them you will help them learn any needed skills.

Alternative Assessment Strategy

- Oral administration is appropriate for younger students or those whose native language is not English. Read the skills title and directions one section at a time. Check students' understanding by asking them to tell you how they will do the first exercise in the group.

Time to the Hour, Half Hour, and Quarter Hour

Write each time.

1.

_____

2.

_____

3.

_____

4.

_____

5.

_____

6.

_____

7.

_____

8.

_____

9.

_____

Time to the Hour,
Half Hour, and Quarter Hour

**MEASUREMENT/
GEOMETRY
2**

Write each time.

1. _____

2. _____

3. _____

4. _____

5. _____

6. _____

7. _____

8. _____

9. _____

© Macmillan/McGraw-Hill

23A

MEASUREMENT AND GEOMETRY 2
PREREQUISITE SKILLS

The skills listed in this chart are those identified as major prerequisite skills for students' success in the Measurement and Geometry lessons. Each skill is covered by one or more assessment items from page 23A as shown in the middle column. The right column provides the page numbers for the lessons in this book that reteach Measurement and Geometry prerequisite skills.

Skill Name	Assessment Items	Lesson Pages
Time to the Hour, Half Hour, and Quarter Hour	1-9	T124-T125

MEASUREMENT
AND GEOMETRY 2
ASSESSMENT

Assessment Goal
This assessment covers skills identified as necessary for success in Measurement and Geometry.

Getting Started
- Allow students time to look over the assessment. Point out the labels that identify the skills covered.
- Have students find math vocabulary terms used in the assessment. List vocabulary terms on the board as students identify them. If necessary, review the meanings of all essential math vocabulary.

Introducing the Assessment
- Explain to students that these pages will help you know if they are ready to start a new topic in their math textbooks.
- Students who have transferred from another school may not have been introduced to some of these skills. Encourage students to do their best and assure them you will help them learn any needed skills.

Alternative Assessment Strategy
- Oral administration is appropriate for younger students or those whose native language is not English. Read the skills title and directions one section at a time. Check students' understanding by asking them to tell you how they will do the first exercise in the group

Measuring Length

How many paper clips long is each object?

1. _____ paper clips

2. _____ paper clips

3. _____ paper clips

4. _____ paper clips

5. _____ paper clips

6. _____ paper clips

7. _____ paper clips

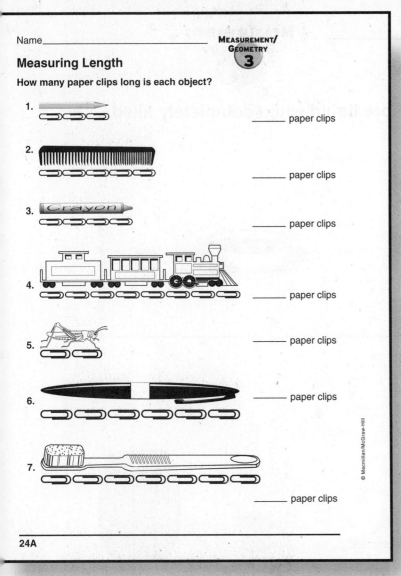

Name_____

Measuring Length

How many paper clips long is each object?

1. _____ paper clips

2. _____ paper clips

3. _____ paper clips

4. _____ paper clips

5. _____ paper clips

6. _____ paper clips

7. _____ paper clips

© Macmillan/McGraw-Hill

24A

MEASUREMENT AND GEOMETRY 3 ASSESSMENT

Assessment Goal

This assessment covers skills identified as necessary for success in Measurement and Geometry.

Getting Started

- Allow students time to look over the assessment. Point out the labels that identify the skills covered.
- Have students find math vocabulary terms used in the assessment. List vocabulary terms on the board as students identify them. If necessary, review the meanings of all essential math vocabulary.

Introducing the Assessment

- Explain to students that these pages will help you know if they are ready to start a new topic in their math textbooks.
- Students who have transferred from another school may not have been introduced to some of these skills. Encourage students to do their best and assure them you will help them learn any needed skills.

Alternative Assessment Strategy

- Oral administration is appropriate for younger students or those whose native language is not English. Read the skills title and directions one section at a time. Check students' understanding by asking them to tell you how they will do the first exercise in the group.

MEASUREMENT AND GEOMETRY 3 PREREQUISITE SKILLS

he skills listed in this chart are those identified as major prerequisite kills for students' success in the Measurement and Geometry lessons. ach skill is covered by one or more assessment items from page 24A as own in the middle column. The right column provides the page num- ers for the lessons in this book that reteach Measurement and eometry prerequisite skills.

Skill Name	Assessment Items	Lesson Pages
Measuring Length	1–7	T126–T127

Capacity

Underline the object that holds more liquid when completely filled.

1.

2.

3.

4.

5.

6.

Name_____

Capacity

Underline the object that holds more liquid when completely filled.

1.

2.

3.

4.

5.

6.

© Macmillan/McGraw-Hill

25A

MEASUREMENT AND GEOMETRY 4 PREREQUISITE SKILLS

The skills listed in this chart are those identified as major prerequisite skills for students' success in the Measurement and Geometry lessons. Each skill is covered by one or more assessment items from page 25A as shown in the middle column. The right column provides the page numbers for the lessons in this book that reteach Measurement and Geometry prerequisite skills.

Skill Name	Assessment Items	Lesson Pages
Capacity	1-6	T128-T129

MEASUREMENT AND GEOMETRY 4 ASSESSMENT

Assessment Goal

This assessment covers skills identified as necessary for success in Measurement and Geometry.

Getting Started

- Allow students time to look over the assessment. Point out the labels that identify the skills covered.

- Have students find math vocabulary terms used in the assessment. List vocabulary terms on the board as students identify them. If necessary, review the meanings of all essential math vocabulary.

Introducing the Assessment

- Explain to students that these pages will help you know if they are ready to start a new topic in their math textbooks.

- Students who have transferred from another school may not have been introduced to some of these skills. Encourage students to do their best and assure them you will help them learn any needed skills.

Alternative Assessment Strategy

- Oral administration is appropriate for younger students or those whose native language is not English. Read the skills title and directions one section at a time. Check students' understanding by asking them to tell you how they will do the first exercise in the group.

Name_____

Classify Shapes

Circle the shape that does not belong.

1.

2.

_____   _____

Identify Sides and Angles

Write the number of sides and angles for each figure.

3.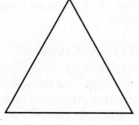

_____ sides

_____ angles

4.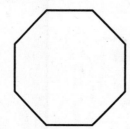

_____ sides

_____ angles

5.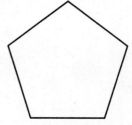

_____ sides

_____ angles

6.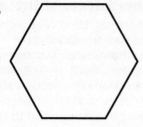

_____ sides

_____ angles

7.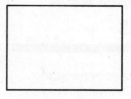

_____ sides

_____ angles

8.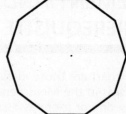

_____ sides

_____ angles

Classify Shapes

**MEASUREMENT/
GEOMETRY
5**

Circle the shape that does not belong.

1.
_____

2.
_____

Identify Sides and Angles

Write the number of sides and angles for each figure.

3.

_____ sides

_____ angles

4.

_____ sides

_____ angles

5.

_____ sides

_____ angles

6.

_____ sides

_____ angles

7.

_____ sides

_____ angles

8.

_____ sides

_____ angles

© Macmillan/McGraw-Hill

26A

MEASUREMENT AND GEOMETRY 5 PREREQUISITE SKILLS

The skills listed in this chart are those identified as major prerequisite skills for students' success in the Measurement and Geometry lessons. Each skill is covered by one or more assessment items from page 26A as shown in the middle column. The right column provides the page numbers for the lessons in this book that reteach Measurement and Geometry prerequisite skills.

Skill Name	Assessment Items	Lesson Pages
Classify Shapes	1-2	T130-T131
Identify Sides and Angles	3-8	T132-T133

MEASUREMENT AND GEOMETRY 5 ASSESSMENT

Assessment Goal
This assessment covers skills identified as necessary for success in Measurement and Geometry.

Getting Started
- Allow students time to look over the assessment. Point out the labels that identify the skills covered.
- Have students find math vocabulary terms used in the assessment. List vocabulary terms on the board as students identify them. If necessary, review the meanings of all essential math vocabulary.

Introducing the Assessment
- Explain to students that these pages will help you know if they are ready to start a new topic in their math textbooks.
- Students who have transferred from another school may not have been introduced to some of these skills. Encourage students to do their best and assure them you will help them learn any needed skills.

Alternative Assessment Strategy
- Oral administration is appropriate for younger students or those whose native language is not English. Read the skills title and directions one section at a time. Check students' understanding by asking them to tell you how they will do the first exercise in the group.

Comparing Angles

Compare each pair of angles. Write > or <.

A ◯ B   C ◯ D   F ◯ G

Measuring Line Segments

Measure the length of each line segment to the nearest $\frac{1}{2}$ inch.

Length

4. |——————————| _____

5. |————————————————| _____

6. |————| _____

Identify Equal Parts

Circle the figures that show equal parts.

7.   8.   9.   10.

  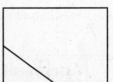 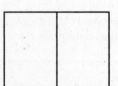

Name_____

Comparing Angles

Compare each pair of angles. Write > or <.

1.

2.

3.

A ◯ B   C ◯ D   F ◯ G

Measuring Line Segments

Measure the length of each line segment to the nearest $\frac{1}{2}$ inch.

Length

4. _____   _____

5. _____   _____

6. _____   _____

Identify Equal Parts

Circle the figures that show equal parts.

7.   8.   9.   10.

© Macmillan/McGraw-Hill

27A

MEASUREMENT AND GEOMETRY 6
PREREQUISITE SKILLS

The skills listed in this chart are those identified as major prerequisite skills for students' success in the Measurement and Geometry lessons. Each skill is covered by one or more assessment items from page 27A as shown in the middle column. The right column provides the page numbers for the lessons in this book that reteach Measurement and Geometry prerequisite skills.

Skill Name	Assessment Items	Lesson Pages
Comparing Angles	1-3	T134-T135
Measuring Line Segments	4-6	T136-T137
Identify Equal Parts	7-10	T138-T139

MEASUREMENT
AND GEOMETRY 6
ASSESSMENT

Assessment Goal

This assessment covers skills identified as necessary for success in Measurement and Geometry.

Getting Started

- Allow students time to look over the assessment. Point out the labels that identify the skills covered.

- Have students find math vocabulary terms used in the assessment. List vocabulary terms on the board as students identify them. If necessary, review the meanings of all essential math vocabulary.

Introducing the Assessment

- Explain to students that these pages will help you know if they are ready to start a new topic in their math textbooks.

- Students who have transferred from another school may not have been introduced to some of these skills. Encourage students to do their best and assure them you will help them learn any needed skills.

Alternative Assessment Strategy

- Oral administration is appropriate for younger students or those whose native language is not English. Read the skills title and directions one section at a time. Check students' understanding by asking them to tell you how they will do the first exercise in the group.

Name_____

Frequency Tables

Complete the table.

Students Who Attend Special Assembly

Class	Tally	Number
3-1	卌 II	7
3-2	卌 卌 I	1. _____
3-3	III	2. _____
3-4	卌 卌 卌 I	3. _____

Kinds of Pets

Pet	Tally	Number
dogs	卌 卌 卌	15
cats	卌 卌 IIII	4. _____
fish	卌 I	5. _____
rabbits	卌 III	6. _____

Frequency Tables

DATA/PROBABILITY
1

Complete the table.

Students Who Attend Special Assembly

Class	Tally	Number
3-1	|||| ||	7
3-2	|||| ||||		1. _____
3-3	|||	2. _____
3-4	|||| |||| ||||		3. _____

Kinds of Pets

Pet	Tally	Number
dogs	|||| |||| ||||	15
cats	|||| |||| ||||	4. _____
fish	||||		5. _____
rabbits	|||| |||	6. _____

DATA AND PROBABILITY 1
PREREQUISITE SKILLS

The skills listed in this chart are those identified as major prerequisite skills for students' success in the Data and Probility lessons. Each skill is covered by one or more assessment items from page 28A as shown in the middle column. The right column provides the page numbers or the lessons in this book that reteach Data and Probability prerequisite skills.

Skill Name	Assessment Items	Lesson Pages
Frequency Tables	1-6	T144-T145

DATA AND PROBABILITY 1 ASSESSMENT

Assessment Goal
This assessment covers skills identified as necessary for success in Data and Probability.

Getting Started
- Allow students time to look over the assessment. Point out the labels that identify the skills covered.
- Have students find math vocabulary terms used in the assessment. List vocabulary terms on the board as students identify them. If necessary, review the meanings of all essential math vocabulary.

Introducing the Assessment
- Explain to students that these pages will help you know if they are ready to start a new topic in their math textbooks.
- Students who have transferred from another school may not have been introduced to some of these skills. Encourage students to do their best and assure them you will help them learn any needed skills.

Alternative Assessment Strategy
- Oral administration is appropriate for younger students or those whose native language is not English. Read the skills title and directions one section at a time. Check students' understanding by asking them to tell you how they will do the first exercise in the group.

Skill Builder
Lessons and Activities

USING THE LESSON

Activity 1 Lesson Goal
- Find which numbers come before, after, and between other numbers.

What the Student Needs To Know
- Read a number line.
- Use place value in one-, two-, and three-digit numbers to find numbers on a number line.
- Recognize numbers *before, after,* and *between* other numbers on a number line.

Getting Started
Ask each student to create a number line from 60 to 65. Ask:
- *What number comes just before 61?* (60)
- *What number comes just after 63?* (64)
- *What number comes between 61 and 63?* (62)

What Can I Do?
- Read the question and the response. Then read and discuss the examples. Display a number line from 365 to 375. Ask:
- *Why is a number line a helpful tool to find number order?* (It can help you see which number is before, after, or between other numbers.)
- *How can you use a number line to figure out the number that comes just before 367?* (Find 367 on the number line. Go back 1. 366 comes just before 367.)
- *When you go back 1 from 367, are you going back in the ones place, tens place, or hundreds place?* (ones place)
- *How can you use a number line to figure out the number that comes just after 372?* (Find 372 on the number line. Go forward 1. 373 comes just after 372.)
- *When you go forward 1 from 372, are you going forward in the ones place, tens place, or hundreds place?* (ones place)

T2 Grade 3, Activity 1

Name _____

Order Numbers

Learn

Use a number line.

<----+----+----+----+----+----+----+----+----+----+----+---->
365 366 367 368 369 370 371 372 373 374 375

> **What Can I Do?**
> I want to find which numbers come before, after, and between other numbers.

What number comes just **before** 367?	What number comes just **after** 372?
Find 367 on the number line.	Find 372 on the number line.
Go back 1.	Go forward 1.
366 comes just **before** 367.	373 comes just **after** 372.

What number comes **between** 369 and 371?

Find 369 and 371 on the number line.
Find the number that comes just before 371 and just after 369.

370 comes **between** 369 and 371.

Try It • Use the number line to answer each question.

<----+----+----+----+----+----+----+----+----+----+----+---->
502 503 504 505 506 507 508 509 510 511 512

1. What number comes just *before* 512? __511__
2. What number comes just *after* 509? __510__
3. What number comes *between* 504 and 506? __505__

2

WHAT IF THE STUDENT CAN'T

Read a Number Line
- Remind the student that a number line can start and end on any number. Discuss the number line from 502 to 512 in Try It, page 6.
- Have the student copy that number line and use it to answer other number order questions. For example, say: *What number comes between 506 and 508?* (507)

Use Place Value in One-, Two-, and Three-Digit Numbers to Find Numbers on a Number Line
- Use place-value models to stress that in a two-digit number like 51, the 5 is in the tens place and the 1 is in the ones place. Explain that to find the number just after 51, go forward 1 in the ones place. Say: *What number is just after 51?* (52)
- Follow a similar procedure for a three-digit number like 260. Say: *What number is just before 260?* (259)

Power Practice • Write the number that comes just *before*. You may draw a number line to help.

4. _____ 14   5. _____ 27   6. _____ 60

7. _____ 95   8. _____ 132   9. _____ 418

10. _____ 521   11. _____ 789   12. _____ 656

Write the number that comes just *after*. You may draw a number line to help.

Learn with Partners & Parents

13. 17 _____   14. 55 _____

15. 113 _____   16. 309 _____

17. 667 _____   18. 800 _____

Write the number that comes *between*. You may draw a number line to help.

19. 4 _____ 6   20. 28 _____ 30

21. 99 _____ 101   22. 310 _____ 312

23. 492 _____ 494   24. 944 _____ 946

I Spy a Number
- Take turns. One player spies a three-digit number in a store, on a license plate, or on a sign. The player must say, "I spy the number _____," and read the number aloud.
- The second player earns 1 point for telling the number that comes just *before* and another point for telling the number that comes just *after* the spied number.
- Write down all the numbers. The first player to get 25 points is the winner.

3

- How can you use a number line to figure out the number that comes between 370 and 372? (Find 370 and 372 on the number line. Go back 1 from 372. Go forward 1 from 370. 371 comes between 370 and 372.)
- Have students read their answers aloud. Ask them to point to their answers on the number line.
- For each incorrect answer, have students draw a number line, write and circle the correct answer, and draw arrows going forward, back, or between.

Power Practice
- Call on volunteers to model their answers on number lines for several of the answers.
- Have students explain how to use a number line to order numbers just before, after, or between other numbers.

Learn with Partners & Parents
- If players disagree about which number comes before or after a given number, they can sketch a number line to help them confirm the correct sequence.

WHAT IF THE STUDENT CAN'T

Recognize Numbers *Before*, *After*, and *Between* Other Numbers on a Number Line
- Remind the student that on a number line, the number just *before* another number is 1 to the left of it. The number just *after* another number is 1 to the right of it. The number just *between* two numbers is 1 to the left of the greater number and 1 to the right of the lesser number.
- Use number lines to illustrate these concepts daily until the student can name numbers just before, after, and between other numbers automatically.

Complete the Power Practice
- Discuss each incorrect answer. Have the student create a number line for any exercise he or she missed. Then ask the student to write the correct answer and read it aloud as a sentence. For example: *945 comes between 944 and 946.*

USING THE LESSON

Activity 2 Lesson Goal
- Order whole numbers from greatest to least.

What the Student Needs to Know
- Understand place value through hundreds.
- Order numbers from 0 to 9.

Getting Started
Find out what students know about ordering whole numbers. Write the following numbers on the board.

429, 16, 95, 3, 700

Ask:
- *Which of these numbers is the greatest?* (700)
- *Which of these numbers is the least?* (3)
- *Which number is greater, 95 or 16?* (95)
- *Which number is less, 95 or 429?* (95)
- *How do you know that one number is greater than another?* (Possible answer: The number that is farther along on a number line is greater.)

What Can I Do?
Read the question and the response. Then read and discuss the example. Ask:
- *Why do you start at the left and work to the right?* (Because the values at the left have the greatest place value, and the place values get less as you move to the right. For example, a hundred is greater than a ten, which is greater than a one.)
- *How do you know that the two numbers that have a value in the hundreds place are greater than the two numbers that don't?* (Because the numbers that don't have a value written in the hundreds place have 0 hundreds, and 0 is less than 1 and less than 3.)

Ordering Whole Numbers

Learn

What Can I Do?
I want to order whole numbers from greatest to least.

Use place value.

Look for the greatest number in each place. Start at the left.

hundreds	tens	ones
1	7	5
	9	8
3	5	2
	3	4

Look at the hundreds place. Two numbers have no hundreds. Since 3 is greater than 1, that number is the greatest.

352, 175, _____, _____

Then look at the tens of the other numbers.

hundreds	tens	ones
✓ 1	7	5
	9	8
✓ 3	5	2
	3	4

Since 9 is greater than 3, that number is next.

352, 175, 98, 34

4

© Macmillan/McGraw-Hill

WHAT IF THE STUDENT CAN'T

Understand Place Value Through Hundreds
- Have the student write a three-digit number and read it aloud. Explain that each digit can be seen as one place in a place-value chart. Then have the student tell you how many hundreds, tens, and ones are in the number.
- Have the student practice writing two-digit and three-digit numbers in a place-value chart until it can be done with ease.

Order Numbers from 0 to 9
- Have the student draw a number line from 0 to 9. Explain that as you move to the right on the line, the numbers are greater. At the same time, as you move left on the number line, the numbers are lesser. Have the student practice finding pairs of numbers on the line and identifying the greater and lesser of each pair.

Name_____

Try It • Use place value. Order from *greatest* to *least*.

1. 65, 28, 76, 82, 13 _____

2. 116, 193, 127, 188, 100 _____

Power Practice • Order from *greatest* to *least*.

3. 73, 88, 79, 94, 65 _____

4. 315, 195, 327, 255, 97 _____

5. 56, 38, 60, 154, 75 _____

6. 465, 856, 246, 365, 754 _____

7. 38, 47, 42, 29, 37 _____

8. 118, 87, 93, 104, 90 _____

9. 159, 167, 219, 178, 146 _____

10. 68, 73, 69, 61, 75 _____

© Macmillan/McGraw-Hill

_____

5

• The number 98 has 9 tens, while 175 has only 7 tens. When you order from greatest to least, which number comes first, 98 or 175? (175 because it has 1 hundred and 98 has 0 hundreds.)

Try It
Look at Exercise 1. Have students write each number in a place-value chart before ordering them from greatest to least. Ask:

• *What is the greatest value in the tens place?* (8) *What is the least value in the tens place?* (1)

• *What is the greatest value in the ones place?* (8) *Which number has this value?* (28) *Where in the order of numbers does 28 fall?* (It is the second-least number.)

Look at Exercise 2. Have students write each number in a place-value chart before ordering them from greatest to least. Ask:

• *Which place value should you use to order the numbers?* (tens place) *Why?* (Because all the numbers have the same value in the hundreds place.)

Power Practice
• Have students complete the practice items. Then review each answer.

• Select a few of the exercises and have students use place value to demonstrate how to order them from greatest to least.

WHAT IF THE STUDENT CAN'T

• Give the student sets of three numbers from 0 to 9. Have the student order each set from greatest to least. The student should continue practicing until the procedure can be done with ease.

Complete the Power Practice
• Discuss each incorrect answer. Have the student write each number in the exercise in a place-value chart. Then have the student order the numbers by comparing digits beginning in the hundreds column and moving right to the next place value or values as needed.

USING THE LESSON

Activity 3 Lesson Goal
- Find the nearest ten.

What the Student Needs To Know
- Count by tens.
- Read a number line.
- Identify which of two whole numbers is less.

Getting Started
Determine what students know about finding the closest ten. Display a number line from 20 to 30, with 23 circled. Say:
- Which two tens is the number 23 between? (20 and 30)
- *Which ten is 23 closer to, 20 or 30?* (20)
- *How can you tell?* (23 is 7 spaces from 30 but only 3 spaces from 20. 3 is less than 7, so 23 is closer to 20 than 30.)
- Display a number line from 60 to 70 with 68 circled. Say: *What two tens is 68 between?* (60 and 70) *Count the number of spaces from 60 to 68.* (8) *Count the number of spaces from 68 to 70.* (2) *Which ten is 68 closer to, 60 or 70?* (70) *Explain your answer.* (2 is less than 8, so 68 is closer to 70 than 60.)

What Can I Do?
- Read the question and the response. Then read and discuss the examples. Ask:
- *How is a number line useful for rounding to the closest ten?* (It shows the two tens a number is between and helps you count the spaces to each ten.)
- *What are the steps to figure out which ten a number is closer to?* (Circle the number on the number line. Count the spaces from the lesser ten to the number. Count the spaces from the number to the greater ten. Compare the amount of spaces. The lesser amount tells you which ten is closer.)

Name ______________________

Round to the Nearest Ten

Activity 3

Learn

Use a number line.

Find the ten that 12 is closer to.

Circle 12 on the number line.

10 11 (12) 13 14 15 16 17 18 19 20

The number 12 is between two tens on the number line. It is between 10 and 20.

Count the number of spaces from 10 to 12. There are 2 spaces.

Count the number of spaces from 12 to 20. There are 8 spaces.

So, 12 is closer to 10.

Find the ten that 27 is closer to.

20 21 22 23 24 25 26 (27) 28 29 30

The number 27 is between the tens 20 and 30.

It is 7 spaces away from 20. It is 3 spaces away from 30.

So, 27 is closer to 30.

Try It • **Choose the closer ten. Circle *a* or *b*.**

1. Which ten is closer to 19?

10 11 12 13 14 15 16 17 18 **19** 20

a. 10 (b. 20)

2. Which ten is closer to 43?

40 41 42 **43** 44 45 46 47 48 49 50

(a. 40) b. 50

© Macmillan/McGraw-Hill

WHAT IF THE STUDENT CAN'T

Count by Tens
- Have the student practice counting by tens from 10 to 100 a few times a day until the student can do so easily.

Read a Number Line
- Read with the student all the numbers on a number line on page 14. Say a number and have the student point to it.
- Help the student draw a number line showing all the numbers between two consecutive tens. Have the student count the spaces from one ten to the next.

Identify Which of Two Numbers is Less
- Write a number line from 0 to 9. Remind the student that in a pair of whole numbers, the number closer to 0 is less than the other. Circle two numbers on the line. Have the student tell which number is closer to 0. Repeat daily until the student can quickly name the lesser whole number in a pair.

Choose the closer ten. Circle a or b.

3. Which ten is closer to 21?

20 **21** 22 23 24 25 26 27 28 29 30

   a. 20   **b.** 30

4. Which ten is closer to 64?

60 61 62 63 **64** 65 66 67 68 69 70

   a. 60   **b.** 70

5. Which ten is closer to 58?

50 51 52 53 54 55 56 57 **58** 59 60

   a. 50   **b.** 60

6. Which ten is closer to 86?

80 81 82 83 84 85 **86** 87 88 89 90

   a. 80   **b.** 90

Power Practice • **Choose the closer ten. Circle a or b. You may draw a number line to help.**

7. 11

   a. 10 **b.** 20

8. 37

   a. 30 **b.** 40

9. 26

   a. 20 **b.** 30

10. 53

   a. 50 **b.** 60

11. 22

   a. 20 **b.** 30

12. 79

   a. 70 **b.** 80

13. 88

   a. 80 **b.** 90

14. 74

   a. 70 **b.** 80

15. 62

   a. 60 **b.** 70

7

Try It

- Call on volunteers to say the number in Exercise 1 and in Exercise 2 and then find it on the number line. Have students identify the two tens on the number line. Ask:
- *Which ten is the number closer to? How can you tell?* (Answers will vary.)
- For each incorrect answer, have students copy the corresponding number line, draw curved arrows while counting the spaces, and explain the correct answer. For example: *19 is 1 space away from 20 and 9 spaces away from 10. 1 is less than 9, so 19 is closer to 20. 43 is 3 spaces away from 40 and 7 spaces away from 50. 3 is less than 7 so 43 is closer to 40.*

Power Practice

- Call on volunteers to model their answers on number lines for several of the answers.
- Have students summarize what they learned by telling what finding the closer ten to a number means. (to go up or down to the ten closer to the number on the number line)

WHAT IF THE STUDENT CAN'T

Complete the Power Practice

- Discuss each incorrect answer. Have the student say the two tens that the number falls between and show on a number line which ten is closer.
- Select several exercises and have volunteers show their work on place-value charts. Compare this method with using number lines to round to the nearest ten. Encourage the student to explain which method he or she prefers.

USING THE LESSON

Activity 4 Lesson Goal
- Round numbers to the nearest ten, hundred, or thousand.

What the Student Needs to Know
- Count by tens, hundreds, and thousands.
- Read a number line.
- Identify digits in the ones, tens, hundreds, and thousands places.

Getting Started
Find out what students know about tens, hundreds, and thousands. Say:
- *Let's count to 100 by tens. I'll start: 10, 20, 30... . Now you continue to count to 100.*
- *Now let's count to 1000 by hundreds. I'll start: 100, 200, 300... . Now you continue to count to 1000.*

What Can I Do?
Read the question and the response. Then read and discuss the examples. Ask:
- *What does "round to the nearest ten" mean?* (to go up or down to the nearest ten on the number line) *When do we round a number down?* (when the ones digit is 1, 2, 3, or 4) *When do we round a number up?* (when the ones digit is 5 or greater) *What is 46 rounded to the nearest ten?* (46 rounded to the nearest ten is 50)
- *How can we round 237 to the nearest hundred?* (Look on the number line and see which hundred it is closest to. It is closest to 200.) *How would we round 250 to the nearest hundred?* (Round up to 300.) *Why doesn't 250 round to 200?* (because there is a 5 in the tens place)
- *Look at the number 3,290. What place is to the right of the thousands place?* (the hundreds place) *What number is in the hundreds place?* (2) *Let's say we want to round 3,590 to the nearest thousand. What should we do?* (Look at the hundreds place, the place to the right of the

---

Name_____

Round to Tens, Hundreds, and Thousands

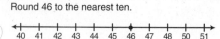

Learn

What Can I Do?
I want to round to the nearest ten, hundred, or thousand.

Use a number line.

Round 46 to the nearest ten.

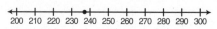
40 41 42 43 44 45 46 47 48 49 50 51

The number 46 is between 40 and 50. It is closer to 50. So, 46 rounded to the nearest ten is 50.

Round 237 to the nearest hundred.

200 210 220 230 240 250 260 270 280 290 300

The number 237 is between 200 and 300. It is closer to 200. So, 237 rounded to the nearest hundred is 200.

Round 3,290 to the nearest thousand without using a number line.

Look at the place to the right of the thousands place.

3,**2**90

If the digit is less than 5, round down.
If the digit is 5 or greater, round up.

2 < 5; so, round 3,290 down to 3,000.

So, 3,290 rounded to the nearest thousand is 3,000.

Try It • Round to the nearest ten. Use the number line to help.

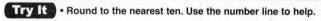
1. 20 21 22 23 24 25 26 27 28 29 30

28 __30__

2. 80 81 82 83 84 85 86 87 88 89 90

83 __80__

8

© Macmillan/McGraw-Hill

WHAT IF THE STUDENT CAN'T

Count by Tens, Hundreds, and Thousands
- Practice counting by tens, hundreds, and thousands a few times each day until the student can do so with ease.
- The student might use tens and hundreds models to count by tens and hundreds.

Read a Number Line
- Sketch on the board three different number lines, one showing tens, one showing hundreds, and one showing thousands. Have the student come to the board and help you insert smaller numbers between the points you have labeled. For example, he or she can add 21, 22, 23, 24, and so on, between 20 and 30; or the student can add 110, 120, 130, and so on, between 100 and 200.

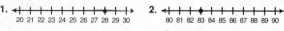

Round to the nearest hundred. Use the number line to help.

3.

700 710 720 730 740 750 760 770 780 790 800

721 _____

4.

400 410 420 430 440 450 460 470 480 490 500

475 _____

Round to the nearest thousand. Look at the digit to the right of the thousands place to round up or round down.

5. 1,341 _____   6. 6,752 _____   7. 4,901 _____

Power Practice • Round to the nearest *ten.*

8. 12 _____   9. 38 _____   10. 59 _____

11. 26 _____   12. 74 _____   13. 63 _____

Round to the nearest *hundred.*

14. 187 _____   15. 313 _____   16. 578 _____

17. 845 _____   18. 529 _____   19. 767 _____

Round to the nearest *thousand.*

20. 2,399 _____   21. 3,860 _____   22. 7,089 _____

23. 8,615 _____   24. 5,453 _____   25. 6,524 _____

9

© Macmillan/McGraw-Hill

---

thousands place. There is a 5 there, so we round up to 4,000.)

Try It

Have students say the number to be rounded and then find it on the number line. Have them identify the lesser ten and the greater ten on the number line. Ask:

- *Is the number closer to the lesser ten or the greater ten?* (Answers will vary.)

- *In 28, what number is in the ones place?* (8) *How does this number help you figure out whether to round up or down?* (I know that if the ones digit is 5 or greater, I should round up. 8 is greater than 5, so I round up to 30.)

- *In 83, what is the ones digit?* (3) *Should you round up or down, and why?* (I should round down, because 3 is less than 5. I'll round down to 80.)

Power Practice

- Select several of the exercises and have volunteers describe some different methods they can use to show that the answer they have written is correct.

- Review some ways that students can help themselves decide whether to round up or down. For example, they can sketch a number line and use it to estimate whether the number they are rounding is closest to the greater or lesser ten, hundred, or thousand. Or they can look at the digit to the right of the place they are rounding to. If that digit is 5 or greater, they should round up. If it is 4 or less, they should round down.

WHAT IF THE STUDENT CAN'T

Identify Digits in the Ones, Tens, Hundreds, and Thousands Places

- Emphasize that in a whole number the last digit is in the ones place. Make sure the student knows that the digit to the left of the ones place is in the tens place. Have the student also point to the hundreds and thousands places.

- Have the student point to each number in the Power Practice and identify the digit in the ones, tens, hundreds, and thousands places as appropriate.

Complete the Power Practice

- Discuss each incorrect answer. Have the student model any exercise he or she missed using a sketched number line.

- Have the student identify the digit to the right of the place he or she is rounding to. Then have him or her round up or down according to the rule.

Activity 5 Lesson Goal

- Round numbers to the nearest ten or hundred.

What the Student Needs to Know

- Count by tens.
- Count by hundreds and thousands.
- Understand place value to thousands.

Getting Started

Find out what students know about tens, hundreds, and thousands. Have them count by 10s to 100, 100s to 1,000, and 1,000s to 10,000. Ask:

- *When you count by 10s, 100s, and 1,000s, what happens to the first (left) digit of the numbers as you count?* (It increases by one.)
- *What happens to the other digits in the numbers?* (They remain zero.)

What Can I Do?

Read the question and the response. Then read and discuss the examples. Ask:

- *What does it mean to say that 26 rounds to 30?* (26 is closer to 30 than 20)
- *What does it mean to say that 302 rounds to 300?* (302 is closer to 300 than 400)
- *What does it mean to say that 3,472 rounds to 3,000?* (3,472 is closer to 3,000 than 4,000)
- *When a digit you are rounding is a 5, do you round up or down?* (up)

Name _____

Rounding

Learn

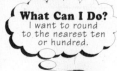

What Can I Do?
I want to round to the nearest ten or hundred.

Round to the given place value.

To round to the nearest **ten**, use the *ones* digit.

26 rounds to 30.   32 rounds to 30.

To round to the nearest **hundred**, use the *tens* digit.

257 rounds to 300.   302 rounds to 300.

To round to the nearest **thousand**, use the *hundreds* digit.

2,901 rounds to 3,000.   3,472 rounds to 3,000.

Try It • Circle the numbers.

1. Circle the numbers that round to 50.

42 43 44 (45 46 47 48 49 50 51 52 53 54) 55 56 57 58

2. Circle the numbers that round to 600.

530 540 (550 560 570 580 590 600 610 620 630 640) 650 660

Round each number to the nearest *ten*.

3. 76 __80__   4. 36 __40__   5. 24 __20__   6. 57 __60__

7. 85 __90__   8. 71 __70__   9. 91 __90__   10. 65 __70__

Round each number to the nearest *hundred*.

11. 631 __600__   12. 923 __900__   13. 349 __300__   14. 558 __600__

15. 815 __800__   16. 128 __100__   17. 644 __600__   18. 157 __200__

10

© Macmillan/McGraw-Hill

WHAT IF THE STUDENT CAN'T

Count by Tens

- Have the student use tens models to illustrate the numbers that result when you count by ten. Then have the student write down the sequence of numbers.

- Have the student practice counting by 10s to 100 until it can be done with ease.

Count by Hundreds and Thousands

- Use models to represent hundreds and thousands. Have the student count the models by ones. Then explain what each model represents and have the student count again, this time identifying what is being counted as a hundred or as a thousand.

- Have the student practice counting by hundreds and thousands until it can be done with ease.

Round to the Nearest Ten, Hundred, or Thousand

Activity 6

Learn

What Can I Do?

I want to round to the nearest ten, hundred, or thousand.

Round 6,803 to the nearest thousand.

Step 1
Look at the place to the right of the thousands place.

6,803

Step 2
If the digit is less than 5, round down to 6,000.

If the digit is 5 or greater, round up to 7,000.

8 > 5, so round 6,803 up to 7,000.

So, 6,803 rounded to the nearest thousand is 7,000.

Try It . Round to the nearest ten, hundred, or thousand. Fill in the blanks.

1. Round 29 to the nearest ten.

29 is between _____ and _____.

29 rounds to _____.

2. Round 538 to the nearest hundred.

538 is between _____ and _____.

538 rounds to _____.

Power Practice • Round to the nearest *ten*.

3. 22 _____

4. 86 _____

5. 45 _____

Round to the nearest *hundred*.

6. 271 _____

7. 749 _____

8. 615 _____

Round to the nearest *thousand*.

9. 4,672 _____

10. 3,333 _____

11. 8,501 _____

11

© Macmillan/McGraw-Hill

WHAT IF THE STUDENT CAN'T

Count by Tens, Hundreds, and Thousands

- Practice counting by tens, hundreds, and thousands a few times each day until the student can do so with ease.
- The student might use tens and hundreds blocks to count by tens and hundreds.

Identify Digits in the Ones, Tens, Hundreds, and Thousands Places

- Emphasize that in a whole number the last digit is in the ones place. Make sure the student knows that the digit to the left of the ones place is in the tens place. Have the

student also point to the hundreds and thousands places.

- Have the student point to each number in the Power Practice and identify the digit in the ones, tens, hundreds, and thousands places as appropriate.

Complete the Power Practice

- Discuss each incorrect answer. Have the student model any exercise he or she missed using a sketched number line.
- Have the student identify the digit to the right of the place he or she is rounding to. Then have him or her round up or down according to the rule.

USING THE LESSON

Activity 6 Lesson Goal

- Round numbers to the nearest ten, hundred, or thousand.

What the Student Needs to Know

- Count by tens, hundreds, and thousands.
- Identify digits in the ones, tens, hundreds, and thousands places.

Getting Started

Write the number 4,321 on the board. Ask:

- *What number is in the hundreds place?* (3) *What number is in the ones place?* (1) *What number is in the thousands place?* (4) *What number is in the tens place?* (2)

What Can I Do?

Read the question and the response. Then read and discuss the examples. Ask:

- *What does "round to the nearest thousand" mean?* (to go up or down to the nearest thousand)
- *Should we round 6,803 up or down?* (up) *Why should we round this number up?* (The digit to the right of the thousands place is 8. 8 is greater than 5, so we round up.)
- *What is 6,803 rounded to the nearest thousand?* (7,000)

Try It

For each of the exercises, have the students say the number to be rounded and then tell which multiples of 10 or 100 it falls between. Ask:

- *Should you round 29 up or down?* (up) *Why?* (because 9 is greater than 5)
- *In Exercise 2, is 538 closer to 500 or 600?* (500) *Should you round up or down?* (down) *Why?* (because 3 is less than 5)

Power Practice

- Have the student complete the practice items. Then review each answer.

Activity 7 Lesson Goal
- Compare two numbers.

What the Student Needs to Know
- Read a number line.
- Use the > and < signs.

Getting Started
Find out what students know about comparing numbers. Write the numbers 16 and 83 on the board. Ask:

- *When you count from 1 to 100, which of these numbers do you come to first?* (16)

Find out what students know about number lines. Draw a number line from 1 to 10 on the board. Ask:

- *In which direction do the numbers on the number line increase or become greater?* (from left to right)

- *In which direction do the numbers decrease?* (from right to left)

What Can I Do?
- Read the question and the response. Then read and discuss the example. Ask:

- *How can you tell that 43 is greater than 34 using the number line?* (43 is to the right of 34 on the number line, and the number to the right is always greater.)

- *How can you use place value to check your answer?* (Check the numbers in the tens place of both numbers. 43 has a 4 in the tens place, and 34 has a 3 in the tens place. Since 4 is greater than 3, you know that 43 is greater than 34.)

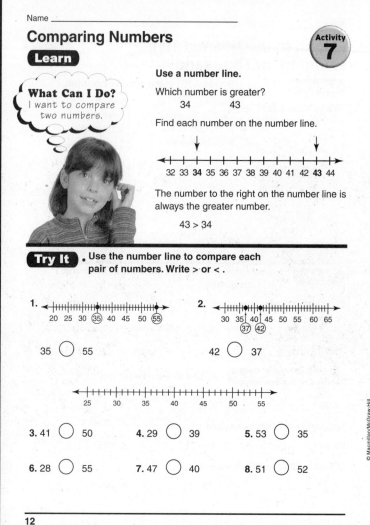

Name _____

Comparing Numbers

Learn

What Can I Do?
I want to compare two numbers.

Use a number line.

Which number is greater?

34   43

Find each number on the number line.

32 33 **34** 35 36 37 38 39 40 41 42 **43** 44

The number to the right on the number line is always the greater number.

43 > 34

Try It . Use the number line to compare each pair of numbers. Write > or < .

1.
20 25 30 (35) 40 45 50 (55)

35 ◯ 55

2.
30 35 40 45 50 55 60 65
(37) (42)

42 ◯ 37

25   30   35   40   45   50   55

3. 41 ◯ 50   4. 29 ◯ 39   5. 53 ◯ 35

6. 28 ◯ 55   7. 47 ◯ 40   8. 51 ◯ 52

12

© Macmillan/McGraw-Hill

WHAT IF THE STUDENT CAN'T

Read a Number Line
- Draw a number line from 10 to 30 and read the numbers aloud. Then have the student do so. Point to numbers on the line and have the student identify them. Be sure the student understands that the numbers increase as you move from left to right
- Have the student draw a number line from 40 to 60, labeling each number.

Use the > and < Signs
- Explain that these signs are used to compare two numbers. In a comparison like 9 > 2, the > sign means that 9 *is greater than* 2. The comparison can also be written 2 < 9, where the < sign means that 2 *is less than* 9.

Name_____

```
←┼┼┼┼┼┼┼┼┼┼┼┼┼┼┼┼┼┼┼┼┼┼┼┼┼┼┼┼┼┼┼┼┼┼┼┼┼┼┼┼→
  50    55    60    65    70    75    80    85    90    95
```

9. 57 ◯ 75   **10.** 66 ◯ 56   **11.** 73 ◯ 83

12. 79 ◯ 59   **13.** 60 ◯ 81   **14.** 77 ◯ 57

15. 82 ◯ 79   **16.** 90 ◯ 59   **17.** 74 ◯ 73

```
←┼┼┼┼┼┼┼┼┼┼┼┼┼┼┼┼┼┼┼┼┼┼┼┼┼┼┼┼┼┼┼┼┼┼┼┼┼┼┼┼→
 100   105   110   115   120   125   130   135   140   145
```

18. 111 ◯ 117

19. 134 ◯ 128

20. 130 ◯ 138

21. 107 ◯ 113

22. 128 ◯ 132

23. 106 ◯ 119

24. 137 ◯ 131

25. 127 ◯ 107

© Macmillan/McGraw-Hill

Learn with Partners & Parents

One More, One Less

Any number of people can play.

• Choose a number from 50 to 59 and write it down. Then look for numbers that are one more than your number and one less than your number. Look in the grocery store, at home, or on license plates and billboards. List where you found the number.

• When you look for numbers, you must find the exact number. If you are looking for 54, then you must find 54. The digits cannot be part of another number, such as 8,542.

• When you find both these numbers, start looking for numbers that are two more and two less than your number. Keep playing until you are looking for zero.

• The person who has found more numbers wins.

13

Try It

Have students look at Exercise 1. Ask:

• *Which number is farther to the right?* (55) *farther to the left?* (35)

Then have the students complete Exercises 1 and 2.

Have students look at Exercise 3. Have a volunteer find both numbers on the number line and identify which is farther right. Then have students complete Exercises 3–8.

Power Practice

• Have students complete the practice items in both sets. Then review each answer.

• Select a few of the exercises from both sets. Have a volunteer find both numbers on the appropriate number line and compare them to one another.

Learn with Partners & Parents

• Suggest that students work in pairs and play the game for a week. Students should also look in text books, newspapers or magazines.

• Have students keep track of the numbers they start with and of those that they find in order to calculate their score after a week.

WHAT IF THE STUDENT CAN'T

• If the student has difficulty writing the signs correctly, mention that the opening in the sign should be toward the greater number. So, if you compare 8 and 4, the open end of the sign will face the 8, and the comparison will either read 8 > 4 or 4 < 8.

• Have the student practice comparing single-digit numbers until the concept becomes clear.

Complete the Power Practice

• Have the student label both number lines by writing "less" on the left side of the line and "greater" on the right side.

• Discuss each incorrect answer. Have the student find both numbers on the number line and identify which is less and which is greater. Then have the student complete the exercise correctly.

Activity 8 Lesson Goal

- Use a number line to complete an addition pattern that goes up by ones.

What the Student Needs To Know

- Count on by ones.
- Read a number line.

Getting Started

Find out what students know about completing an addition pattern. Say:

- *Let's start with the numbers in the pattern 1, 2, 3. Each number goes up by 1. Start at 3. What number comes just after 3?* (4)
- *Now, you continue the pattern up to 10. Start at 5.* (5, 6, 7, 8, 9, 10)

What Can I Do?

Read the question and the response. Then read and discuss the examples. Ask:

- *What do the dark arrows on the number line from 0 to 12 mean?* (They show the direction in the number pattern.)
- *How can you figure out the missing numbers in the pattern?* (Each number goes up by 1, so count on by ones from 7 to find the missing numbers.)
- *Is the addition pattern going up or down?* (up)
- Do the same for the number line in the second example.

Try It

Have students say each number in the pattern and point to it on the number line. Have them count on by ones to complete each pattern. Ask:

- *Is the addition pattern going up on the number line or down on the number line?* (up)

Power Practice

- Have the student complete the practice items. Then review each answer.

Name _____

Counting On

Learn

What Can I Do? I want to complete an addition pattern.

Use a number line to count on.

Complete the addition pattern.

0 1 2 3 4 5 6 7 8 9 10 11 12

Each number goes up by 1. Count on by ones. Start at 7.

7, 8, 9, 10, _11_, _12_

Complete the addition pattern.

65 66 67 68 69 70 71 72 73 74 75

Each number goes up by 1. Count on by ones. Start at 65.

65, 66, 67, 68, _69_, _70_

Try It • Complete each addition pattern. Use the number line to help.

1.
12 13 14 15 16 17 18 19 20 21 22

13, 14, 15, 16, _____, _____

2.
54 55 56 57 58 59 60 61 62 63 64

56, 57, 58, 59, _____, _____

Power Practice • Complete each addition pattern.

3. 2, 3, 4, 5, _____, _____

4. 9, 10, 11, 12, _____, _____

5. 38, 39, 40, 41, _____, _____

6. 87, 88, 89, 90, _____, _____

7. 110, 111, 112, 113, _____, _____

8. 525, 526, 527, 528, _____, _____

14

© Macmillan/McGraw-Hill

WHAT IF THE STUDENT CAN'T

Count on By Ones

- Have the student practice counting on by ones, starting with different two-digit numbers, a few times a day until he or she can do so easily.
- Have students use counters to help them count on by ones.

Read a Number Line

- Read all the numbers on a number line. Say a number and have the student point to it. Ask the student to name the next number.

- Have the student draw a number line showing all the numbers between two consecutive tens. Ask the student to read each number aloud.

Complete the Power Practice

- Discuss each incorrect answer. Have the student count on by ones to complete the pattern correctly.
- Remind students to proofread their work to make sure each number is in the correct place in the pattern.

Name _____

Skip Counting

Activity **9**

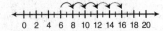 **Learn**

Use a number line to skip count.

Complete the addition pattern.

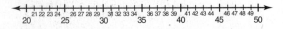

0 2 4 6 8 10 12 14 16 18 20

What Can I Do?
I want to complete an addition pattern.

Skip count by 2s. Start at 6.
6, 8, 10, 12, __14__, __16__

Complete the addition pattern.
Skip count by 5s. Start at 10.
10, 15, 20, 25, __30__, __35__

Complete the addition pattern.
Skip count by 10s. Start at 30.
30, 40, 50, 60, __70__, __80__

Try It . Complete each addition pattern.
Use the number line to help.

20 21 22 23 24 25 26 27 28 29 30 31 32 33 34 35 36 37 38 39 40 41 42 43 44 45 46 47 48 49 50

1. 32, 34, 36, 38, ____,____   **2.** 20, 25, 30, 35, ____,____

Power Practice . Complete each addition pattern.

3. 3, 6, 9, 12, ____,____   **4.** 10, 20, 30, 40, ____,____

5. 45, 50, 55, 60, ____,____   **6.** 56, 58, 60, 62, ____,____

7. 80, 90, 100, 110, ____,____   **8.** 275, 280, 285, 290, ____,____

© Macmillan/McGraw-Hill

15

WHAT IF THE STUDENT CAN'T

Skip Count by 2s, 5s, and 10s
- Have the student practice skip counting by 2s, 5s, and 10s a few times a day until he or she can do so easily.

Read a Number Line
- Ask the student to read all the numbers on a number line. Say a number and have the student point to it. Ask the student to read the next few numbers, using the arrows as a guide.
- Have the student draw a number line showing all the numbers between two consecutive tens. Ask the student to read each number aloud.

Identify Place Value in Patterns
- Help students use a place-value chart to model what happens to the ones, tens, and hundreds places, if applicable, in the patterns they missed.

Complete the Power Practice
- Discuss each incorrect answer. Have the student count on by 2s, 5s, or 10s to complete the pattern correctly.
- Have students create number lines for the patterns they missed.

USING THE LESSON

Activity 9 Lesson Goal
- Complete an addition pattern.

What the Student Needs To Know
- Skip count by 2s, 5s, and 10s.
- Read a number line.
- Identify place value in patterns.

Getting Started
Find out what students know about completing an addition pattern. Say:
- *Think about the numbers in the pattern 2, 4, 6. Each number goes up by 2. Start at 6. What is the next number in the pattern?* (8)
- *Let's count to 20 by 2s. I'll start. 8, 10, 12....*

What Can I Do?
Read the question and the response. Then read and discuss the examples. Ask:
- *How can using a number line help you complete an addition pattern?* (You can count the spaces between two numbers, then skip count by that amount.)
- *Do patterns that skip in 2s end in odd numbers or even numbers?* (even numbers)
- *What digit is in the ones place in patterns that skip in 10s?* (0) *What digits are in the ones place in patterns that skip in 5s?* (5 or 0)

Try It
Ask students to say each number in the pattern and point to it on the number line. Have them count the spaces on the number line to determine what each pattern is. Ask:
- *What does the first pattern go up by?* (2s)
- *What does the second pattern go up by?* (5s)

Power Practice
- Have students complete the practice items. Then review each answer.

Patterns Skill Builder **T15**

Activity 10 Lesson Goal
- Complete a subtraction pattern.

What the Student Needs to Know
- Use a number line.
- Count back by ones.

Getting Started
Draw on the board a number line from 0 to 10. Place your finger on 10 and begin counting backward. Say 9, 8, 7, 6 and so on. Ask:
- *What am I doing?* (counting back by ones)
- *How can I count back by ones from 5?* (5, 4, 3, 2, 1, 0)

What Can I Do?
Read the question and the response. Then read and discuss the examples. Ask:
- *If I start at 9 on the number line and count back by ones, what should I say?* (9, 8, 7, 6, 5, 4)
- *If I start at 264 and count back by ones, what should I say?* (264, 263, 262, 261, 260, 259)

Try It
Have students say the series of numbers after they complete them. Ask:
- *What follows 13 in the pattern in Exercise 1?* (12) *What follows 12?* (11)
- *What follows 79 in the pattern in Exercise 2?* (78) *What follows 78?* (77)

Power Practice
- Have students complete the practice items. Then review each answer.

Name_____

Count Back

Learn

What Can I Do?
I want to complete a subtraction pattern.

Use a number line to count back.
Complete each subtraction pattern.

0 1 2 3 4 5 6 7 8 9 10

Count back by ones. Start at 9.
9, 8, 7, 6, __5__, __4__

255 256 257 258 259 260 261 262 263 264 265

Count back by ones. Start at 264.
264, 263, 262, 261, __260__, __259__

Try It • Complete each subtraction pattern. Use the number line to help.

1.
10 11 12 13 14 15 16 17 18 19 20

16, 15, 14, 13, _____, _____

2.
72 73 74 75 76 77 78 79 80 81 82

82, 81, 80, 79, _____, _____

Power Practice • Complete each subtraction pattern.

3. 25, 24, 23, 22, _____, _____   4. 44, 43, 42, 41, _____, _____

5. 587, 586, 585, _____, _____   6. 152, 151, 150, _____, _____

7. 770, 769, 768, _____, _____   8. 803, 802, 801, _____, _____

16

WHAT IF THE STUDENT CAN'T

Use a Number Line
- Have the student use a number line to practice counting forward by ones. For example, say:
- *Start at 5 and count forward by ones.* (5, 6, 7, 8, 9, 10)
- *Let's draw a number line from 250 to 260. Start at 252 and count forward by ones.* (252, 253, 254, 255, 256....)

Count Back by Ones
- Have the student use number lines to practice counting back by ones. For example, say:

- *Now start at 5 and count back by ones.* (5, 4, 3, 2, 1, 0)
- *Let's draw a number line from 50 to 60. Start at 55 and count back by ones.* (55, 54, 53, 52, 51, 50)
- Repeat with other subtraction patterns until the student can follow the steps with ease.

Complete the Power Practice
- Discuss each incorrect answer. Have the student model any exercise he or she missed using a sketched number line.

Name _____

Skip Count Backward
Learn

What Can I Do?
I want to complete a skip counting pattern.

Use a number line.

Each number in the pattern decreases or goes down by 2.

Skip count backward by 2s. Start at 14.

```
←+—+—+—+—+—+—+—+—+—+—+—+—+—+—+—+→
  0  1  2  3  4  5  6  7  8  9 10 11 12 13 14 15
```

Count back 14, 12, 10, 8, 6.

14, 12, 10, 8, __6__

Try It • Complete each skip counting pattern. Use the number line to help.

```
←+—+—+—+—+—+—+—+—+—+—+—+—+—+—+—+—+—+—+—+—+→
  0 1 2 3 4 5 6 7 8 9 10 11 12 13 14 15 16 17 18 19 20
```

1. 18, 15, 12, 9, _____   **2.** 20, 16, 12, 8, _____

Power Practice • Write the next number in each skip counting pattern.

3. 30, 25, 20, 15, _____   **4.** 36, 32, 28, 24, _____

5. 27, 24, 21, 18, _____   **6.** 60, 54, 48, 42, _____

17

© Macmillan/McGraw-Hill

WHAT IF THE STUDENT CAN'T

Read a Number Line
• Review the format of a number line and how it can be used for counting.

Skip Count *Forward*
• Use counters to form groups for skip counting. Show the student that by gathering the counters into groups of, say, 4, they can count 1-2-3-4, then 5-6-7-8, and so on. The last number in each group of 4 becomes the next number in the skip counting.

Skip Count *Backward*
• Use the same counters to form groups for skip counting

backwards. Show students that by gathering the counters into groups of, say, 4, they can start with 20 and remove four counters, one at a time: 20-19-18-17. They have 16 left. Then remove four more counters: 16-15-14-13. There are 12 left. Have students continue until they have only four counters left. Ask: *What is the skip counting pattern?* (20, 16, 12, 8, 4)

Complete the Power Practice
• Discuss each incorrect answer. Help the student see where he or she went wrong.

USING THE LESSON

Activity 11 Lesson Goal
• Use a number line to complete a skip counting pattern backwards.

What the Student Needs to Know
• Read a number line.
• Skip count *forward*.
• Skip count *backward* to get decreasing numbers.

Getting Started
Review skip counting. Say:
• *Let's skip count to 20 by 2s.* (2, 4, 6, 8, . . .)

Have volunteers skip count by 3s to 30s, 4s to 40, and so on, through 9s to 90.

Tell students that they can also skip count backwards.

What Can I Do?
Read the question and the response. Then discuss the example. Ask:
• *What is shown here?* (skip counting backwards by 2s)
• *What number comes next?* (6)

Draw a number line on the board.
• *Let's see how we would show this on the number line.* (Draw arrows backward from 14 to 12, and then from 12 to 10. Then have students finish down to 0.)

Try It
Use a large number line on the board or individual number lines from 1 to 20 to complete the skip-counting patterns in Exercises 1 and 2.

Power Practice
• Have students complete the practice items. Then review each answer.

Activity 12 Lesson Goal
- Skip count by 5s to complete a pattern.

What the Student Needs to Know
- Recognize and continue an addition pattern.
- Understand skip counting.
- Add 5 to different multiples of 5.

Getting Started
Find out what students know about patterns. Ask:
- *What comes next in this pattern: ababa? (b) What comes next in this pattern: 1, 2, 3, 4? (5)*
- *How would you describe this pattern: 2, 4, 6, 8? (skip counting by 2s beginning with 2) How would you describe this pattern: 0, 5, 10, 15? (skip counting by 5s, beginning with 0)*

What Can I Do?
Read the question and the response. Then read and discuss the example. Ask:
- *How would you describe this pattern? (skip counting by 5s beginning with 10)*
- *How can you find the next number in the pattern? (Add 25 + 5, which equals 30.) What comes after 30 in the pattern? (35)*

Try It
For Exercise 4, have students describe their thinking. To prompt them, ask:
- *How would you describe this pattern? (skip counting by 5s beginning with 35)*
- *What number comes before the blank? (50) What number comes next in the pattern? (55)*

Power Practice
- Have the student complete the practice items. Then review each answer.

Name_____

Skip Count by 5s

Activity 12

Learn

What Can I Do?
I want to complete a pattern.

Skip count to complete the pattern. Each number in the pattern increases or goes up by 5.

Skip count by 5s. Start at 10.

Count 10, 15, 20, 25, 30, 35.

10, 15, 20, 25, __30__, __35__

Try It
• Skip count by 5s. Write the next number in each pattern.

1. 5, 10, 15, 20, _____
2. 20, 25, 30, 35, _____
3. 15, 20, 25, 30, _____
4. 35, 40, 45, 50, _____

Power Practice
• Write the next two numbers in each pattern.

5. 25, 30, 35, 40, _____, _____
6. 0, 5, 10, 15, _____, _____
7. 35, 40, 45, 50, _____, _____
8. 30, 35, 40, 45, _____, _____
9. 45, 50, 55, 60, 65, _____, _____
10. 20, 25, 30, 35, _____, _____
11. 60, 65, 70, 75, 80, _____, _____
12. 10, 15, 20, 25, _____, _____

18

© Macmillan/McGraw-Hill

WHAT IF THE STUDENT CAN'T

Recognize and Continue an Addition Pattern
- Tell the student that in an addition pattern such as 2, 4, 6, 8, the same number (in this case, 2) is added over and over again.
- Write several simple addition patterns on the board and have the student continue them. Repeat a few times a day until the student can continue such patterns with ease.

Understand Skip Counting
- Have the student practice skip counting by 2s, 5s, and 10s on the number line, saying the numbers aloud. Next, have him or her skip count without using a number line.

Add 5 to Different Multiples of 5
- Have the student create several 5-cube trains of connecting cubes and then count the cubes in 1 train, 2 trains, 3 trains, and so on.

Complete the Power Practice
- Discuss each incorrect answer. Have the student model any exercise he or she missed using connecting cubes or a sketched number line.

Name_____

Ordinal Numbers

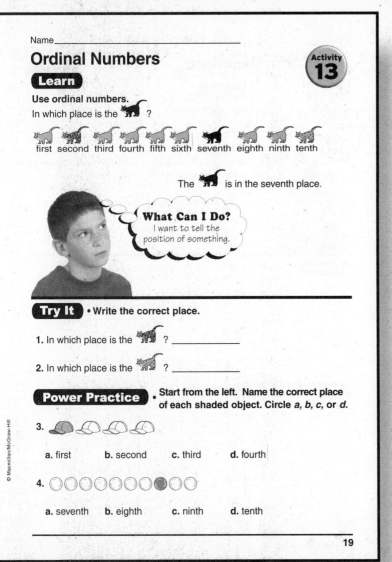

Learn

Use ordinal numbers.
In which place is the 🐱 ?

first second third fourth fifth sixth seventh eighth ninth tenth

The 🐱 is in the seventh place.

What Can I Do?
I want to tell the position of something.

Try It • Write the correct place.

1. In which place is the 🐱 ? _____

2. In which place is the 🐱 ? _____

Power Practice • Start from the left. Name the correct place of each shaded object. Circle *a, b, c,* or *d.*

3.
   a. first   **b.** second   **c.** third   **d.** fourth

4.
   a. seventh   **b.** eighth   **c.** ninth   **d.** tenth

19

© Macmillan/McGraw-Hill

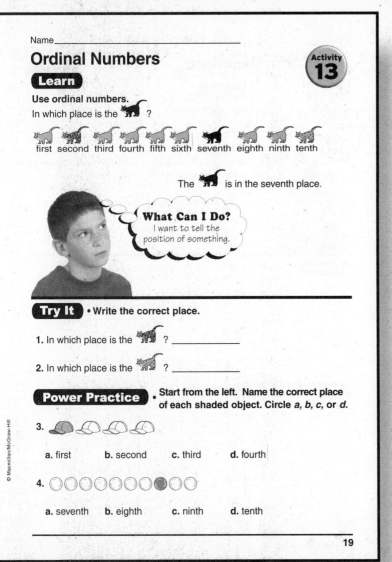

WHAT IF THE STUDENT CAN'T

Understand That Ordinal Numbers Correspond to Cardinal Numbers

• Have the student write the numbers 1 through 10 on a sheet of paper. Below these cardinal numbers, he or she can write the corresponding ordinal number words. For example, under numeral 5, he or she should write "fifth."

• Ask, for example: *If there are 3 people in a line, what place in line does the last one have?* (the third) *If there are 7 people in a line, what position does the last person have?* (the seventh)

Complete the Power Practice

• Discuss each incorrect answer. Have the student model any exercise he or she missed by counting from left to right.

Activity 13 Lesson Goal

• Use ordinal numbers.

What the Student Needs to Know

• Ordinal numbers that correspond to cardinal numbers.

Getting Started

Find out what students know about ordinal numbers. Ask:

• *If you are the third person in line, how many people are in front of you?* (2)

• *What is the next word in this pattern: first, second, third....?* (fourth)

What Can I Do?

Read the question and the response. Then read and discuss the example. Ask:

• *How many cats are in front of the black cat?* (6)

• *Which place in line does the cat in front of the black cat have?* (the sixth place) *Which place in line does the cat behind the black cat have?* (the eighth place)

Try It

Ask:

• *How many cats are in front of the striped cat?* (1) *Which place in line does the striped cat have?* (the second place)

• *How many cats are in the line?* (10) *Which cat is last in line?* (the spotted cat) *Which place in line does the last cat have?* (the tenth place)

Power Practice

• Have the student complete the practice items. Then review each answer.

Activity 14 Lesson Goal

- Skip count backwards by 6s and 7s, using only numbers that are products of 6 or 7.

What the Student Needs to Know

- Count forward by 6s and 7s.
- Read a number line.
- Understand the relationship between counting *forward* and *backward*.

Getting Started

Find out what students know about counting by 6s and 7s. Ask:

- *As you count forward by 6s, what pattern do you see in the numbers?* (Each number is 6 greater than the number that comes before it.)
- *If you want to count forward by 7s, how do you do it?* (add 7 to each number)

What Can I Do?

Read the question and the response. Then read and discuss the examples. Ask:

- *As you count backwards by 6s, what pattern do you see in the numbers?* (Each number is 6 less than the number that comes before it.)
- *As you count backwards by 7s, what pattern do you see in the numbers?* (Each number is 7 less than the number that comes before it.)

Try It

Have students complete Exercises 1 and 2 by continuing each skip counting sequence and then reading it aloud. Then have them read each sequence backwards.

Power Practice

- Have students complete the practice items. Review each answer. For each incorrect answer, first have students identify the skip counting pattern. Then ask them to correct their counting.

Name_____

Skip Count Backward by 6 and 7

Activity 14

What Can I Do?
I want to count backwards by 6s and 7s.

Learn   Use number lines.

When counting backwards by 6s, start at 60.

0 5 10 15 20 25 30 35 40 45 50 55 60

When counting backwards by 7s, start at 70.

10 15 20 25 30 35 40 45 50 55 60 65 70

Try It • Count forward.

1. Count by 6s up to 60.

6, _____, _____, _____, _____, _____, _____, _____, _____, _____

2. Count by 7s up to 70.

7, _____, _____, _____, _____, _____, _____, _____, _____, _____

Power Practice • Complete each skip counting pattern.

3. 60, 54, _____, 42, 36, _____   4. 70, _____, 56, _____, 42, 35

5. 42, _____, 30, _____, 18, 12   6. 48, 42, _____, 30, 24, _____

7. 35, _____, 21, _____, 7, 0   8. _____, 24, 18, _____, 6, 0

9. _____, 49, 42, _____, 28, 21   10. 63, _____, 49, _____, 35, 28

20

WHAT IF THE STUDENT CAN'T

Count Forward By 6s and 7s

- Use drawings or counters to illustrate the numbers that are encountered when counting by 6s and 7s.
- Have the student practice counting by 6s to 60 and 7s to 70 until he or she can do so easily.

Read a Number Line

- Tell the student the number of each mark on a 10-digit section of the number line. Then say a number and have the student point to it. Show how the same principle applies to other sections of the number line.

Understand the Relationship Between Counting *Forward* and *Backward*

- Have the student count from 1 to 20 by ones. Then illustrate how the same thing can be done in reverse, from 20 to 1.
- Have the student practice counting forward and backwards by ones until the student can do it easily.

Complete the Power Practice

- Have the student identify the counting pattern in each exercise. Then guide the student in completing the pattern correctly.

Name_____

Skip Count Backward by 8 and 9

What Can I Do?
I want to count backward by 8s and 9s.

Learn

Use number lines.

When counting backward by 8s, start at 80.

20 25 30 35 40 45 50 55 60 65 70 75 80

When counting backward by 9s, start at 90.

30 35 40 45 50 55 60 65 70 75 80 85 90

Try It • Count backward.

1. Count by 8s starting at 80.

80 _____, _____, _____, _____, _____, _____, _____, _____, _____

2. Count by 9s starting at 90.

90 _____, _____, _____, _____, _____, _____, _____, _____, _____

Power Practice • Complete each skip counting pattern.

3. 80, _____, 64, _____, 48, 40   4. _____, 81, 72, _____, 54, 45

5. 40, 32, _____, 16, _____, 0   6. 64, _____, 48, 40, _____, 24

7. 54, 45, _____, _____, 18, 9   8. 45, 36, _____, 18, 9, _____

9. _____, 48, 40, _____, 24, 16   10. 72, 64, _____, 48, _____, 32

© Macmillan/McGraw-Hill

21

WHAT IF THE STUDENT CAN'T

Count Forward By 8s and 9s

- Use counters to illustrate the numbers that are encountered when counting by 8s and 9s.
- Practice counting by 8s to 80 and 9s to 90 until the student can do so easily.

Read a Number Line

- Tell the student the number of each mark on a 10-digit section of the number line. Then say a number and have the student point to it. Show how the same principle applies to other sections of the number line.
- Help the student draw a 20-digit section of a number line.

Understand the Relationship Between Counting *Forward* and *Backward*

- Have the student count from 1 to 20 by ones. Then illustrate how the same thing can be done in reverse, from 20 to 1.
- Have the student practice counting forward and backwards by ones until the student can do it easily.

Complete the Power Practice

- Have the student identify the counting pattern in each exercise. Then guide the student in completing the pattern correctly.

USING THE LESSON

Activity 15 Lesson Goal

- Skip count backwards by 8s and 9s, using only numbers that are products of 8 or 9.

What the Student Needs to Know

- Count forward by 8s and 9s.
- Read a number line.
- Understand the relationship between counting *forward* and *backward*.

Getting Started

Find out what students know about counting by 8s and 9s. Ask:

- *As you count forward by 8s, what pattern do you see in the numbers?* (Each number is 8 greater than the number that comes before it.)
- *As you count forward by 9s, what pattern do you see in the numbers?* (Each number is 9 greater than the number that comes before it.)

What Can I Do?

Read the question. Then read and discuss the examples. Ask:

- *As you count backwards by 8s, what pattern do you see in the numbers?* (Each number is 8 less that the number that comes before it.)
- *As you count backwards by 9s, what pattern do you see in the numbers?* (Each number is 9 less than the number that comes before it.)

Try It

Have students complete Exercises 1 and 2 by completing each skip-counting sequence and then reading it aloud. Then have them read each sequence backwards.

Power Practice

- Have students complete the practice items. Review each answer. For each incorrect answer, first have students identify the skip-counting pattern. Then ask them to correct their counting.

Activity 16 Lesson Goal

- Identify and continue number and shape patterns.

What the Student Needs to Know

- Recognize shape patterns.
- Recognize number patterns.
- Understand that patterns follow rules.

Getting Started

- Write the word patterns on the board and ask: *What is a pattern?* Allow students to share their ideas. Explain: *In mathematics, a pattern is something that repeats in a special way. Patterns can include shapes or numbers. If you know how a pattern repeats, you can find the next shape or number in the pattern.*

- Write this series of numbers on the board: 1, 2, 3, 4, 5, 6, 7. Ask: *What number could come next?* (8). *Why?* (It is 1 higher than 7.)

- Write this series of shapes on the board: circle, square, square, circle, square, square, circle. *What shape could come next?* (square) *Why?* (Because each circle is followed by two squares.)

What Can I Do?

- Read the question and the response. Then read and discuss the examples. Draw students' attention to the shape pattern under "Look for Changes." Point out that this pattern goes from top to bottom. The first figure shows four squares and one triangle. The second figure shows three squares and two triangles.

- Ask: *How many shapes are in the first line?* (5) *How many shapes are in the second line?* (5) *In the third line?* (5) *How many shapes do you think will be in the fourth line?* (5) *Why?* (The number of shapes stays the same.) *What changes?* (the number of squares and triangles)

Name _____

Number Patterns

Learn

Look for changes.

What could be the next figure in this pattern?

■ ■ ■ ■ ▲
■ ■ ■ ▲ ▲
■ ■ ▲ ▲ ▲

To find the next figure, look at how the pattern changes.

- First: four squares and one triangle
- Second: three squares and two triangles
- Third: two squares and three triangles

In each figure, there is one more triangle and one less square. So, the next figure will have one square and four triangles.

■ ▲ ▲ ▲ ▲

Look for repeats.

What could be the next number in this pattern?

8, 8, 7, 2, 8, 8, 7, 2, 8, 8, 7

Saying a pattern aloud can help you find how it repeats.

Say "eight, eight, seven, two, eight, eight, seven, two, eight, eight, seven."

The repeated pattern is 8, 8, 7, 2. A 2 comes after every 7. So, the next number is a 2.

What Can I Do?

How can I see a pattern?

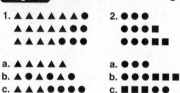

Try It • Circle the letter of the figures that comes next.

1. ▲ ▲ ▲ ▲ ▲ ▲ ●
   ▲ ▲ ▲ ▲ ● ●
   ▲ ▲ ▲ ● ● ●

   a. ▲ ▲ ▲ ▲ ▲
   b. ▲ ● ▲ ● ▲ ●
   c. ▲ ▲ ▲ ● ● ● ●

2. ● ● ●
   ● ● ■
   ● ● ■ ■

   a. ● ● ●
   b. ● ● ● ■ ■ ■
   c. ■ ■ ■ ● ●

3. ● ● ● ● ● ● ▲
   ● ● ● ● ● ▲
   ● ● ● ● ▲

   a. ● ● ● ▲
   b. ● ● ● ▲ ▲
   c. ● ● ● ▲ ▲ ▲

22

© Macmillan/McGraw-Hill

WHAT IF THE STUDENT CAN'T

Recognize Shape Patterns

- Encourage the student to use construction paper cut-outs to model the figures. After reproducing the patterns shown, the student can use the manipulative shapes to find the next figure in the pattern. You may wish to help the student by providing the correct shapes. For example, to solve Exercise 6, the student should first recreate the series shown. Then give him or her four circles and two squares with the request to find the correct order.

Recognize Number Patterns

- Point out to the student that the number patterns in this lesson go from left to right. Encourage the student to read each series of numbers aloud to hear the repeating pattern. The student can also use the pitch of the voice to accentuate patterns. For example, to read the pattern in Exercise 12, the student might use a high pitch for every 5, a low pitch for every 9, and a medium pitch for every 3.

Name _____

Write the repeating pattern.

4. 9, 9, 3, 2, 9, 9, 3, 2, 9, 9, 3, 2, 9, 9, 3, 2   ____ ____ ____ ____

5. 6, 7, 1, 5, 6, 7, 1, 5, 6, 7, 1, 5, 6, 7, 1, 5   ____ ____ ____ ____

Power Practice • Draw the set of figures that come next.

6. ●■■■■■
●●■■■■
●●●■■■

7. ▲■
▲■■
▲■■■

8. ▲■▲■
▲■▲■▲
▲■▲■■

_____ _____ _____

9. ●●●●●●●●
●●●●●●
●●●●●●

10. ■■■■■■■■●
■■■■■■●
■■■●●●●●

11. ■●■●■●■
●■●■●
■●■●■

_____ _____ _____

Write what the next number in each pattern could be.

12. 5, 9, 3, 5, 9, 3, 5, 9, 3, 5, ____

13. 8, 2, 1, 0, 8, 2, 1, 0, 8, 2, 1, ____

14. 3, 3, 4, 9, 3, 3, 4, 9, 3, 3, 4, 9, ____

15. 8, 2, 9, 7, 7, 8, 2, 9, 7, 7, 8, 2, 9, 7, ____

16. 6, 0, 3, 1, 3, 6, 0, 3, 1, 3, 6, 0, 3, ____

17. 1, 1, 2, 2, 3, 3, 4, 4, 5, 5, 6, ____

18. 1, 3, 5, 7, 9, 11, 13, 15, 17, 19, ____

Learn with Partners & Parents

Secret Patterns

One player writes down a secret pattern using these shapes: ▲ ■ ●

The other player asks yes or no questions to guess the pattern. For example: Does the first shape have straight sides? Are there four figures in the pattern?

When you think you know the pattern, write it down. Find out if your guess is correct. Then switch roles and play again.

23

WHAT IF THE STUDENT CAN'T

Understand that Patterns Follow Rules

• Have the student practice identifying the rules that produce familiar patterns, such as the following:

1, 3, 5, 7, 9, 11

2, 4, 6, 8, 10, 12

5, 10, 15, 20, 25, 30, 35

Have the student name the rule that each pattern follows.

Complete the Power Practice

• After completing the activities, suggest that students work together to review one another's work. Encourage students to describe each pattern and the rules it follows.

• After finding the fourth figure in the pattern, students can continue the pattern to find the fifth figure. *How many triangles will there be?* (5) *How many squares?* (0)

• Have students look at the number pattern under Look for Repeats. Have students read the numbers aloud. The rhythm of reading the pattern will often help students identify the repeating pattern.

• Ask: *What number always comes after a 2?* (8) *Could this pattern continue forever?* (Yes.) *How?* (You could keep repeating 8, 8, 7, 2 endlessly.)

Try It

• Explain that the patterns in Exercises 1–3 all go from top to bottom. Ask: *How many shapes are in the first row of Exercise 1?* (7) *In the second row?* (7) *In the third row?* (7) *How many shapes will be in the fourth row?* (7)

Power Practice

• You may wish to select examples from Exercises 6–18 to complete as a class. Assign remaining exercises for individual practice.

• Remind students that the patterns in Exercises 6–11 go from top to bottom. Encourage them to begin by counting how many shapes are in each row.

Learn with Partners & Parents

• Tell students to begin by choosing secret patterns that use circles, squares, and triangles. After several rounds, they can change to number patterns.

USING THE LESSON

Activity 17 Lesson Goal

- Complete addition facts (sums through 20).

What the Student Needs to Know

- Use a number line to count on.
- Double numbers from 1 through 9.
- Recognize pairs of addends that sum to 10.

Getting Started

Draw on the board a number line from 0 to 20. Ask a student to come to the board and use the line to find the sum of 6 + 4. For example, say:

- *Where should you start on the number line to add 6 + 4?* (at 6)
- *How many numbers should you move to the right, or count on?* (4 numbers to the right)
- *Where did you end up?* (at 10)
- *What is the sum of 6 + 4?* (10)

What Can I Do?

Read the question and the response. Then read and discuss the examples. Ask:

- *How can I use the number line to add 7 + 4?* (Start at 7, and count on 4. You end up at 11, so the sum is 11.)
- *Doubles of numbers such as 8 + 8 = 16 may be easier to remember than some other addition facts, such as 8 + 9 = 17. Even if I don't remember the sum of 6 + 7, I do remember how to double 6. What addition sentence means "double 6"?* (6 + 6 = 12)
- *My second addend is 7. How many more than 6 is 7?* (1 more) *What does 6 + 6 + 1, or 12 + 1 equal?* (13)
- *Name some pairs of numbers that sum to 10.* (Examples: 5 + 5; 2 + 8; 7 + 3; 9 + 1)

Name_____

Addition Facts to 20

Activity 17

Learn You can count on, use doubles, or make a ten to add.

Find 7 + 3.

Use the number line to count on.

0 1 2 3 4 5 6 7 8 9 10 11 12 13 14 15

Start with the greater number. Start at 7.
Count on 3 spaces. You end at 10.

So, 7 + 3 = 10.

What Can I Do?
I want to add two 1-digit numbers.

Find 6 + 7.	Find 9 + 5.
Use doubles to add.	Make a ten to add.

6 + 6 = 12
6 + 7 is 1 more.
So, 6 + 7 = 13.

Add 9 + 1 to make a ten.

You made a ten and have 4 left over.

10 + 4 = 14

So, 9 + 5 = 14.

Try It • Count on to add. Draw a number line to help.

1. 4 + 1 = _____   2. 2 + 9 = _____   3. 5 + 3 = _____

4.　3   5.　7   6.　2   7.　2
　 + 6   　+ 2   　+ 8   　+ 5

24

© Macmillan/McGraw-Hill

WHAT IF THE STUDENT CAN'T

Use a Number Line to Count On

- Have the student use a number line to practice addition facts to 10. For example, say:
- *To add 2 + 3, place your finger on 2, the first number. How many times will you need to jump to the right to find 2 + 3?* (3 times)
- Count aloud together as the student jumps his or her finger three numbers to the right: *three, four, five.* Then ask: *What is 2 + 3?* (5)
- Repeat with other addition facts to 10 until the student can follow the steps automatically. Next, have him or her use a number line to practice addition facts to 20.

Double Numbers from 1 through 9

- Have the student set out 1 through 9 counters of one color, and then set out the same number of another color, doubling the original number. Invite the student to arrange the counters in memorable symmetrical patterns and count the sum. He or she might copy the patterns on cards using colored markers.
- Practice doubling numbers aloud until the student can do so with ease.

Name_____

Use doubles to add.

8. 2 + 3 = _____   **9.** 3 + 4 = _____   **10.** 5 + 6 = _____

11. 7   **12.** 8   **13.** 4   **14.** 7
 + 8   + 9   + 5   + 6

Make a ten to add.

15. 9 + 2 = _____   **16.** 7 + 5 = _____   **17.** 8 + 4 = _____

18. 7   **19.** 5   **20.** 9   **21.** 4
 + 4   + 8   + 6   + 9

Power Practice • Add.

22. 2 + 1 = _____   **23.** 4 + 3 = _____   **24.** 3 + 6 = _____

25. 5 + 4 = _____   **26.** 3 + 3 = _____   **27.** 8 + 3 = _____

28. 6 + 6 = _____   **29.** 5 + 7 = _____   **30.** 9 + 6 = _____

31. 6   **32.** 3   **33.** 8   **34.** 7
 + 4   + 9   + 8   + 4

35. 9   **36.** 5   **37.** 8   **38.** 7
 + 7   + 9   + 9   + 8

25

© Macmillan/McGraw-Hill

WHAT IF THE STUDENT CAN'T

Recognize Addend Pairs that Sum to 10

- Use connecting cubes or counters of two different colors to model addition facts with sums of 10 (2 + 8 = 10; 6 + 4 = 10; 1 + 9 = 10; and so on). The student might copy the models on cards using colored markers.

Complete the Power Practice

- Discuss each incorrect answer. Have the student model any fact he or she missed using a number line or counters and then write the correct sum.

- To help me add 9 + 2, I want to make a ten first. What number do I need to add to 9 to make a ten? (1) What number do I have left over after taking 1 from 2? (1) What is 10 + 1? (11) Now I want to make a ten to help me add 9 + 5. After I add 9 + 1 to make a ten, what is left over from 5? (4) What is 10 + 4? (14)

Try It

- Check students' understanding of how to use a number line, doubles, and making tens to solve addition facts.

- For Exercises 15–21, students might begin by modeling the addition sentences using counters. For example, for 7 + 5 they might set out 7 red counters and 5 black ones. Then they might set 3 of the black counters next to the 7 red ones to make 10. This will help them visualize 10 + 2 = 12. Encourage them to rewrite one or more of the facts as follows:

     7   +   5
   + 3   − 3
    10   +   2   = 12

Power Practice

- Review with students the different methods they have learned to help them add. Tell them they may use mental math for the facts they have memorized. Before students begin, ask how they will decide which methods to use. For example, they will probably use mental math for Exercises 26, 28, and 33, since these facts are doubles.

- Select several of the exercises and have volunteers explain which methods they can use to show that the sums they have written are correct. For example, an exercise in which 9 is one of the addends might best be solved by making 10 to add.

Activity 18 Lesson Goal

- Complete addition facts with 2-digit addends (sums through 99).

What the Student Needs to Know

- Add 2 one-digit numbers with sums through 9.
- Understand place value.
- Use a place-value chart.

Getting Started

Ask what students would do to add the ages of two teenagers: Victoria, 13, and Pablo, 14. Draw a place-value chart on the board. For example, say:

- *Where should I write the 1 in 13?* (in the tens place) *Where should I write the 3 in 13?* (in the ones place)

- Have a volunteer write 14 under 13 in the place-value chart. Ask: *To add these two numbers, what should I do first?* (Add 3 + 4, and write 7 at the bottom of the ones column.)

- *What should I do next?* (Add 1 and 1, and write 2 at the bottom of the tens column.) *So 13 + 14 = __?__.* (27)

What Can I Do?

Read the question and the response. Then read and discuss the examples. Ask:

- *Why do we put the 1 in 15 in the tens column?* (because 15 has 1 ten) *Why do we put the 5 in the ones column?* (because 15 has 5 ones)

- *How would you write 32 in the place-value chart?* (Put the 3 in the tens place and the 2 in the ones place.)

- *Which column should we add first?* (the ones column) *What does 5 + 2 equal?* (7)

- *Which column should we add next?* (the tens column) *What does 1 + 3 equal?* (4) So 15 + 32 = __?__ (47)

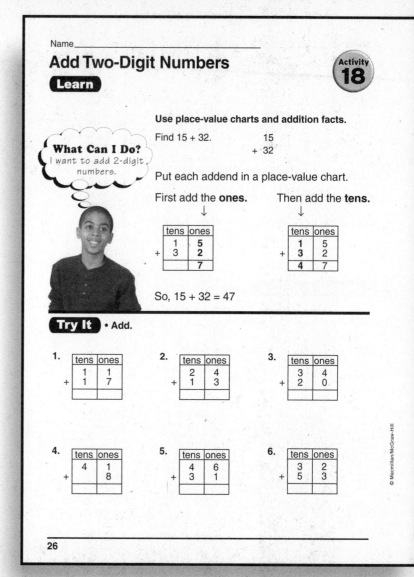

WHAT IF THE STUDENT CAN'T

Add 2 One-Digit Numbers with Sums through 9

- Have the student practice arranging 9 counters to model addition facts with sums through 9. Then they might make models of the facts using sticky dots on cards.

- Practice using mental math to complete addition facts with sums through 9 until the student can do so with ease.

Understand Place Value

- Have the student use connecting cubes to model numbers of tens and ones in two-digit numbers. For example, give the student 11 unconnected cubes and ask him or her to show how many tens and how many ones there are. He or she can connect ten cubes and show that there is 1 left over.

- Have the student model two-digit numbers using base-ten rods and ones cubes.

Name_____

7. 18	8. 26	9. 33	10. 15
+ 11	+ 12	+ 13	+ 34

11. 50	12. 24	13. 38
+ 17	+ 61	+ 31

Learn with
Partners & Parents

14. 41	15. 55	16. 11
+ 52	+ 22	+ 67

11, 22, 33 Challenge

17. 34	18. 79	19. 94
+ 53	+ 20	+ 4

- Play with a partner. You will need 2 number cubes. Toss one number cube to see who goes first, then take turns.

20. 16	21. 44	22. 43
+ 82	+ 44	+ 36

- The first player tosses both number cubes and makes a two-digit number using the digits shown on the number cubes. The digits can be used in any order.

23. 18 + 51 = _____   24. 5 + 52 = _____

- The second player chooses another number for the first player to add to the number tossed. That number must be 11, 22, or 33.

25. 33 + 33 = _____   26. 23 + 21 = _____

- The first player adds the two numbers. You must show the addition on paper. A correct sum earns 5 points. No points are earned for an incorrect sum. The first player to earn 75 points is the winner.

27. 53 + 32 = _____   28. 26 + 43 = _____

© Macmillan/McGraw-Hill

27

WHAT IF THE STUDENT CAN'T

Use a Place-Value Chart

- Have the student use a place-value mat to model two-digit numbers using connecting cubes and/or base-ten rods and ones cubes. Then have him or her draw place-value charts and show the same numbers with numerals.

- For example, he or she might model 23 on a place-value mat by placing two 10-cube trains in the tens column and 3 cubes in the ones column. Then he or she can write the number as follows:

Tens	Ones
2	3

Complete the Power Practice

- Discuss each incorrect answer. Have the student model any fact he or she missed using place-value charts or base-ten rods and ones cubes.

Try It

- Check students' understanding of how to use a place-value chart to find addition facts with two-digit addends.

- Students might begin by modeling the addition sentences using base-ten rods and ones cubes. For example, for Exercise 1, (11 + 17), they might set out 1 tens rod next to 1 ones cube a few inches away from 1 tens rod next to 7 ones cubes. Then they can combine the rods and cubes to make 2 rods and 8 cubes, or 28.

Power Practice

- Review with students the different methods they have learned to help them add two-digit numbers. Tell them they do not need to draw a place-value chart unless they want to. Suggest that it may be helpful to draw a vertical line between the ones and tens places.

- Select several of the exercises and have volunteers explain which methods they can use to show that the sums they have written are correct. For example, they might model the addition facts using place-value charts or base-ten rods and ones cubes.

Learn with Partners & Parents

- If the players disagree about the sum, they can use place-value models to double-check the answer.

Activity 19 Lesson Goal
- Add more than 2 one- or two-digit numbers.

What the Student Needs to Know
- Add using basic facts.
- Add 2 two-digit numbers with and without regrouping.

Getting Started
Find out what students know about addition. Say:

- *Let's add. How much is 1 + 4?* (5) *How much is 7 + 6?* (13) *How much is 5 + 1?* (6)
- *Draw a place-value chart on the board. In the chart write 17 + 46.*

tens	ones
1	7
+ 4	6

- *Where should I begin adding?* (in the ones place) *How much is 7 + 6?* (13)
- *Can I write 13 ones in the ones column of the sum?* (no) *What do I need to do instead?* (regroup) *How many tens and how many ones are in 13?* (1 ten, 3 ones) *Which number do I write in the ones place in the sum?* (3) *Where do I write the 1 ten?* (in the tens place)
- *What should I do next?* (Add 1 + 1 + 4, and write 6 at the bottom of the tens column.) *So 17 + 46 = _?_ .* (63)

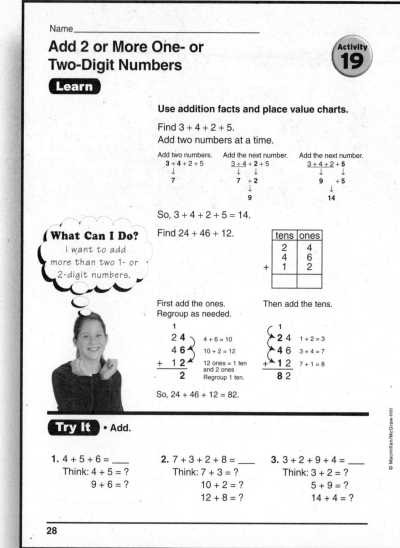

Name_____

Add 2 or More One- or Two-Digit Numbers

Activity 19

Learn

Use addition facts and place value charts.

Find 3 + 4 + 2 + 5.
Add two numbers at a time.

Add two numbers.
$3 + 4 + 2 + 5$
↓
7

Add the next number.
$3 + 4 + 2 + 5$
↓
7 + 2
↓
9

Add the next number.
$3 + 4 + 2 + 5$
↓
9 + 5
↓
14

So, 3 + 4 + 2 + 5 = 14.

Find 24 + 46 + 12.

tens	ones
2	4
4	6
+ 1	2

What Can I Do?
I want to add more than two 1- or 2-digit numbers.

First add the ones. Regroup as needed.

```
  1
  2 4     4 + 6 = 10
  4 6     10 + 2 = 12
+ 1 2     12 ones = 1 ten
    2     and 2 ones
          Regroup 1 ten.
```

Then add the tens.

```
  1
  2 4     1 + 2 = 3
  4 6     3 + 4 = 7
+ 1 2     7 + 1 = 8
  8 2
```

So, 24 + 46 + 12 = 82.

Try It • Add.

1. 4 + 5 + 6 = ____
   Think: 4 + 5 = ?
   9 + 6 = ?

2. 7 + 3 + 2 + 8 = ____
   Think: 7 + 3 = ?
   10 + 2 = ?
   12 + 8 = ?

3. 3 + 2 + 9 + 4 = ____
   Think: 3 + 2 = ?
   5 + 9 = ?
   14 + 4 = ?

28

WHAT IF THE STUDENT CAN'T

Add Using Basic Facts
- Have the student practice adding basic facts using a number line or counters.
- You may wish to have the student identify 4–6 facts that he or she finds particularly troublesome. The student can write those facts on separate index cards with the sums on the backs of the cards.
- Practice using mental math with these troublesome facts until the student can do them with ease. Continue practicing and then retiring/replacing cards until the student can quickly add using any basic fact.

Use a Place-Value Chart
- Have the student use connecting cubes or base-ten blocks to model two-digit numbers on a place-value mat. Then have the student draw place-value charts that represent the same numbers.
- For example, ask the student to model 45 on the place-value mat by placing 4 tens rods in the tens column and 5 ones cubes in the ones column. Then the student can record the number of tens and ones he or she used in the place-value chart.

tens	ones
4	5

Name_____

Add.

4.
tens	ones
1	8
1	2
+ 3	4

5.
tens	ones
2	3
1	5
+ 1	7

6.
tens	ones
1	0
3	5
+ 2	5

7. 52 + 12 + 31 = _____

8. 14 + 34 + 22 + 8 = _____

Power Practice • Add.

9. 4 + 6 + 9 + 1 = _____

10. 3 + 8 + 1 + 3 = _____

11. 5 + 1 + 1 + 6 = _____

12. 32 + 46 + 9 = _____

13. 14 + 23 + 34 + 17 = _____

14. 11 + 12 + 13 + 14 = _____

15.
29
33
+ 24

16.
72
14
+ 9

17.
16
47
22
+ 4

18.
33
22
+ 9

19.
18
26
31
+ 10

20.
46
13
19
+ 7

29

WHAT IF THE STUDENT CAN'T

Regroup

- Give the student 10 or more loose connecting cubes. Have the student count the cubes and name the number. Then have him or her connect groups of ten cubes into trains. Have the student identify the number of tens and the number of ones that equal the total number of cubes.

- Have the student draw a place-value chart and record the tens and ones in the chart.

Complete the Power Practice

- Discuss each incorrect answer. Have the student use a number line, connecting cubes, or base-ten blocks to model any exercise that he or she missed.

- For addition with two-digit numbers, help students decide if they need to regroup the ones. Have them name the number of tens and ones in the sum. Then guide them in writing the tens and ones in the appropriate places in the place-value chart.

What Can I Do?

Read the question and the response. Then read and discuss the examples. Ask:

- *How many numbers do we add at a time?* (2) *What is the first addition we do?* (3 + 4 = 7) *Which number do we add to 7?* (2) *How much is 7 + 2?* (9) *What number do we add to 9?* (5) *What is the sum of 9 + 5?* (14) *So how much is 3 + 4 + 2 + 5?* (14)

- *Let's look at the next example. Do we add the tens or the ones first?* (the ones) *What is the first addition we do?* (4 + 6 = 10) *What number must we add to 10?* (2) *What is 10 + 2?* (12)

- *Do we need to regroup the 12?* (yes) *What do we do next?* (write 2 at the bottom in the ones place and write the 1 ten at the top of the tens column)

- *Which two tens do we add first?* (1 ten + 2 tens = 3 tens) *How much is 3 tens and 4 tens?* (7 tens) *What do we do next?* (add 7 tens + 1 ten = 8 tens) *Where do we write the 8 tens?* (at the bottom of the tens column) *How much is 24 + 46 + 12?* (82)

Try It

- Check students' understanding of adding more than 2 one- or two-digit numbers. They might use base ten blocks and a place-value mat to model the additions.

- For Exercises 8 and 9, draw a place-value chart on the board. Have students tell you how to record the addends in the chart. Have students draw their own place-value charts as they add.

Power Practice

- Have students complete the practice items. Then review each answer.

Activity 20 Lesson Goal

- Add two one-digit numbers (sums through 18).

What the Student Needs to Know

- Count on mentally.
- Double numbers from 1 through 9.
- Recognize pairs of addends that sum to 10.

Getting Started

Find out what students know about adding 2 one-digit numbers. Ask, for example:

- *How could you use doubles to add 4 + 5?* (First, double 4 for a sum of 8. 5 is 1 more than 4, so add 1 to 8 for a sum of 9.)

What Can I Do?

Read the question and the response. Then read and discuss the examples. Ask:

- *What addition sentence means "double 7"?* (7 + 7 = 14) *How many more than 7 is 8?* (1 more) *What does 7 + 7 + 1 equal?* (15)

- *How can I count on mentally to add 4 + 3?* (Start at 4, and count on 3 times: 5, 6, 7. The sum is 7.)

- *To help me add 8 + 6, I want to make a ten first. What number do I need to add to 8 to make a ten?* (2) *What number do I have left over after taking 2 from 6?* (4) *What is 10 + 4?* (14)

Try It

- Help students decide which method to use to help them add. For example, they might use counting on mentally for Exercise 1; doubles for Exercises 2 and 7; and making tens for Exercises 3–6.

Power Practice

- Have students complete the practice items. Then review each answer.

Name_____

Basic Addition Facts

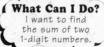

Learn

What Can I Do? I want to find the sum of two 1-digit numbers.

Use doubles to add.	**Count on to add.**
Find 7 + 8.	Find 4 + 3.
You know that 7 + 7 = 14. 7 + 8 is 1 more. So, 7 + 8 = 15.	Start at 4. Say 5, 6, 7. So, 4 + 3 = 7.
	Make a ten to add.
	Find 8 + 6.
	Add 8 + 2 to make a ten with 4 left over.
	10 + 4 = 14 So, 8 + 6 = 14.

Try It • Count on, use doubles, or make a ten to find each sum.

1. 3 + 2 = _____   2. 4 + 5 = _____   3. 9 + 4 = _____

4. 8   5. 4   6. 9   7. 6
   + 5   + 7   + 8   + 6

Power Practice • Find each sum.

8. 3 + 7 = _____   9. 2 + 0 = _____   10. 4 + 8 = _____

11. 8 + 3 = _____   12. 7 + 7 = _____   13. 1 + 9 = _____

14. 7   15. 0   16. 8   17. 9
   + 5   + 9   + 6   + 7

30

WHAT IF THE STUDENT CAN'T

Count on Mentally

- Have the student use a number line to practice adding one-digit numbers by counting on. Repeat until the student can follow the steps automatically.

- Next, have him or her add one-digit numbers by counting on mentally.

Double Numbers from 1 through 9

- Have the student set out 1 through 9 counters of one color, and then set out the same number of another color, doubling the original number. Invite him or her to arrange the doubles in mem-

orable patterns and copy the patterns on cards using stick-on dots.

Recognize Addend Pairs That Sum to 10

- Use connecting cubes or counters of two different colors to model addition facts with sums of 10 (2 + 8 = 10; 6 + 4 = 10; 1 + 9 = 10; and so on).

Complete the Power Practice

- Discuss each incorrect answer. Have the student model any fact he or she missed by counting on, making doubles, or making tens to add.

Name _____

Using an Addition Table

Learn

What Can I Do?
I want to use an addition table.

Add.

To find 8 + 7, look across the 8 row until you are under the 7. Answer: 15

Subtract.

To find 13 – 5, look across the 5 row until you find 13. Look in the top row for the answer, 8.

Addition Table

+	0	1	2	3	4	5	6	7	8	9	10
0	0	1	2	3	4	5	6	7	8	9	10
1	1	2	3	4	5	6	7	8	9	10	11
2	2	3	4	5	6	7	8	9	10	11	12
3	3	4	5	6	7	8	9	10	11	12	13
4	4	5	6	7	8	9	10	11	12	13	14
5	5	6	7	8	9	10	11	12	13	14	15
6	6	7	8	9	10	11	12	13	14	15	16
7	7	8	9	10	11	12	13	14	15	16	17
8	8	9	10	11	12	13	14	15	16	17	18
9	9	10	11	12	13	14	15	16	17	18	19
10	10	11	12	13	14	15	16	17	18	19	20

Try It • Use the addition table.

1. Look in the 7 row. Where is the answer to 7 + 6? _____

_____

2. Look in the 4 row. Where is the answer to 12 – 4? _____

_____

Power Practice • Find each sum or difference using the table.

3. 16 – 9 = _____   **4.** 7 + 6 = _____   **5.** 13 – 8 = _____

6. 9 + 5 = _____   **7.** 14 – 8 = _____   **8.** 9 + 6 = _____

9. 13 – 6 = _____   **10.** 8 + 6 = _____   **11.** 15 – 6 = _____

12. 14 – 9 = _____   **13.** 8 + 4 = _____   **14.** 9 + 8 = _____

31

© Macmillan/McGraw-Hill

WHAT IF THE STUDENT CAN'T

Understand the Relationship between Addition and Subtraction

- Use counters to illustrate addition facts, such as 4 + 9 = 13. Then demonstrate with counters how the same numbers are in the related subtraction fact 13 – 9 = 4.

- Have the student practice by using subtraction facts to write addition facts until the student can do so with ease. For example: 14 – 8 = 6; 6 + 8 = 14.

Complete the Power Practice

- Discuss each incorrect answer. Guide the student in finding the appropriate numbers on the table. Then have the student demonstrate the correct answer to the exercise.

Activity 21 Lesson Goal

- Use an addition facts table to add and subtract.

What the Student Needs to Know

- Understand the relationship between addition and subtraction.

Getting Started

Draw an addition facts table from 0 to 3 on the board. Show how row 1 and column 3 meet at 4, and write 1 + 3 = 4 to represent this fact. Then ask:

- *What are some other addition facts that can be found in this table?* (Possible answers: 2 + 0 = 2; 3 + 3 = 6)

What Can I Do?

Read the question and the response. Then read and discuss the examples. Ask:

- *What is the difference between the way you use the table for addition and for subtraction?* (In addition, you know the row and column, so you look in the table to find the sum where those numbers meet. In subtraction, you know the row and the sum in the table, so you look at the top of the column to find the other numbers.)

Try It

Have students demonstrate how they found the answers to Exercises 1 and 2. Then have them write each exercise as its own equation.

Power Practice

- Have students complete Exercises 3–14. Then review each answer. For each incorrect answer, have students use the table to demonstrate the correct answer for you.

Activity 22 Lesson Goal

- Double a number.

What the Student Needs to Know

- Identify the ones and tens places in a two-digit number.
- Choose addition strategies.
- Recognize doubled numbers.

Getting Started

Find out what students know about doubling numbers. Display 2 blue cubes. Say:

- *What is the double of 2?* (4) Display 2 red cubes, Say *Let's check. Count the 2 blue cubes and the 2 red cubes.* (4) *So, 2 + 2 = 4.*

- *How can doubling 2 help you if you need to add 2 + 3?* (Double 2 and count on by 1.) *So, how much is 2 + 3?* (5) Display the 2 red and the 2 blue cubes. *Let's check. The double of 2 is 4. Display 1 more red cube. Count on 1 from 4.* (5). *So, 2 + 3 = 5.*

What Can I Do?

Read the question and the response. Then read and discuss the examples. Ask volunteers to model the examples with colored connecting cubes. Ask:

- *What addition sentence means the same as "double 3"?* (3 + 3)

- *Why is it easier to find the sum of 4 + 5 if you double 4 first?* (It is faster to double 4 and add 1 than to use the counting on method.)

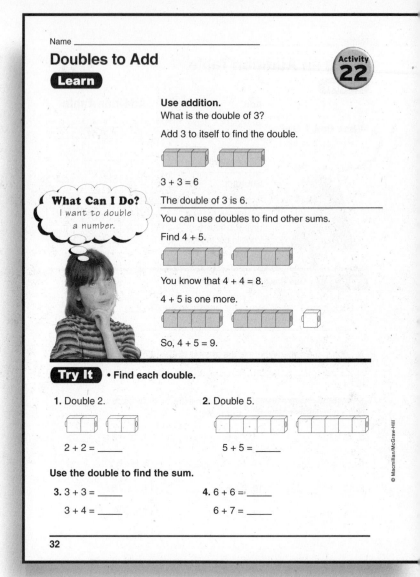

Name _____

Doubles to Add

Learn

Use addition.
What is the double of 3?

Add 3 to itself to find the double.

3 + 3 = 6

What Can I Do?
I want to double a number.

The double of 3 is 6.

You can use doubles to find other sums.

Find 4 + 5.

You know that 4 + 4 = 8.

4 + 5 is one more.

So, 4 + 5 = 9.

Try It • Find each double.

1. Double 2.

2 + 2 = _____

2. Double 5.

5 + 5 = _____

Use the double to find the sum.

3. 3 + 3 = _____

3 + 4 = _____

4. 6 + 6 = _____

6 + 7 = _____

32

WHAT IF THE STUDENT CAN'T

Identify the Ones and Tens Places in Two-Digit Numbers

- Direct the student's attention to Exercise 6. Ask what the double of 6 is. (12) Have students identify the number of tens and ones. (1 ten, 2 ones) Do the same with the sums of Exercises 2, 6, 7, 8, and 10. Stress that doubling whole numbers from 5 to 9 will produce two-digit numbers.

Choose Addition Strategies

- Have the student use flash cards to practice basic addition facts until he or she can use these addition strategies: counting on, using doubles, using doubles plus 1, or using doubles minus 1.

Name _____

Power Practice • Find each sum.

5. 4 + 4 = _____   6. 6 + 6 = _____   7. 9 + 9 = _____

8. 7 + 7 = _____   9. 1 + 1 = _____   10. 8 + 8 = _____

Use the double to find the sum.

11. 5 + 5 = _____   12. 7 + 7 = _____   13. 10 + 10 = _____

    5 + 6 = _____   7 + 8 = _____   10 + 11 = _____

14. 8   9   **15.** 6   7
    + 8   + 8   + 6   + 6

16. 7   8   **17.** 9   10
    + 7   + 7   + 9   + 9

Add. Write the double you can use.

18. 7 ☐   **19.** 5 ☐
    + 6 + ☐   + 4 + ☐

20. 8 ☐   **21.** 6 ☐
    + 9 + ☐   + 5 + ☐

22. 8 ☐   **23.** 4 ☐
    + 5 + ☐   + 7 + ☐

24. 7 ☐   **25.** 3 ☐
    + 8 + ☐   + 6 + ☐

33

Try It

Have students complete Exercises 1–4. Review their answers. Call on volunteers to show their work on number lines. Ask:

- *Did you use mental math to find the doubles? Why or why not?* (Possible answer: Yes, because I know that 2 + 2 = 4, 5 + 5 = 10, 3 + 3 = 6, and 6 + 6 = 12.)

- *How did you use doubles to find the new sums?* (I used mental math to find the double and then I counted on by 1.)

- *How can you practice your mental math?* (Possible answer: You can use flash cards.)

Power Practice

- Have students complete the practice exercises. Then review each answer.

WHAT IF THE STUDENT CAN'T

Recognize Doubled Numbers

- Remind the student that an addition sentence that adds a number to itself means doubling that number.

- Ask the student to create an illustrated chart showing the doubles of numbers from 1 to 10.

Complete the Power Practice

- Discuss each incorrect answer. Have the student draw pictures to show the correct answers.

USING THE LESSON

Activity 23 Lesson Goal
- Add greater numbers mentally.

What the Student Needs to Know
- Basic addition facts (sums to 20).
- Count by tens and hundreds.
- Understand place value.

Getting Started
Find out what students know about patterns among ones, tens, and hundreds. Ask:
- *What does 1 + 5 equal?* (6) *What does 10 + 50 equal?* (60) *What does 100 + 500 equal?* (600)
- *How could you use the addition sentence 8 + 5 = 13 to figure out what 80 + 50 equals?* (I could add a 0 after 13 to make 130. Then I would know that 80 + 50 = 130.)

What Can I Do?
Read the question and the response. Then read and discuss the example. Ask:
- *How can you use 7 + 5 = 12 to figure out what 70 + 50 equals?* (I can add a 0 after 12 to make 120.)
- *How can you use 7 + 5 = 12 to figure out what 700 + 500 equals?* (I can add two zeros after 12 to make 1,200.)

Try It
For Exercise 1, have students describe their thinking. To prompt them, ask:
- *How did you use 4 + 1 = 5 to figure out the next sum?* (I added a 0 after 5 to make 50.)
- *How did you use 4 + 1 = 5 to figure out what 400 + 100 equals?* (I added two zeros after 5 to make 500.)

Power Practice
- Have the student complete the practice items. Then review each answer.

Name_____

Addition Patterns

Learn

What Can I Do?
I want to add greater numbers mentally.

Use basic facts and patterns to find sums mentally.

Find 700 + 500.

You know the basic fact 7 + 5 = 12.

7 + 5 = 12
Think: 7 ones + 5 ones = 12 ones

70 + 50 = 120
Think: 7 tens + 5 tens = 12 tens

700 + 500 = 1,200
Think: 7 hundreds + 5 hundreds = 12 hundreds

So, 700 + 500 = 1,200.

Try It • Write each sum.

1. 4 + 1 = _____
   40 + 10 = _____
   400 + 100 = _____

2. 5 + 6 = _____
   50 + 60 = _____
   500 + 600 = _____

Power Practice • Add. Use mental math.

3. 200 + 600 = _____
4. 30 + 40 = _____
5. 80 + 10 = _____
6. 600 + 600 = _____
7. 800 + 500 = _____
8. 70 + 30 = _____
9. 900 + 600 = _____
10. 500 + 500 = _____
11. 90 + 90 = _____
12. 70 + 80 = _____

34

© Macmillan/McGraw-Hill

WHAT IF THE STUDENT CAN'T

Complete Basic Addition Facts with Sums to 20
- Have the student use counters or connecting cubes to practice addition facts with sums to 20. The student might copy the models he or she creates on cards using colored markers. Have the student write the addition sentence below each drawing.

Count by Tens and Hundreds
- Practice counting by tens and hundreds a few times each day until the student can do so with ease.
- The student might use tens and hundreds models to count by tens and hundreds.

Understand Place Value
- Have the student use hundreds, tens, and ones blocks and a place-value mat to model a series of numbers such as 7, 70, and 700.
- Then he or she can write each number in a place-value chart as follows:

hundreds	tens	ones
7	0	0

Complete the Power Practice
- Discuss each incorrect answer. Have the student model any exercise he or she missed using tens and hundreds blocks.

Addition Patterns

Learn

Activity **24**

Look at the value of
each picture, then add.

What Can I Do?
I want to use
pictures to add.

If ☐ = 2 then

☐ ☐ ☐ ☐ = _____

You know that one ☐ = 2.

☐ ☐ ☐ ☐

Add: 2 + 2 + 2 + 2 = 8

Try It • Complete.

1. If △ = 3 then

△ △ △ = _____

___ + ___ + ___ = _____

2. If ◯ = 5 then

◯ ◯ = _____

___ + ___ = _____

Power Practice • Complete.

3. If ☐ = 5 then

☐ ☐ ☐ ☐ ☐ = _____

4. If ◯ = 10 then

◯ ◯ ◯ ◯ = _____

© Macmillan/McGraw-Hill

35

WHAT IF THE STUDENT CAN'T

Connect Symbols with Numerical Values

- Talk with the student about the words "stands for." For example, a nickel stands for, or is worth, 5 pennies.
- Use attribute blocks and counters. Tell the student that, for example, a triangle is worth 3 counters. Make exchanges with the student. For example, exchange 2 triangles for 6 counters.

Add Several One-Digit Numbers

- Have the student use a number line to practice adding several one-digit numbers. Say:
- *To add 3 + 3 + 3, place your finger on the first number. How many times will you need to jump to the right to find 3 + 3? (3 times) What is 3 + 3? (6)*
- *What should you do to add the last 3? (Jump 3 more numbers to the right.) What does 3 + 3 + 3 equal? (9)*

Complete the Power Practice

- Discuss each incorrect answer. Have the student model any exercise he or she missed by exchanging attribute blocks for counters.

USING THE LESSON

Activity 24 Lesson Goal

- Use picture symbols to add.

What the Student Needs to Know

- Connect symbols with numerical values.
- Add several one-digit numbers.

Getting Started

Draw a star on the board. Tell students that the star stands for 2. Then ask:

- *If each star stands for 2, what would 2 stars equal? (4) What would 3 stars equal? (6, or 2 + 2 + 2)*

What Can I Do?

Read the question and the response. Then read and discuss the example. Ask:

- *What does 1 square equal? (2) What would 2 squares equal? (2 + 2, or 4)*
- *What would 3 squares equal? (2 + 2 + 2, or 6)*
- *How can you write an addition sentence to show the value of 4 squares? (2 + 2 + 2 + 2 = 8)*

Try It

Have students describe their thinking. To prompt them, ask:

- *What does 1 triangle equal? (3) If you add 3 triangles, and each equals 3, what do you get? (9)*
- *What does 1 circle equal? (5) What is the quickest way to add 2 circles (2 fives)? (count by 5s — 5, 10)*

Power Practice

- Have students complete the practice items. Make sure they understand that in Exercise 3, a square is worth 5, rather than 2 (as in the example at the top of the page).

Activity 25 Lesson Goal

- Write a different addition sentence using the same addends and sum.

What the Student Needs to Know

- Identify the missing number as an addend.
- Use the Commutative Property of Addition.

Getting Started

Find out what students know about writing different addition sentences using the same addends and sum. Display 4 red cubes and 2 blue cubes. Say:

- *Write a number sentence for the cubes.* (4 + 2) *What is the sum?* (6)
- *Change the order of the cubes. Write another addition sentence.* (2 + 4) *What is the sum?* (6)
- *Does the order in which you add the red cubes and the blue cubes matter?* (No.) *Why?* (The sum is the same.)

What Can I Do?

Read the question and the response. Then read and discuss the example. Ask volunteers to model the example with colored connecting cubes. Ask:

- *Which numbers can you reorder in an addition sentence?* (the addends)
- *How can you tell which numbers in an addition sentence are the addends?* (The addends are on either side of the addition sign.)
- *How can you tell which number in an addition sentence is the sum?* (The sum is by itself after the equals sign.)
- *Can you reorder a sum and an addend to make two addition sentences that are equal?* (No.)

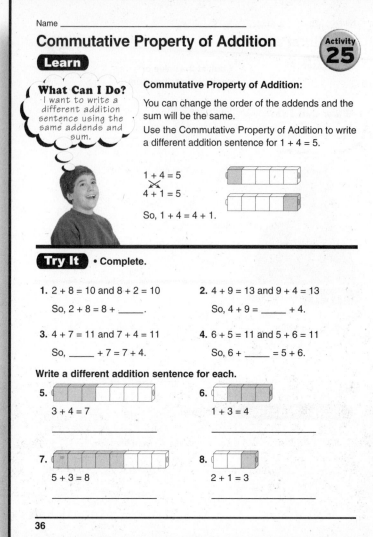

WHAT IF THE STUDENT CAN'T

Identify the Missing Number as an Addend

- For Exercises 1–4 and 9–18, the student may incorrectly write the sum in the blank instead of the missing addend. Emphasize that the student is combining the same addends, just in a different way. Have the student use counters to demonstrate each addition sentence missed.

Use the Commutative Property

- Direct the student's attention to Exercise 1. Explain that the Commutative Property of Addition can help him or her find 8 + 2 if he or she knows that 2 + 8 = 10. Have the student use flashcards to change the order of addends in basic addition facts until this can be done with ease.

Name _____

9. $2 + 6 = 6 +$ _____

10. $8 + 1 =$ _____ $+ 8$

11. $4 +$ _____ $= 5 + 4$

12. _____ $+ 3 = 3 + 9$

13. $7 +$ _____ $= 8 + 7$

14. _____ $+ 9 = 9 + 5$

15. $8 + 4 =$ _____ $+ 8$

16. $6 + 1 = 1 +$ _____

17. _____ $+ 5 = 5 + 2$

18. $6 +$ _____ $= 7 + 6$

Write a different addition sentence for each.

19. $2 + 7 = 9$

_____

20. $3 + 1 = 4$

_____

21. $5 + 7 = 12$

_____

22. $6 + 9 = 15$

_____

23. $8 + 5 = 13$

_____

24. $3 + 2 = 5$

_____

25. $6 + 3 = 9$

_____

26. $9 + 2 = 11$

_____

Write two different addition sentences for each model. Use the same addends and sum for each.

27.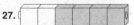

_____

_____

28.

_____

_____

© Macmillan/McGraw-Hill

37

Try It

- Have students complete Exercises 1–8. Encourage them to use cubes or counters to model the two different sentences.

- Review their answers and have students explain how their models show that their answers are correct.

Power Practice

- Have students complete the practice exercises. Then review each answer.

WHAT IF THE STUDENT CAN'T

Use the Same Addends and Sum to Write a Different Addition Sentence

- Have the student use red and blue connecting cubes to model the sentence. Have the student write the number of red cubes on one self-stick note and the number of blue cubes on another self-stick note.

- Have the student match the order of the addends to the order of the cubes and write the addition sentence. Then have the student change the order of the colors of the cubes. The student can then match the order of the self-stick notes to the new order of the cubes and write the new addition sentence.

Complete the Power Practice

- Discuss each incorrect answer. Have the student use colored squares to help show the correct answer.

USING THE LESSON

Activity 26 Lesson Goal
- Complete subtraction facts to 20.

What the Student Needs to Know
- Count back by ones.
- Double numbers from 1 through 9.

Getting Started
Draw on the board a number line from 0 to 10. Place your finger on 8. Ask:
- *How can I use the number line to subtract 8 – 3?* (Count back 3 numbers, 7, 6, 5.) *What is 8 – 3?* (5)

What Can I Do?
Read the question and the response. Then read and discuss the examples. Ask:
- *If I start at 11 and count back to subtract 11 – 3, what should I say?* (10, 9, 8) *What does 11 – 3 equal?* (8)
- *What do you get if you double 3?* (6) *So what does 6 – 3 equal?* (3)
- *What do you get if you double 6?* (12) *So what does 12 – 6 equal?* (6)

Try It
- Have students identify the exercises for which they will use doubles to subtract (Exercises 3–7). Ask:
- *In Exercise 1, at what number will you start?* (6) *How many times should you count back?* (2 times) *Let's try it: 5, 4. So what does 6 – 2 equal?* (4)
- *In Exercise 4, how will you use doubles to subtract?* (9 + 9 = 18, so 18 – 9 = 9)

Power Practice
- Have students complete the practice items. Then review each answer.

Name_____

Subtraction Facts to 20

Learn

What Can I Do?
I want to find the difference between two numbers.

Count back to subtract.
Find 11 – 3.
Start at 11. Count back 3.
Say 10, 9, 8.
So, 11 – 3 = 8.

Use doubles to subtract.
Find 12 – 6.
You know that 6 + 6 = 12.
So, 12 – 6 = 6.

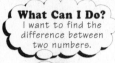

Try It • Count back or use doubles to subtract.

1. 6 – 2 = ____   2. 4 – 3 = ____   3. 8 – 4 = ____

4. 18   5. 10   6. 14   7. 16
   – 9   – 5   – 7   – 8

Power Practice • Subtract.

8. 3 – 1 = ____   9. 9 – 4 = ____   10. 12 – 5 = ____

11. 12 – 7 = ____   12. 16 – 9 = ____   13. 13 – 4 = ____

14. 11 – 6 = ____   15. 14 – 8 = ____   16. 16 – 7 = ____

17. 6   18. 10   19. 8   20. 17
    – 3   – 8   – 0   – 9

38

© Macmillan/McGraw-Hill

WHAT IF THE STUDENT CAN'T

Count Back by Ones
- Have the student use a number line to practice counting back by ones. For example, say:
- *Start at 9 and count back by ones.* (9, 8, 7, 6, 5, 4, 3, 2, 1, 0)
- *Let's use the number line to subtract 9 – 4. Where should we start?* (at 9) *Now what should we do?* (Count back 4 numbers.) *Let's say this together: 8, 7, 6, 5. What does 9 – 4 equal?* (5)
- Next, follow a similar process using mental math instead of a number line.

Double Numbers from 1 through 9
- Have the student set out counters of one color, and then set out the same number of another color, doubling the original number. On a separate sheet of paper the student should write an addition sentence for the double shown.

Complete the Power Practice
- Discuss each incorrect answer. Have the student model any exercise missed using connecting cubes.

Name _____

Subtraction

Learn

Activity 27

What Can I Do?
I want to subtract whole numbers.

Find 53 − 26.

Step 1 Start with the ones digits.

```
  53 ←ones
− 26
```

Step 2 Regroup if you need to.

```
  4 13
  5̶3̶
− 26
  27
```

Try It • Find each difference

1.   71
  − 24
    7
	2. 45
	  − 27
	    8
		3. 50
		  − 16
		    4
			4. 82
			  − 35
			    7
				5. 63
				  − 19
				    4

Power Practice • Find each difference.

6.   61
  − 28
	7. 80
	  − 64
		8. 74
		  − 39
			9. 36
			  − 14
				10. 58
				  − 29

11.   87
  − 28
	12. 56
	  − 23
		13. 73
		  − 35
			14. 42
			  − 27
				15. 82
				  − 54

16.   62
  − 36
	17. 85
	  − 19
		18. 30
		  − 14
			19. 91
			  − 48
				20. 64
				  − 13

© Macmillan/McGraw-Hill

39

WHAT IF THE STUDENT CAN'T

Recall Basic Subtraction Facts

- Use counters to illustrate subtraction facts. Have the student write a number sentence for each subtraction fact as you demonstrate it.
- Have the student practice completing subtraction sentences using counters and on paper until the student is able to do so with ease.

Understand Place Value up to Tens

- Have the student write a two-digit number and read it aloud. Explain that each digit can be seen as one place in a place-value chart. Then have

the student tell you how many tens and ones are in the number.

- Use grid strips and squares to illustrate how you can regroup in a place-value chart by taking a ten and breaking it into ones. Explain that this kind of regrouping is often necessary in subtracting.

Complete the Power Practice

- Discuss each incorrect answer. Have the student tell you whether regrouping is necessary in the problem. If so, have the student regroup appropriately. Then have the student subtract tens and ones.

USING THE LESSON

Activity 27 Lesson Goal

- Subtract two-digit whole numbers, regrouping when necessary.

What the Student Needs to Know

- Recall basic subtraction facts.
- Understand place value up to tens.

Getting Started

Find out what students know about regrouping. Write the following number in a place value chart on the board:

tens	ones
7	2

Ask:

- *What number is shown in the place value chart?* (72)
- *If you convert one of the tens to ones, how many ones will there be?* (10 + 2 = 12 ones)

What Can I Do?

- Read the question and the response. Then discuss the example. Ask:
- *Why is the number 53 regrouped as 4 in the tens column and 13 in the ones column?* (Because the top number in the ones column needs to be higher than the bottom number in order to subtract.)
- *When you regroup one of the 5 tens, how many tens are left?* (4)

Try It

Have students look at exercise 1 and tell you what to do to find the answer. Be sure they understand that regrouping means that the tens digit in the first number will be reduced by one. Then have them complete Exercises 2–5.

Power Practice

- Have the students complete the practice items. Then review each answer.

Operations Skill Builder **T39**

Activity 28 Lesson Goal

- Use mental math or subtract with regrouping to find the difference between a one- and a two-digit number.

What the Student Needs to Know

- Recall subtraction facts through 20.
- Use subtraction fact patterns.
- Understand how to regroup.

Getting Started

Find out what students know about using mental math. Say:

- *In subtracting one number from another, you often find that the number you are subtracting in the ones column is larger than the number you are subtracting from, for example, 11 – 4.*
- *If you don't remember the subtraction fact, how can you find the difference between the numbers using mental math?* (You think of a subtraction fact you know and then add or subtract from there.)
- *For example, if you don't remember 11 – 4, what subtraction fact might you think of?* (possible answer: 14 – 4 = 10).
- *Since 11 is 3 less than 14, the answer will be 3 less than what?* (10)—or in other words—? (7)

What Can I Do?

Read the question and the response. Then discuss the first example. Ask:

- *If you can't remember 12 – 3, what can you do?* (Subtract 13 – 3 and then subtract 1.)

Read the second example. Ask:

- *How would you regroup to solve this problem?* (Think: 7 ones is more than 2 ones, so you have to exchange 1 ten for 10 ones.)

Name _____

Subtraction

Learn

Activity 28

What Can I Do?
I want to subtract a 1-digit number from a 2-digit number.

Use mental math or subtract with regrouping.

Find 12 – 3.

Use mental math for subtraction facts through 20.

So, 12 – 3 = 9.

Find 42 – 7.

Think: 7 ones > 2 ones, so regroup 1 ten for 10 ones.

Subtract the tens.
$\overset{3\ 12}{4\!\!\!/2}$
$- 7$
$3\,5$

Regroup to subtract the ones.

$$\overset{3\ 12}{4\!\!\!/2}$$
$$- 7$$
$$5$$

4 tens 2 ones = 3 tens 12 ones

So, 42 – 7 = 35.

Try It • Subtract. Use mental math.

1. 9 – 3 = _____ **2.** 12 – 4 = _____ **3.** 18 – 9 = _____

4. 17 – 9 = _____ **5.** 15 – 7 = _____ **6.** 13 – 8 = _____

Regroup to subtract.

7. 24
  – 6

8. 32
  – 4

9. 35
  – 7

10. 46
  – 9

40

© Macmillan/McGraw-Hill

WHAT IF THE STUDENT CAN'T

Recall Basic Subtraction Facts

- Practice basic subtraction facts through 20 for 10 to 15 minutes daily until the student can recall the differences for the subtraction facts automatically.

Use Subtraction Fact Patterns

- Review how to use mental math. Help students develop proficiency by using subtraction fact patterns, for example: 14 – 6 = 8 so 24 – 6 = 18, 34 – 6 = 28, and so on.

Power Practice • Subtract.

| 11. | 8
− 2 | 12. | 24
− 4 | 13. | 20
− 5 | 14. | 27
− 9 |

| 15. | 56
− 7 | 16. | 16
− 8 | 17. | 36
− 9 | 18. | 54
− 6 |

Learn with Partners & Parents

19. $14 - 7 =$ _____ 20. $42 - 6 =$ _____

21. $81 - 9 =$ _____ 22. $53 - 8 =$ _____

23. $75 - 7 =$ _____ 24. $61 - 9 =$ _____

25. $14 - 6 =$ _____ 26. $40 - 9 =$ _____

27. $57 - 9 =$ _____ 28. $34 - 5 =$ _____

29. $22 - 7 =$ _____ 30. $91 - 6 =$ _____

31. $44 - 5 =$ _____ 32. $60 - 2 =$ _____

Odd Subtraction

You will need two number cubes and a spinner numbered 0–9. Two or more players can play.

- Players take turns. First toss the number cubes. Use numbers to make a two-digit number. The digits may be in any order.
- Next spin the spinner. Subtract the number on the spinner from the number made with the number cubes.
- If the difference is correct and an even number, the player gets 1 point. If the difference is correct and an odd number, the player gets 2 points. The first player to get 25 points wins.

© Macmillan/McGraw-Hill

41

WHAT IF THE STUDENT CAN'T

Understand How to Regroup
- Use cubes or counters to physically represent the tens and the ones. Show the conversion of 1 ten to 10 ones and back again.

Complete the Power Practice
- Discuss each incorrect answer. Have the student model any fact he or she missed, using cubes or counters along with written numbers.

- If I add the 10 ones to the number already in the ones column, how many will I have? (12)
- If I subtract 7 from 12, how much will be left? (5)
- Now what do I have to do? (Subtract the tens.)
- How many tens are left after the regrouping? (3)
- What is $42 - 7$? (35)

Try It
Have students read each difference aloud and tell how they can use mental math or regrouping to subtract.

Power Practice
Have students complete the practice items. Then review each answer.

Learn with Partners & Parents
You may wish to review these rules with students:

even number − even number = ? (even number)

even number − odd number = ? (odd number)

odd number − odd number = ? (even number)

odd number − even number = ? (odd number)

Familiarity with these rules will allow each player to predict the subtraction result as odd or even. The following variation will introduce an element of strategy to the game. Each player first spins the spinner to find the number that will be subtracted. Then each player rolls the number cubes and forms the two-digit number.

Activity 29 Lesson Goal

- Complete subtraction facts with two-digit numbers.

What the Student Needs to Know

- Subtract one-digit numbers.
- Understand place value.
- Use a place-value chart.

Getting Started

Write the numbers 39 and 21 on the board. Ask what students would do to find out how many years older a 39-year-old is than a 21-year-old. Draw a place-value chart on the board. For example, say:

- *Where should I write the 3 in 39?* (in the tens place) *Where should I write the 9 in 39?* (in the ones place)

- Have a volunteer write 21 under 39 in the place-value chart. Ask: *To subtract 21 from 39, what should I do first?* (Subtract 1 from 9, and write 8 at the bottom of the ones column.)

- *What should I do next?* (Subtract 2 from 3, and write 1 at the bottom of the tens column.) *So 39 – 21 = _?_.* (18)

What Can I Do?

Read the question and the response. Then read and discuss the example. Ask:

- *Why do we put the 5 in 59 in the tens column?* (because 59 has 5 tens) *Why do we put the 9 in the ones column?* (because 59 has 9 ones)

- *How would you write 24 in the place-value chart?* (Put the 2 in the tens place and the 4 in the ones place.)

- *Which column should we subtract first?* (the ones column) *What does 9 – 4 equal?* (5)

- *What should we do next?* (Subtract the numbers in the tens column.) *What does 5 – 2 equal?* (3) *So 59 – 24 = _?_.* (35)

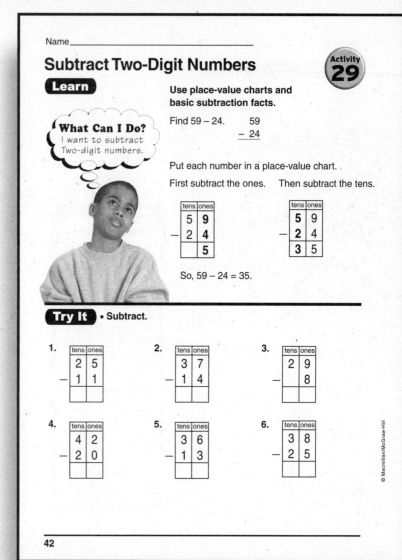

WHAT IF THE STUDENT CAN'T

Subtract One-Digit Numbers

- Have the student use 9 connecting cubes to model subtraction sentences with 1-digit numbers. For example, he or she might begin with an 8-cube train and take away 2 cubes to create a 6-cube train. Then have the student draw each model on a card. He or she should write the subtraction sentence below the picture.

- The student should practice using mental math to complete subtraction facts with one-digit numbers until he or she can do so with ease.

Understand Place Value

- Have the student use tens and ones blocks to model two-digit numbers. For example, the student can model 11 by setting out 1 tens block and 1 ones block. He or she can model 95 by setting out 9 tens blocks and 5 ones blocks.

- Have the student practice identifying the numbers of tens and ones in two-digit numbers.

Name_____

Power Practice • Subtract.

7. 19
− 11

8. 27
− 12

9. 46
− 15

10. 48
− 34

11. 54
− 24

12. 65
− 21

13. 34
− 11

14. 49
− 24

15. 74
− 33

16. 66
− 22

17. 58
− 46

18. 79
− 41

19. 94
− 13

20. 88
− 17

21. 75
− 44

22. 99
− 75

23. 38 − 13 = _____

24. 29 − 6 = _____

25. 45 − 21 = _____

26. 66 − 35 = _____

27. 87 − 34 = _____

28. 76 − 53 = _____

Learn with Partners & Parents

99 Subtraction

Play with a partner. You need four sets of digit cards 0–9, paper, and a pencil.

• Mix the cards well. Place them facedown in the middle of the table. Take turns drawing 2 cards each, but do not show them to the other player.

• Each player makes a number with the two digits on the cards and subtracts that number from 99. The player with the greatest difference gets 2 points. The player with the most points after all the cards are used wins the game.

43

© Macmillan/McGraw-Hill

Try It

Check students' understanding of how to use a place-value chart to find subtraction facts.

• Students might begin by modeling the subtraction sentences using tens and ones blocks.

• For example, for 25 − 11, they can set out 2 tens blocks and 5 ones blocks and then take away 1 tens block and 1 ones block, leaving 1 tens block and 4 ones blocks, or 14.

Power Practice

• Review with students the steps they can follow to help them subtract two-digit numbers. Tell them they do not need to draw place-value charts unless they want to. Suggest that it may be helpful to draw a vertical line between the ones and tens columns.

• Select several of the exercises and have volunteers describe the steps they followed to find the differences.

Learn with Partners & Parents

• As an alternative, have students make cards for several two-digit numbers. Students can take turns drawing cards and subtracting the number on the card from 99.

WHAT IF THE STUDENT CAN'T

Use a Place-Value Chart

• Have the student use a place-value mat to model two-digit numbers using tens and ones blocks. Then have him or her draw place-value charts and show the same numbers with numerals.

• For example, he or she might model 35 on a place-value mat by placing 3 tens blocks in the tens column and 5 ones blocks in the ones column. Then he or she can write the number as follows:

tens	ones
3	5

Complete the Power Practice

• Discuss each incorrect answer. Have the student model any fact he or she missed using place-value charts or tens and ones blocks.

Activity 30 Lesson Goal

- Complete addition/subtraction fact families.

What the Student Needs to Know

- Complete addition and subtraction facts.
- Understand the relationship between addition and subtraction.

Getting Started

Find out what students know about the relationship between addition and subtraction. Write the following addition facts on the board:

$5 + 7 = 12$

Ask:

- *What is a subtraction fact you can write using the same numbers?* (12 – 7 = 5; 12 – 5 = 7)

Have students write another addition fact, along with a related subtraction fact.

What Can I Do?

Read the question and the response. Then read and discuss the examples. Ask:

- *What three numbers appear in each addition and subtraction fact?* (3, 5, 8)
- *Where does 8 appear in the addition facts?* (as the sum or after the equals sign) *Where does 8 appear in the subtraction facts?* (as the first number)
- *How many facts are in the fact family for 3, 5, and 8?* (4) *How many numbers are in each fact?* (3)
- *Do the numbers in a family of facts change from fact to fact, or do they remain the same?* (remain the same)
- *Do any of the facts in a fact family repeat themselves, or are they all different?* (all different)

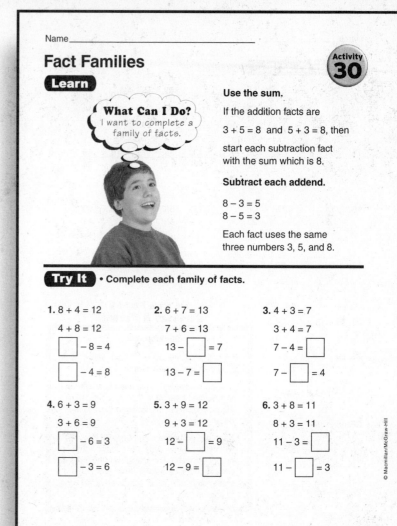

Name _____

Fact Families

Learn

What Can I Do?
I want to complete a family of facts.

Use the sum.

If the addition facts are

$3 + 5 = 8$ and $5 + 3 = 8$, then

start each subtraction fact with the sum which is 8.

Subtract each addend.

$8 - 3 = 5$
$8 - 5 = 3$

Each fact uses the same three numbers 3, 5, and 8.

Try It • Complete each family of facts.

1. $8 + 4 = 12$
   $4 + 8 = 12$
   $\boxed{} - 8 = 4$
   $\boxed{} - 4 = 8$

2. $6 + 7 = 13$
   $7 + 6 = 13$
   $13 - \boxed{} = 7$
   $13 - 7 = \boxed{}$

3. $4 + 3 = 7$
   $3 + 4 = 7$
   $7 - 4 = \boxed{}$
   $7 - \boxed{} = 4$

4. $6 + 3 = 9$
   $3 + 6 = 9$
   $\boxed{} - 6 = 3$
   $\boxed{} - 3 = 6$

5. $3 + 9 = 12$
   $9 + 3 = 12$
   $12 - \boxed{} = 9$
   $12 - 9 = \boxed{}$

6. $3 + 8 = 11$
   $8 + 3 = 11$
   $11 - 3 = \boxed{}$
   $11 - \boxed{} = 3$

44

WHAT IF THE STUDENT CAN'T

Complete Addition and Subtraction Facts

- Use counters to demonstrate the principle of addition. Start with smaller numbers, and work up to showing that $9 + 9 = 18$.
- Use counters to demonstrate the principle of subtraction. Start with simple subtraction facts such as $3 - 1 = 2$, and work up to show that $18 - 9 = 9$.
- Have the student write basic addition and subtraction facts on flash cards. Then have the student practice with flash cards until the facts can be recalled with ease.

Understand the Relationship between Addition and Subtraction

- Use counters to illustrate addition facts, such as $3 + 9 = 12$. Then demonstrate with counters how the same numbers are in the related subtraction fact $12 - 9 = 3$.
- Have the student practice by using addition facts to write subtraction facts until the student can do so with ease. For example: $8 + 7 = 15$; $15 - 7 = 8$.

Name_____

Power Practice • Write the pair of related subtraction facts for each pair of addition facts.

7. $9 + 7 = 16$
$7 + 9 = 16$

_____

_____

8. $9 + 1 = 10$
$1 + 9 = 10$

_____

_____

9. $6 + 8 = 14$
$8 + 6 = 14$

_____

_____

10. $4 + 6 = 10$
$6 + 4 = 10$

_____

_____

11. $7 + 4 = 11$
$4 + 7 = 11$

_____

_____

12. $9 + 4 = 13$
$4 + 9 = 13$

_____

_____

13. $6 + 2 = 8$
$2 + 6 = 8$

_____

_____

14. $8 + 9 = 17$
$9 + 8 = 17$

_____

_____

Learn with Partners & Parents

Fact Family Roll

You will need two 1–6 number cubes.

• Toss the cubes to get two numbers to add. If the numbers are the same, toss again.

• The first player to write two addition and two subtraction facts gets one point.

• Play the game until one player has 7 points.

15. $7 + 5 = 12$
$5 + 7 = 12$

_____

_____

16. $8 + 5 = 13$
$5 + 8 = 13$

_____

_____

45

Try It

Have students look at Exercises 1 and 2. Ask:

• *How do you know which number to start with in the subtraction facts?* (You start with the number that is the sum of the addition facts.)

• *How do you know which of the lesser numbers is missing from the subtraction facts?* (by comparing the subtraction facts with the addition facts; by solving one of the equations)

• Have students complete Exercises 1–6. Check to be sure that students understand that the numbers in a fact family remain consistent.

Power Practice

• Select one of the exercises and have students complete it. Be sure students understand how to convert an addition fact into 2 related subtraction facts.

• Have students complete the remaining practice items. Then review each answer.

Learn with Partners & Parents

• Remind the players they are to write the addition and subtraction fact families in this game.

WHAT IF THE STUDENT CAN'T

Complete the Power Practice

• Discuss each incorrect answer. Have the student compare each incorrect subtraction fact with a corresponding addition fact. Then have the student use counters to demonstrate the correctness of the revised subtraction fact or facts.

Activity 31 Lesson Goal

- Complete addition and subtraction facts.

What the Student Needs to Know

- Add 2 one-digit numbers.
- Subtract one-digit numbers.
- Use addition to check subtraction.

Getting Started

- Write 2 + 4 = 6 on the board. Say: *This is an addition fact. It is always true.* Then write 6 − 1 = 5 on the board. Say: *This is a subtraction fact. It is always true.*

- Remind students that they use addition and subtraction facts when they solve many different kinds of problems. Some facts, such as 2 + 2 = 4, are easy to remember. But sometimes you might forget an addition or subtraction fact. This lesson will help them review ways they can find an answer when they forget a fact.

What Can I Do?

- Read the question and the response. Then read and discuss the examples. Begin with the example under "Rearrange and Count On." Use models to demonstrate 3 + 8. Then switch the order of the groups to show 8 + 3. Ask: *Have I changed the number of things?* (No.) So 3 + 8 is always equal to 8 + 3.

- Point out that counting on is useful when you are adding a small number, such as 1, 2, 3, or 4. Counting on can be confusing if you are adding on a larger number, such as 8 or 9.

- Next, discuss how counting back can help you subtract. You may wish to use models to demonstrate 12 − 3. Ask: *How could you count back to find the answer to 14 − 5?* (Start at 14 and then count back five numbers: 14, 13, 12, 11, 10, 9.)

Name _____

Addition and Subtraction Facts

Learn

What Can I Do?
I forgot an addition fact.

Count On

Think: 3 + 8 = ?

Remember that 3 + 8 is the same as 8 + 3.

You can count on from the greater number.
Think: 8, 9, 10, 11
8 + 3 = 11

Fact with 10

Think: 9 + 8 = ?

You might remember that 10 + 8 = 18. You know that 9 + 8 will be 1 less,
so 9 + 8 = 17

Count Back

Think: 12 − 3 = ?

You can't rearrange subtraction facts. Count back to find the difference.
Think: 12, 11, 10, 9
12 − 3 = 9

Related Facts

Think: 13 − 5 = ?

You may remember that 5 + 8 = 13. Then you can find 13 − 5 = 8. Use related addition facts to help solve subtraction.

Try It • Rearrange and add.

1. 3 + 9

9 + _____ = _____

2. 4 + 7

_____ + _____ = _____

3. 2 + 9

_____ + _____ = _____

Count back to subtract.

4. 11 − 3 = _____

5. 9 − 2 = _____

6. 11 − 2 = _____

Use a fact with 10 to help you add or subtract.

7. 9 + 6 = ?
10 + 6 = 16

So, 9 + 6 = _____.

8. 17 − 9 = ?
17 − 10 = 7

So, 17 − 9 = _____.

9. 18 − 9 = ?
18 − 8 = 10

So, 18 − 9 = _____.

46

WHAT IF THE STUDENT CAN'T

Add 2 One-Digit Numbers

- Have the student use manipulatives to model each fact. Using manipulatives for addition can help with understanding why groups can be re-ordered without changing the total amount (4 + 8 = 8 + 4).

- Have the student create addition fact flash cards to practice learning common facts.

Subtract 2 One-Digit Numbers

- Have the student use manipulatives to model each fact. Using manipulatives for subtraction can help with understanding the meaning of subtraction. Remind the student that subtracting refers to taking some away.

Name _____

Add or subtract. Then check your answer.

10. $8 + 7 =$ _____   11. $14 - 8 =$ _____   12. $12 + 6 =$ _____

_____ $- 7 = 8$ _____ $+ 8 = 14$ _____ $- 6 = 12$

Power Practice • Add or subtract

13. $6 + 9 =$ _____   14. $15 - 8 =$ _____

15. $9 + 7 =$ _____   16. $19 - 9 =$ _____

17. $16 - 7 =$ _____   18. $13 - 5 =$ _____

19. $9 + 3 =$ _____   20. $11 - 9 =$ _____

21. $12 - 5 =$ _____   22. $14 - 6 =$ _____

23. $4 + 8 =$ _____   24. $8 + 3 =$ _____

25. $8 + 1 =$ _____   26. $16 - 9 =$ _____

27. $17 - 9 =$ _____   28. $14 - 8 =$ _____

29. $12 + 7 =$ _____   30. $18 - 6 =$ _____

Learn with Partners & Parents

The Answer Is...

This game can help you remember addition and subtraction facts. Try this game with 2 to 4 players.

• Write the numbers 10 to 20 on index cards and mix them.

• Turn one card over. Players take turns writing addition or subtraction problems that have the answer shown.

• If a player writes an incorrect problem or cannot think of another problem to add to the list, he or she is out for the round.

• Keep playing until no one can add another problem. The last player to add a problem gets to keep the card.

• Turn the next card over to begin the next round. The player with the most cards at the end of the game is the winner.

47

• Next, point out that facts with 10 can be easy to remember. Thinking of a fact with 10 can help you remember a forgotten fact.

• Talk about how using related addition facts can help you subtract. Ask: *How could knowing $7 + 8 = 15$ help you to subtract $15 - 7$?* (You know that $7 + 8 = 15$, so $15 - 7$ must equal 8.)

Try It

• Have students complete Exercises 1–12 to help them practice the four strategies for finding addition and subtraction facts. Encourage students to talk about how they solved each exercise.

Power Practice

• Partners can work together on Exercises 13–30. Each partner finds one answer and then they compare their numbers to see if they are equal or not equal. Review the terms *equal* and *not equal* before students begin these activities.

Learn with Partners & Parents

• Model the activity by writing 11 on the board. Say: *Suppose you pick the 11 card. What addition facts might you write?* (1 + 10; 2 + 9; 3 + 8; 4 + 7; 5 + 6) *What subtraction problems have an answer of 11?* (12 – 1, 13 – 2, 14 – 3, and so on)

• You may wish to have students begin using only addition facts. After one or two rounds, students can add subtraction facts to the game.

WHAT IF THE STUDENT CAN'T

Use Addition to Check Subtraction

• Have the student write an addition fact, such as $5 + 3 = 8$. Then have him or her write two subtraction facts that use the same numbers. ($8 - 5 = 3$; $8 - 3 = 5$) Then have the student solve a subtraction fact, such as $12 - 7 = 5$.

• Explain that the student can use addition to make sure the answer is correct by adding the two smaller numbers to see if they equal the largest number ($5 + 7 = 12$).

Encourage the student to use manipulatives to demonstrate each subtraction problem and then "undo" the subtraction using addition.

Complete the Power Practice

• Have partners check one another's answers. Guide students to use one of the strategies for adding or subtracting when they do not know the answer.

Activity 32 Lesson Goal
• Add 3 or more numbers.

What the Student Needs to Know
• Add pairs of whole numbers mentally.
• Understand the Associative Property of Addition.

Getting Started
Find out what students know about grouping numbers to make addition easier. Write on the board:

$2 + 8 + 7 =$ _____. Say:

• *Add 2 + 8. (10) Add 10 + 7. (17)*
• *How does adding 2 + 8 first make the addition easier?* (You can use mental math to add 2 + 8 quickly to get 10, then add 10 to 7.)
• *Which is easier, adding the group 2 + 8 first or the group 8 + 7?* (Answers will vary.)

What Can I Do?
• Read the question and the response. Remind students that the parentheses mean "do this first." Then read and discuss the example. Ask:
• *What is the first step in adding 3 or more numbers?* (Group the numbers in pairs.)
• *How does grouping pairs of numbers make adding easier?* (You can use mental math to add 2 numbers quickly.)

Try It
Have students use parentheses to show how they grouped the numbers. Remind students that there is no right or wrong way to group them.

Power Practice
• Have students complete the practice items. Then review each answer.

Learn with Partners & Parents
• Encourage players to use parentheses to show how they grouped numbers.

Name _____

Add 3 or More Numbers

Activity 32

Learn

What Can I Do?
I want to add 3 or more numbers.

Use the Associative Property to add two numbers at a time.

Find $4 + 2 + 8$.

Group the numbers to make addition easier.

$4 + (2 + 8) =$
$\downarrow$
$4 + \quad 10 \quad = 14$ Make a ten. Add mentally.

So, $4 + 2 + 8 = 14$.

Try It
Add. Show how you grouped the numbers.

1. $3 + 2 + 9 =$ _____

2. $5 + 5 + 6 =$ _____

Power Practice
Add.

3. $7 + 1 + 2 =$ _____

4. $5 + 3 + 4 =$ _____

5. $2 + 2 + 5 + 3 =$ _____

6. $4 + 6 + 6 =$ _____

48

Learn with Partners & Parents

Number Cube Roll
You need four 1–6 number cubes.
• The first player tosses the four cubes.
• The second player writes a number sentence to add the four numbers tossed.
• The first player then writes a number sentence in which the numbers are grouped differently.
• Each player checks the other's number sentence. If both players agree, both get a point for the round, and the second player tosses. If a player misses a sentence, that player loses a point, and the other player tosses.
• Play until one or both players have earned 10 points.

© Macmillan/McGraw-Hill

WHAT IF THE STUDENT CAN'T

Use Mental Math to Add Whole Numbers
• Have the student practice adding pairs of whole numbers using flash cards until he or she can do so with ease.

Understand the Associative Property of Addition
• Discuss the meaning of "Associative Property" (when adding or multiplying, the grouping of the numbers does not affect the result). Then have the student write the term, its meaning, and an example in the math journal.

Complete the Power Practice
• Discuss each incorrect answer. Have the student use connecting cubes to check his or her work, or group different pairs to see if the addition is easier.

Name _____

Repeated Addition

Activity 33

Learn

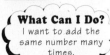

What Can I Do?
I want to add the same number many times.

Use skip counting.

Find 4 + 4 + 4 + 4 + 4.

Look at the number of 4s. There are five 4s.

Skip count by 4s five times.

4 + 4 + 4 + 4 + 4

4,   8,   12,   16,   20

So, 4 + 4 + 4 + 4 + 4 = 20

Try It • Find each sum. Skip count to help.

1. 2 + 2 + 2 + 2 = _____

Skip count by 2s.

_____, _____, _____, _____

2. 5 + 5 + 5 = _____

Skip count by 5s.

_____, _____, _____

Power Practice • Find each sum.

3. 3 + 3 + 3 + 3 + 3 = _____   4. 6 + 6 + 6 = _____

5. 4 + 4 + 4 + 4 = _____   6. 5 + 5 + 5 + 5 + 5 + 5 = _____

7. 7 + 7 + 7 + 7 = _____   8. 8 + 8 + 8 + 8 = _____

9. 2 + 2 + 2 + 2 + 2 + 2 = _____   10. 9 + 9 + 9 + 9 + 9 + 9 = _____

© Macmillan/McGraw-Hill

49

WHAT IF THE STUDENT CAN'T

Use Skip Counting

- Use counters to form groups for skip counting. Show the student that by gathering the counters into groups of, say, 4, they can count 1-2-3-4, then 5-6-7-8, and so on. The last number in each group of 4 becomes the next number in the skip counting pattern.

- Practice selected addition facts daily for 5 or 10 minutes: adding equal numbers, such as 4 + 4, then 4 to the sum of that (8 + 4), and so on. Repeat until the student can recall the sums for these addition facts automatically.

Complete the Power Practice

- Discuss each incorrect answer.

- Perhaps the student will understand the concept of skip counting if presented in a different modality; for example, doing artwork (color every fourth frog he or she draws) or playing a game (every fourth student stands up).

Activity 33 Lesson Goal
- Use skip counting to add the same number three or more times.

What the Student Needs to Know
- Use skip counting.

Getting Started
Ask students to look at this example: 2 + 2 + 2. Say:
- When you add these numbers, you skip the numbers between them.
- *The numbers you count are __?__.* (2, 4, 6)
- *The numbers you skip are __?__.* (3, 5)

What Can I Do?
Read the question and the response. Then look at the example. Ask:
- *How many 4s are being added?* (5)
- *How many times do you skip count 4?* (5)

Skip count with students: 4, 8, 12, 16, 20. You may want to have students count the in-between numbers with fingers: Say: *4; use fingers when counting 5, 6, and 7.*

Try It
- Have students read Exercise 1 and count the number of 2s. Have students write the correct numbers on the lines at the bottom of the example and place the answer on the top write-on line.
- Have students follow the same procedure for Exercise 2.

Power Practice
- Have students complete the practice items. Then review each answer.

Activity 34 Lesson Goal

- Add more than 2 two-digit or three-digit numbers.

What the Student Needs to Know

- Recall basic addition facts.
- Add more than 2 one-digit numbers.
- Understand place value through hundreds and regrouping.

Getting Started

Find out what students know about adding more than two numbers. Write the following addition sentence on the board:

2 + 9 + 5 = _____ (16)

Ask:

- *How can you find the sum of these three numbers?* (Add two of the numbers together, then add the third number to the sum of the first two.)
- *Does it matter in which order you add the numbers?* (No.)
- *What is the sum of the numbers?* (16)

Then write the following addition sentence on the board:

4 + 1 + 9 + 8 = _____ (22)

Ask:

- *What are some ways you can find the sum of these four numbers?* (Possible answers: Find the sum of the first two and the last two, then add them together; add the first two numbers, add the third to that sum, and add the fourth to that sum to get the answer.)

Have volunteers demonstrate different methods of solving the problem. Be sure students understand that each method should result in the same answer (22).

What Can I Do?

Read the question and the response. Then read and discuss the example. Ask:

- *In which order should you add the columns?* (Start with the ones, then add the tens.)

Name _____

Add 3 or More Addends

Learn

Use basic facts and regrouping.

Find 13 + 25 + 18.

Step 1 Add the ones. Regroup if you need to.

What Can I Do?
I want to add more than 2 numbers.

```
  1
  13
  25
+ 18
───────
   6
```

Step 2 Then add the tens. Remember to add the number of tens you regrouped.

```
  1
  13
  25
+ 18
───────
  56
```

Try It . Use basic facts and regrouping. Complete to find each sum.

1.	2.	3.	4.
1	1		
24	16	12	34
16	44	51	22
+ 13	+ 12	+ 25	+ 45
3	2	8	1

© Macmillan/McGraw-Hill

50

WHAT IF THE STUDENT CAN'T

Recall Basic Addition Facts

- Practice addition facts for 10 to 15 minutes daily until the student can recall the sums for the addition facts easily.

Add More than 2 One-Digit Numbers

- Have the student write out the following addition sentence:

5 + 2 + 9 = _____

Use counters to illustrate how you can solve an addition sentence of three or more numbers by adding the numbers in order. Have the student write the sum of the first two numbers in the number sentence (7). Then have the student add this number to the last number of the sentence to arrive at the correct answer (16).

- Have the student practice solving addition sentences of three or more one-digit numbers until it can be done with ease.

Understand Place Value Through Hundreds and Regrouping

- Have the student write a 3-digit number and read it aloud. Explain that each digit can be seen as one place in a place-value chart. Then have the student tell you how many hundreds, tens, and ones are in the number.

Power Practice • Find each sum.

5. 15 15 + 15	**6.** 12 24 + 36	**7.** 34 26 + 31	**8.** 23 33 + 43
9. 44 55 + 66	**10.** 27 23 + 38	**11.** 84 23 + 16	**12.** 123 123 + 123
13. 200 500 + 300	**14.** 34 34 + 34	**15.** 47 48 + 49	**16.** 400 300 + 700

17. 25 + 42 + 19 = _____

18. 113 + 243 + 115 = _____

19. 19 + 19 + 19 = _____

20. 300 + 400 + 200 = _____

21. 18 + 52 + 18 + 52 = _____

22. 900 + 800 + 700 = _____

23. 400 + 600 + 300 = _____

24. 24 + 35 + 46 + 57 = _____

© Macmillan/McGraw-Hill

Learn with Partners & Parents

Exercise Exchange

• Working by yourself, write six exercises. Three of the exercises should involve adding four two-digit numbers. The other exercises should involve adding four three-digit numbers.

• Create an answer key for your exercises.

• Then exchange exercises with your partner. Find the answers to your partner's exercises.

• For any answers that disagree, work with your partner to determine the correct sum.

51

WHAT IF THE STUDENT CAN'T

• Have the student practice writing two-digit and three-digit numbers in a place-value chart until it can be done with ease.

• Use grid strips and squares to illustrate a situation where regrouping is required. For example, show the student how 6 ones + 7 ones = 13 ones. Since a place value needs to be 9 or less, 10 of the ones are regrouped, giving you 1 ten and 3 ones.

• Have the student practice regrouping ones into tens until it can be done with ease.

Complete the Power Practice

• Discuss each incorrect answer. Have the student write out an addition sentence for each column, including regrouping. As the student finds the sum of each column, have him or her write a digit in the answer to the exercise. When all columns have been added, have the student read off the answer.

• If the student has difficulty adding the numbers correctly, have him or her use counters for assistance.

• What is the sum of the ones column? (16) What do you do with the 6? (Write it underneath the ones column.) What do you do with the 1? (Add it to the tens column.)

• What happens if you forget to add the tens you regroup when you add the tens column? (You will get the wrong digit in the tens place of your sum.)

Try It

Have students look at Exercise 1. Ask:

• What is the sum of the numbers in the ones column? (13)

• What is the sum of the numbers in the tens column? (4 tens + 1 ten = 5 tens)

Then have students complete Exercises 1–4.

Power Practice

Have the students look at Exercise 9. Ask:

• What is the sum of the tens column? (15 tens + 1 ten from the grouping = 16 tens) How do you write this sum in the answer? (Write the 6 in the tens place of the answer, and create a hundreds place to write the 1 in.)

• Have students write Exercises 17–24 in vertical form before they find the sum.

• Have students complete the practice items. Then review each answer.

• Select several of the problems. Have volunteers come up to the board and demonstrate how they arrived at the correct answer.

Learn with Partners & Parents

• After students exchange their exercises and do the problems they were given, they should give the exercises back to their partners. Partners should circle the answers and the addition to be sure that their partners added correctly.

Acivity 35 Lesson Goal

- Add 3 one-, two-, three-, or four-digit numbers in vertical form.

What the Student Needs to Know

- Add one-, two-, three-, or four-digit numbers.
- Understand place value through thousands.

Getting Started

- Write the following problem on the board in vertical form: 7 + 4. Have students add. (11) Then write the problem 11 + 3 on the board in vertical form. Have the students add. (14) Ask:

- *How could you write these two addition problems as one addition problem?* (Students might suggest writing the three addends, 7, 4, and 11, in a column.)

- Write the problem 7 + 4 + 3 on the board in vertical form. Have students add the numbers, two at a time, and compare their result to the sum of 11 + 3. (Both have the same sum, 14.)

- *When you add three numbers, does it make any difference in what order you add them?* (No)

What Can I Do?

Read the question and the response. Then read and discuss the example. Say:

- *If the sum of the first column is 15, what number goes in the ones place?* (5) *What number is added to the tens column?* (1)

- *What is the sum of the tens column?* (10) *How do you write this in the answer?* (Put a zero in the tens place, add one to the hundreds column.)

- *What is the sum of the hundreds column?* (7) *If the sum were 12, how would you write it?* (Put a two in the hundreds place, and create a thousands place to put a one in.)

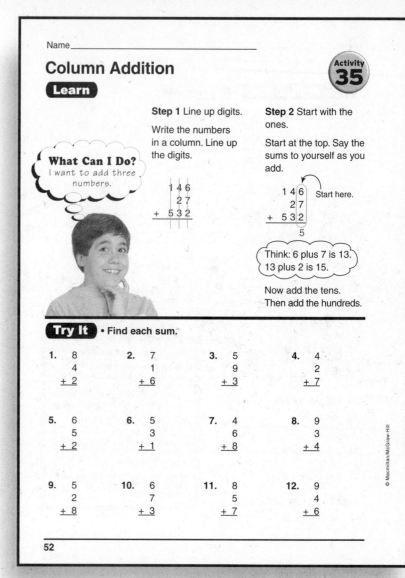

WHAT IF THE STUDENT CAN'T

Add One-, Two-, Three-, or Four-Digit Numbers

- Use place-value models to illustrate how two four-digit numbers can be added. Demonstrate regrouping by trading 10 ones for 1 ten, 10 tens for 1 hundred, and 10 hundreds for 1 thousand. Then give the student pairs of four-digit numbers to add using models.

- Have the student practice adding four-digit numbers to numbers of 1 to 4 digits until the student can do so with ease.

Understand Place Value Through Thousands

- Have the student write a four-digit number and read it aloud. Point out that each digit occupies one place in the number. Have the student tell you how many thousands, hundreds, tens, and ones are in the number. If necessary, let the student refer to a place-value chart for help.

- Have the student practice writing three-digit and four-digit numbers in a place-value chart until it can be done with ease.

Name_____

Find each sum.

13.	25	14.	59	15.	87	16.	29
	83		43		63		93
	+ 32		+ 72		+ 54		+ 38

17.	56	18.	38	19.	6	20.	15
	17		6		52		87
	+ 4		+ 81		+ 48		+ 6

Power Practice • Find each sum.

21.	58	22.	63
	9		147
	+ 72		+ 41

Learn with Partners & Parents

23.	368	24.	413
	210		67
	+ 512		+ 529

┌─────────────────────────┐
│ **Three Number Addition** │
│ Two or three players │
│ can play. │
│ • Take turns. Each player │
│   names a three-digit or a │
│   four-digit number until │
│   three numbers are │
│   named. │
│ • Write down each │
│   number as it is named. │
│   Add the three numbers. │
│ • The first player to get the │
│   correct sum wins one │
│   point. │
│ • Play until one player has │
│   11 points. │
└─────────────────────────┘

25.	2,158	26.	6,215
	1,749		4,670
	+ 5,321		+ 1,912

27.	802	28.	5,106
	157		853
	+ 4,016		+ 29

© Macmillan/McGraw-Hill

53

WHAT IF THE STUDENT CAN'T

• Have the student write a three-digit number and a four-digit number. Ask the student to describe each number in terms of place values. Then have the student write the numbers in a vertical addition problem. Be sure the student understands that each column of numbers correspond to a place value.

Complete the Power Practice

• For each incorrect answer, have the student identify each addend in terms of place value. Then have the student add or use counters to arrive at the correct answer one digit at a time.

Have students look at Exercise 1. Have them write the sum of the first two numbers (12) before adding the third. Have students use counters to illustrate the correct answer. Then have students complete Exercises 1–12. For each incorrect answer, have them use counters to demonstrate the correct sum.

Then have students complete Exercises 13–20. For each incorrect answer, have them use counters to demonstrate the correct sum of the tens column.

Power Practice

• Select a few of the exercises and have students add the numbers one by one to show the correct answer.

• Have students complete the practice exercises. Then review each answer.

┌─────────────────────────┐
│ **Learn with Partners & Parents** │
│ • Players may want to extend │
│   the game to adding four │
│   numbers that are three- and │
│   four-digit numbers, or to │
│   include five-digit numbers │
│   as well. │
└─────────────────────────┘

USING THE LESSON

Activity 36 Lesson Goal
- Add three-digit money amounts.

What the Student Needs to Know
- Add without regrouping.
- Add with regrouping.
- Estimate sums.

Getting Started
- Have students review basic addition facts using flash cards or number cards. Have students describe strategies for remembering addition facts.
- Write 62 + 35 on the board. Have students explain how they can find the sum. Students may want to write a stacked addition problem to help them add. Ask: *What numbers are in the ones place?* (2 and 5) *What is 2 + 5?* (7) *What numbers are in the tens place?* (6 and 3) *What is 6 tens + 3 tens?* (9 tens) *What is the total?* (97)
- Write 28 + 37 on the board. Have a volunteer write the problem as a stacked addition problem. Make sure students align the ones and tens. Ask: *What numbers are in the ones place?* (8 and 7) *What is 8 + 7?* (15) *What numbers are in the tens place?* (2 and 3) *What is 2 tens + 3 tens?* (5 tens) *What is 5 tens + 15?* (65)

What Can I Do?
Read the question and the response. Then read and discuss the examples.

- Tell students that they will follow the same steps to add three-digit money amounts as they used for two-digit numbers.
- Help students understand how to rewrite addition problems by stacking the numbers. Explain that stacking can help line up the ones, tens, and hundreds. Write $5.78 + $0.98 on the board. Ask: *How many ones are in each number?* (8 and 8) *What is 8 + 8?* (16)

Name _____

Adding Money

Learn

> **What Can I Do?**
> I want to add three-digit numbers.

Rewrite the problem.

What is $5.78 + $0.98?

Write this problem by stacking the numbers. Remember to stack the numbers so that the ones are above the ones.

To add, start with the ones.

Think: 8 + 8 = 16
Write the 6 and regroup the 10 ones as 1 ten.

Think: 1 ten + 7 tens + 9 tens = 17 tens.
Write the 7 and rename 10 tens as 1 hundred.

Think: 1 hundred + 5 hundreds = 6 hundreds.
Write the 6.

$$
\begin{array}{cccc}
\$5.78 & \overset{1}{\$5.78} & \overset{1\ 1}{\$5.78} & \overset{1\ 1}{\$5.78} \\
+0.98 & +0.98 & +0.98 & +0.98 \\
\hline
 & 6 & 76 & \$6.76
\end{array}
$$

So, $5.78 + $0.98 = $6.76.

Estimate before you add.

What is $3.85 + $5.17?

Round each amount to the nearest dollar.

Think: $3.85 is close to $4.
       $5.17 is close to $5.

So, the answer will be close to $4 + $5, or $9.

Rewrite the problem to add.

$$
\begin{array}{r}
\$3.85 \\
+\ 5.17 \\
\hline
\$9.02
\end{array}
$$

The answer is $9.02. It is close to your estimate of $9.

54   Grade 3, Chapter 28

Activity **36**

© Macmillan/McGraw-Hill

WHAT IF THE STUDENT CAN'T

Add Without Regrouping
- Have the student practice addition facts to 18. Give the student number cards from 1 to 9 and have him or her practice selecting two cards and finding the sum. A partner can evaluate the responses.
- Make sure that the student aligns numbers accurately before adding. The student might use a place-value chart to help with the alignment of ones, tens, and hundreds.

Add With Regrouping
- Have the student use place-value manipulatives to practice renaming 10 ones as 1 ten and 10 tens as 1 hundred. The student can model each of the exercises to help with the visualization of the addition.
- Make sure the student remembers to write down the 1 or other number when he or she regroups. Check the student's work to see that he or she is using accurate annotations to keep track of regrouping.

Try It • Rewrite each problem. Then find the sum.

1. $2.26 + $3.67   **2.** $7.35 + $1.19   **3.** $8.20 + $4.51

$___.___ ___ $___.___ ___ $___.___ ___

+$___.___ ___   +___.___ ___   +$___.___ ___
_____   _____   _____
$___.___ ___ $___.___ ___ $___.___ ___

Estimate. Then find the exact sum. Use your estimate to check your answer.

4. $6.08 + $5.89   **5.** $7.17 + $8.25

$6.08 is close to _____. $7.17 is close to _____.

$5.89 is close to _____. $8.25 is close to _____.

The answer will be close to _____. The answer will be close to _____.

Exact sum = _____   Exact sum = _____

Power Practice • Find each sum.

6. $4.84   **7.** $7.04   **8.** $9.32
     + 2.73   + 6.09   + 5.12

9. $3.89   **10.** $6.49   **11.** $8.02
     + 8.02   + 8.86   2.20
                                               + 0.79

12. $5.32 + $1.26 = _____   **13.** $6.25 + $1.04 = _____

14. $5.12 + $2.95 = _____   **15.** $4.10 + $3.27 = _____

16. $7.42 + $3.27 = _____   **17.** $3.89 + $3.99 = _____

© Macmillan/McGraw-Hill

55

WHAT IF THE STUDENT CAN'T

Estimate Sums
• Allow the student to practice estimating. Write several 3-digit numbers, such as 213, 877, 692, 541, and 368 and have the student round each to the nearest hundred. Then repeat with three-digit money amounts, asking the student to round to the nearest dollar.

Complete the Power Practice
• Have the student work with a partner to complete the activities. Suggest that partners take turns finding sums and then checking the sum to make sure it is accurate.

• *How can you rename the 1 in 16?* (the 1 equals 1 ten) Follow the rest of the addition as described.

• In the second example, have students discuss how estimating can help you check your answers. Remind students that they might round to the nearest dollar or the nearest hundred.

Try It
• Students practice writing stacked addition problems in Exercises 1–3. Remind students to line up ones, tens, and hundreds.

• Students practice estimating and finding exact sums in Exercises 4–5. Have students compare their estimates and their exact answers.

Power Practice
• Encourage students to estimate each sum before adding. Remind students to show renaming. Before students begin an exercise, they can also predict whether or not they will need to rename ones or tens to solve the exercise.

• Allow students to use a second piece of paper to write stacked addition problems to solve Exercises 12–17.

• If students are confused by the decimal points in problems dealing with money, help them see that they can simply add the numbers as though they were hundreds and then add the decimal point in the sum. Estimating should help students decide where to place the decimal point.

Activity 37 Lesson Goal
- Subtract three-digit money amounts

What the Student Needs to Know
- Subtract without regrouping.
- Subtract with regrouping.

Getting Started
- Write 28 – 13 on the board. Ask a volunteer to write the problem as a stacked problem. Make sure the student aligns ones and tens. Ask: *Do you need to regroup to find the answer?* (No.) *Why not?* (Because you can take 3 from 8 without regrouping and 1 from 2 without regrouping.) *What is the difference?* (15)

- Write 51 – 18 on the board. Ask: *Can you subtract 8 from 1?* (No.) *How can regrouping help you find the difference?* (You can regroup 1 ten as 10 ones.) Have a volunteer continue the subtraction. *What is the difference?* (33)

What Can I Do?
Read the question and the response. Then read and discuss the example. Have a volunteer read the reasoning strategy aloud. Ask:

- *How do you know you can subtract $1.87 from $4.62?* (Because $1.87 is less than $4.62.) *Why do you need to regroup to find this difference?* (Because you cannot subtract 7 from 2 and you cannot subtract 8 tens from 5 tens.)

- Have students discuss why addition helps them check their answer. Ask: *What if you add your answer to the number you are subtracting and you do not get the third number in the problem?* (Your answer is probably incorrect.)

- You may wish to model additional subtraction problems that require no regrouping ($8.54 – $6.23); regrouping only tens ($3.52 – $2.49); regrouping only hundreds ($7.02 – $6.11); or regrouping tens and hundreds ($4.28 – $3.79).

Name _____

Subtracting Money

Learn

What Can I Do?
I want to subtract 187 from 462.

Regroup tens and hundreds.

Write the subtraction problem.

$$\begin{array}{r} \$4.62 \\ -\ 1.87 \\ \hline \end{array}$$

Think: I can't subtract 7 from 2 because 7 is greater than 2. I need to regroup.

Look at the tens column.

The 6 in the tens column equals 6 tens. It can also equal 5 tens plus 10 ones by regrouping 1 ten as 10 ones.

$$\begin{array}{r} \overset{5\ 12}{\$4.\cancel{6}\cancel{2}} \\ -\ 1.87 \\ \hline 5 \end{array}$$

Think: $12 - 7 = 5$

Now look at the tens.
You can't subtract 8 tens from 5 tens. Look at the hundreds column.

The 4 in the hundreds column equals 4 hundreds. It can also equal 3 hundreds and 10 tens by regrouping 1 hundred as 10 tens.

Finally, subtract 100 from 300.

$$\begin{array}{r} \overset{15}{\underset{3\ \$\ 12}{}} \\ \$4.62 \\ -\ 1.87 \\ \hline \$2.75 \end{array}$$

Check your answer with addition.

$2.75 + $1.87 = $4.62

$$\begin{array}{r} \overset{15}{\underset{3\ \$\ 12}{}} \\ \$4.62 \\ -\ 1.87 \\ \hline \$0.75 \end{array}$$

Think: 15 tens – 8 tens = 7 tens

56

© Macmillan/McGraw-Hill

WHAT IF THE STUDENT CAN'T

Subtract Without Regrouping
- Have the student create flash cards to help him or her remember basic subtraction facts. Allow partners to quiz one another on these facts.

- Make sure the student is aligning subtraction problems accurately. Suggest that the student use place-value charts to help with the alignment ones, tens, and hundreds.

Subtract With Regrouping
- Have the student use place-value manipulatives to help with regrouping for subtraction. Partners can model each exercise and then check their answers by adding.

Name _____

1. 685
   – 222 __ __

2. 712
   – 431 ____

3. $2.99
   – 1.57 ____

4. 902
   – 374 ____

5. 843
   – 255 ____

6. $1.28
   – 0.97 ____

Complete.

7. 8 tens = 7 tens and _____ ones

8. 6 hundreds = 5 hundreds and _____ tens

9. 9 tens = _____ tens and 10 ones

10. 4 hundreds = _____ hundreds and 10 tens

Power Practice • Find each difference.

11. $9.57
   – 7.23

12. 843
   – 757

13. 736
   – 98

14. 406
   – 389

15. 600
   – 217

16. $7.04
   – 0.88

17. 837 – 225 = _____

18. 756 – 657 = _____

19. $5.62 – $3.79 = _____

20. 336 – 63 = _____

21. 400 – 282 = _____

22. $772 – $108 = _____

23. $7.83 – $6.94 = _____

24. 405 – 317 = _____

© Macmillan/McGraw-Hill

57

Try It

- Deciding whether or not regrouping will be necessary can help students choose subtraction strategies. After students answer Exercises 1–6, you may wish to have them check the subtractions by adding.

- The number sentences in Exercises 7–10 will give students practice in regrouping. Students can use place-value manipulatives to model each equation.

Power Practice

- Encourage students to decide whether or not they will need to regroup to solve each exercise. Students may also wish to estimate before subtracting.

- Students can check their answers by adding.

WHAT IF THE STUDENT CAN'T

Complete the Power Practice

- Have the student read several subtraction problems and answers aloud. Then have the student practice writing and reading the related addition problem. For example: $8.37 minus $2.25 equals $6.12. $6.12 plus $2.25 equals $8.37.

- If the student forgets how to form the related addition sentence, encourage him or her to recall a simpler subtraction fact: 8 – 2 = 6; 6 + 2 = 8.

- For exercises that have money amounts, remind the student to ignore the dollar sign and decimal point and subtract following the same steps as for other numbers. Then after subtracting, the student can place the decimal point two places from the right. Encourage the students to work with a partner who can estimate to help with the placement of the decimal point.

Activity 38 Lesson Goal
- Describe equal groups.

What the Student Needs to Know
- Recognize equal groups.
- Count the number of equal groups and the number in each group.

Getting Started
Determine what students know about equal groups. Display 6 groups of 2 connecting cubes each. Write on the board "Number of groups" and "Number in each group." Ask the following questions and record the answers under the correct heading:

- *How many groups are there?* (6) *How many cubes are in each group?* (2) *Are the groups equal?* (Yes.) *So, there are 6 groups of 2.*
- If necessary, repeat the steps with 3 groups of 3 pencils each.

What Can I Do?
Read the question and the response. Then discuss the example. Ask:

- *What is the first step?* (Count the number of groups.) *What is the second step?* (Count the number in each group.) *Why is it helpful to do these steps in order?* (To help you keep track of the number of groups, then the number in each group.)
- *How do the pictures help you count the groups or items in each group?* (You can point to each item or group as you count.)
- *Why is it important to count then recount the number of groups?* (to make sure you counted correctly)

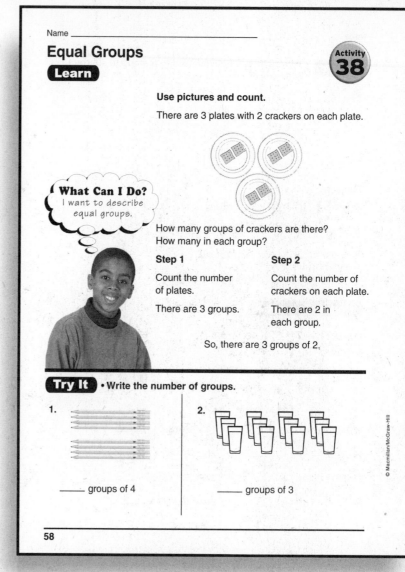

Name _____

Equal Groups

Learn

Activity **38**

Use pictures and count.

There are 3 plates with 2 crackers on each plate.

What Can I Do?
I want to describe equal groups.

How many groups of crackers are there? How many in each group?

Step 1

Count the number of plates.

There are 3 groups.

Step 2

Count the number of crackers on each plate.

There are 2 in each group.

So, there are 3 groups of 2.

Try It • Write the number of groups.

1. _____ groups of 4

2. _____ groups of 3

58

© Macmillan/McGraw-Hill

WHAT IF THE STUDENT CAN'T

Recognize Equal Groups
- Display 2 equal groups of 4 connecting cubes each and 2 unequal groups, one with 3 connecting cubes and one with 5. Have the student count the number in each group to find the pair of equal groups. (the pair with 4 cubes each) Have the student draw and label pictures of equal groups in his or her math journal.

Count the Number of Equal Groups and the Number in Each Group
- Draw four circles on the board with two stars in each.

Tell the student that each circle is a group of stars. Have him or her count the groups. (4) Have him or her count the stars in each group. (2) Then have the student repeat after you, "4 groups of 2." Practice daily until the student can follow the steps without hesitation.

- Help the student correct any errors. Remind the student that he or she can tally the items in one group while counting on by ones, or circle the items while counting. Make sure the student remembers to recount before completing the work.

Name _____

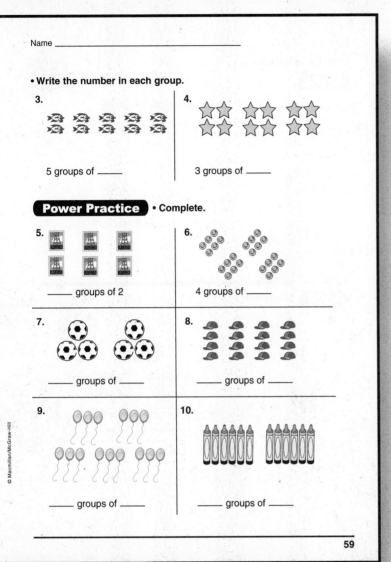

• Write the number in each group.

3.

5 groups of _____

4.

3 groups of _____

Power Practice • Complete.

5.

_____ groups of 2

6.

4 groups of _____

7.

_____ groups of _____

8.

_____ groups of _____

9.

_____ groups of _____

10.

_____ groups of _____

© Macmillan/McGraw-Hill

59

Check students' understanding of counting equal groups. Look at Exercise 1 and ask:

• *What do you count first?* (the number of groups) *How many groups are there?* (2) *How many pencils are in each group?* (4) *Are the groups equal?* (Yes.) Repeat the procedure for Exercise 2.

For Exercises 3–4, make sure students are counting the number in each group. Review students' answers. Ask:

• *What number are you asked to find in Exercises 3 and 4?* (the number in each group) *Is that the first step or second step in describing equal groups?* (the second step)

Power Practice

Have students complete the practice exercises. Review students' answers and have them make corrections as needed. Call on volunteers to model several of their answers with connecting cubes.

WHAT IF THE STUDENT CAN'T

Complete the Power Practice

• Discuss each incorrect answer. Have the student model any missed exercise using connecting cubes or pictured sets.

• The most common error that will occur in Exercises 5–10 is that students will miscount the number of groups. Determine if students understand "3 groups of 2," for instance, by having them draw pictures.

Activity 39 Lesson Goal
- Write a multiplication sentence to describe a number picture.

What the Student Needs to Know
- Recall basic addition and multiplication facts.
- Recognize multiplication as repeated addition.

Getting Started
- Ask students to think of an addition fact for a double, such as 3 + 3. For example, say:
- *Think of 3 + 3 as 2 threes or 2 × 3. Since 3 + 3 = 6, then 2 × 3 = __?__ . (6)*
- *Think of 3 × 3 as 2 × 3 + __?__ . (3)*
- *I'm going to skip count by 3s. When I stop, say the next number. 3, 6, __?__ . (9)*
- *You know that 2 × 3 = 6, that 3 × 3 = 2 × 3 + 3, and that 6 + 3 = 9. So 3 × 3 = __?__ . (9)*
- *What if I have 4 rows of fours? I add another 4: 4 + 4 + 4 + 4. If 3 × 4 was 12, then what do I get if I add 4 more? (16) So 4 × 4 = 16.*
- *What do I get if I have 5 rows of 4? (20) How do I get that? (by adding 4 to 16; 4 + 4 + 4 + 4 + 4 = 20; 5 × 4 = 20)*

What Can I Do?
- Read the question and the response. Then read and discuss the example. Ask:
- *If I count 5 apples in each of 4 groups, how do I show how many counters I have? (5 + 5 + 5 + 5 = 20)*
- *I have 4 groups of 5 apples. That is the same as adding 4 fives. So 5 + 5 + 5 + 5 = 4 × 5 = 20.*
- *What if I have 5 groups of 5? I would add another 5. If 4 × 5 is 20, then what do I get if I add 5 more? (25) So 5 × 5 = 25.*
- *What do I get if I have 6 rows of 5? (30) How do I get that? (by adding 5 to 25)*

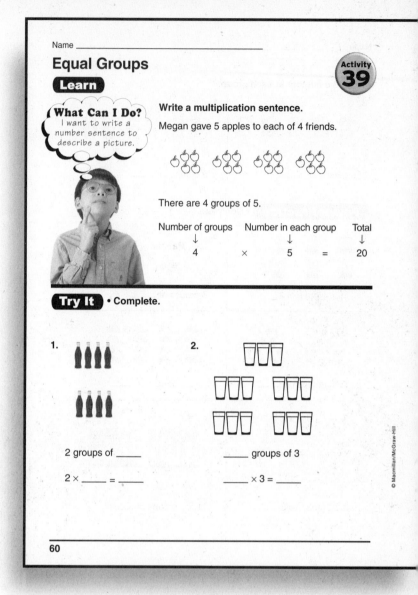

WHAT IF THE STUDENT CAN'T

Recall Basic Addition and Multiplication Facts
- Practice addition and multiplication facts for 10 to 15 minutes daily until the student can recall the sums for addition facts automatically.

Recognize Multiplication as Repeated Addition
- Have the student repeatedly use counters or other objects in equal groups or draw their own equal groups. Have them start with simple numbers—say, up to 5 rows of 5 counters each. Have them count by 1s if necessary. Ask them to write a multiplication sentence for each array of group.

Name _____

Complete.

3.

4.

_____ groups of _____

_____ × _____ = _____

_____ groups of _____

_____ × _____ = _____

Power Practice

Write the multiplication sentence that each picture shows.

5.

_____ × _____ = _____

6.

_____ × _____ = _____

Learn with Partners & Parents

Spinning Groups

- You will need a spinner numbered 1 to 8, and many counters, pennies, or beans in a paper bag.

- Take turns. The first player spins the spinner, and takes a handful of counters from the bag without looking.

- Make equal groups using the counters. Each group should have the number of counters shown on the spinner. (If there are any left over counters, put them back in the bag.)

- Players get 2 points for each equal group. For instance, if you make 5 equal groups of 3 counters each, you get 10 points.

- Each player gets 10 turns. The player with the most points after 10 turns wins the game.

61

WHAT IF THE STUDENT CAN'T

Complete the Power Practice

- Discuss each incorrect answer. Have the student model any fact he or she missed, using physical counters rather than drawn ones.

Try It

- Check students' understanding of how to use a multiplication fact they already know to find another multiplication fact.

- For Exercises 1–4, students might think of the multiplication sentence they would write if they had just 1 group of objects. For example in Exercise 1 they could start with 4 bottles: $1 \times 4 = 4$. From that, they could add another 4 bottles to give them 8 in all, which is the same as 2×4. In Exercise 2, if they already know 3×3, they could add another 3 to get 4×3, then another to get 5×3.

Power Practice

- For each of the exercises, have volunteers describe some different methods they can use to show that the product they have written is correct. (count the number of objects, use counters, use a number line)

- Review that if a product does not immediately come to mind, students can add to a product they know.

- Remind students they can use addition to check their work.

Learn with Partners & Parents

- Players should realize that the least number of counters in any group will be 1, and the greatest number of counters in any group will be 8.

- Tell players that they could decide to give a player 2 points for writing a correct multiplication statement for the array of groups he or she has created; for example, for 5 groups of 3 the statement would be $5 \times 3 = 15$.

Activity 40 Lesson Goal

- Draw a picture to find the total number of items in a problem with groups of items.

What the Student Needs to Know

- Draw recognizable objects.
- Multiply to find the total number of objects.

Getting Started

- Present students with a picture or a physical group of 20 objects scattered about in no particular order. Then present students with the same 20 objects arranged in groups of 4. Ask:

- *Which (fill in name of object) are easier to count? Why? (Answers may vary.)*

- *Once you have grouped the objects, how could you go about finding the total number? (count by 1s, skip count, multiply)*

- *If I'm going to skip count to find the total number in these groups, by what number should I skip count? (by 4s)*

- *How many times should I skip count by 4s? (5)*

- *This is the same as multiplying what two numbers? (5 x 4)*

What Can I Do?

Read the question and the response. Then discuss the example. Ask:

- *How many pencils are in a box? (6)*

- *How many boxes of pencils are there? (4)*

- *Here is a picture that shows 4 boxes with 6 pencils each.*

- *How shall I find how many pencils I have all together? (count by 1s, skip count, multiply)*

- *How will you skip count? (6, 12, 18, 24)*

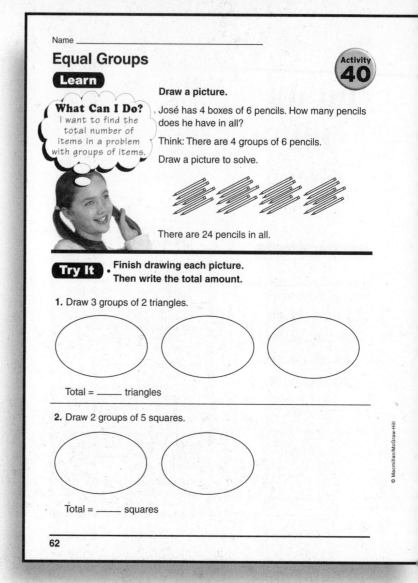

Name _____

Equal Groups

Learn

What Can I Do?
I want to find the total number of items in a problem with groups of items.

Draw a picture.

José has 4 boxes of 6 pencils. How many pencils does he have in all?

Think: There are 4 groups of 6 pencils.

Draw a picture to solve.

There are 24 pencils in all.

Try It • Finish drawing each picture. Then write the total amount.

1. Draw 3 groups of 2 triangles.

Total = _____ triangles

2. Draw 2 groups of 5 squares.

Total = _____ squares

62

© Macmillan/McGraw-Hill

WHAT IF THE STUDENT CAN'T

Draw Recognizable Objects

- Have the student make dots, draw small circles, or use counters.
- Have students practice this skill during "free time."

Multiply to Find the Total Number of Objects

- Practice basic multiplication facts for 10 to 15 minutes daily until the student can recall the products for multiplication facts automatically.

Power Practice • Draw each picture.
Then write the total amount.

3. 5 groups of 5 rectangles	**4.** 4 groups of 7 rectangles
Total = _____ rectangles	Total = _____ rectangles
5. 2 groups of 9 circles	**6.** 6 groups of 3 triangles
Total = _____ circles	Total = _____ triangles
7. 7 groups of 8 squares	**8.** 9 groups of 4 circles
Total = _____ squares	Total = _____ circles

© Macmillan/McGraw-Hill

63

- *How will you show multiplication?*
  (4 x 6)
- *What is the total number of*
  pencils? (24)

Try It

- Have students make their drawings as clear and organized as possible.
- Check students' drawings for Exercises 1 and 2.
- Have volunteers tell you how they go from their drawings to totaling the number of objects.

Power Practice

- For each of the exercises, have volunteers draw their answers on the board. Have them tell what method they use to total the number of objects.

WHAT IF THE STUDENT CAN'T

Complete the Power Practice

- Discuss each incorrect answer. Have the student model any fact he or she missed, using physical counters rather than drawn ones.

Activity 41 Lesson Goal

- Write a multiplication sentence for an array.

What the Student Needs to Know

- Recall basic addition facts.
- Recognize an array as a model for multiplication.

Getting Started

- Ask students to think of an addition fact for a double, such as 4 + 4. Then say:
- *Think of 4 + 4 as 2 fours or 2 × 4. Since 4 + 4 = 8, then 2 × 4 also = __?__. (8)*
- *I'm going to place those 2 fours into 2 rows of counters, each with 4 in a row. That is how we can picture 2 × 4.*

What Can I Do?

- Read the question and the response. Then read and discuss the example. Ask:
- *If I count across 4 counters on each of 3 rows, how do I show how many counters I have? (4 + 4 + 4 = 12)*
- *I have 3 rows of 4 counters. That is the same as adding 3 fours. So 4 + 4 + 4 = 3 × 4 = 12.*
- *What if I have 4 rows of fours?*
  I add another 4: 4 + 4 + 4 + 4. If 3 × 4 was 12, then what do I get if I add 4 more? (16) So 4 × 4 = 16.
- *What multiplication sentence can you write for 6 rows of 4? (6 × 4 = 24) For 7? (7 × 4 = 28)*

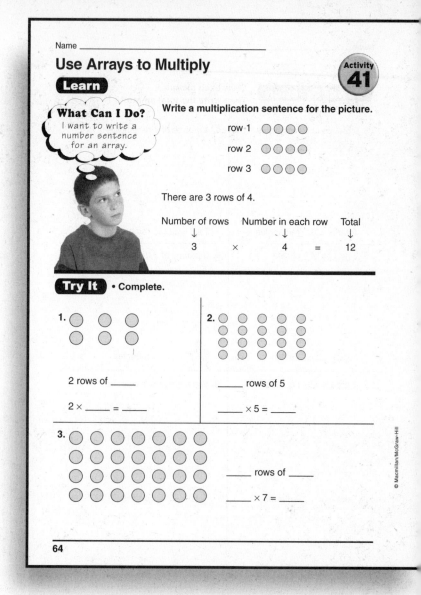

WHAT IF THE STUDENT CAN'T

Recall Basic Addition Facts

- Practice basic addition facts for 10 to 15 minutes daily until students can recall the sums for addition facts automatically.

Recognize an Array as a Model for Multiplication

- Have the student repeatedly use counters or draw arrays. Have the student start with simple numbers—say, up to 5 rows of 5 counters each. Have him or her count by 1s if necessary. Ask the student to write a multiplication sentence for each array.

Name _____

Complete.

4.

_____ rows of _____

_____ × _____ = _____

5.

_____ rows of _____

_____ × _____ = _____

Power Practice • Write the multiplication sentence that each array shows.

6.

_____ × _____ = _____

7.

_____ × _____ = _____

8.

_____ × _____ = _____

9.

_____ × _____ = _____

© Macmillan/McGraw-Hill

65

- For Exercises 1–4, students might think of the multiplication sentence they would write if they had just 1 row of counters. For example in Exercise 1, there are 3 counters: $1 \times 3 = 3$. From that, they can add another 3 to give them 6, which is the same as 2×3. They need not start with 1 row each time. For example, in Exercise 2, if they already know 2×5, they could add another 5 to get 3×5, then another to get 4×5.

Power Practice

- For each exercise, have volunteers describe some different methods they can use to show that the product they have written is correct. (count the number of counters, use a drawing, use a number line)

- Remind students they can use addition to check their work.

WHAT IF THE STUDENT CAN'T

Complete the Power Practice

- Discuss each incorrect answer. Have the student model any fact he or she missed, using physical counters rather than drawn ones.

Activity 42 Lesson Goal

- Practice multiplication facts through 5s by skip counting on a number line.

What the Student Needs to Know

- Skip count by numbers from 2 through 5.
- Recognize which number to use to skip count.

Getting Started

- Write on the chalkboard the multiplication fact 5×2.
- Ask students to tell how to find the answer by skip counting. (2, 4, 6, 8, 10.) Then say:
- *Now we are going to show this on a number line.*

  Use an existing number line or draw one. Then say:
- *I am marking the number line at each 2 through 10: 2, 4, 6, 8, 10.*
- Count the number of 2s: 1, 2, 3, 4, 5.

What Can I Do?

- Read the question and the response. Use an existing number line or draw a new one and mark it as in the lesson. Demonstrate skip counting by 5s, as is shown on the number line.

Try It

- Have students do Exercise 1. Be sure students understand the number by which they are going to skip count (5) and the number of times that they are going to count it (3).
- Check students' marked number lines. (arrows from 0 to 5; 5 to 10; 10 to 15)

Power Practice

- Have students complete the practice items. Then review each answer.

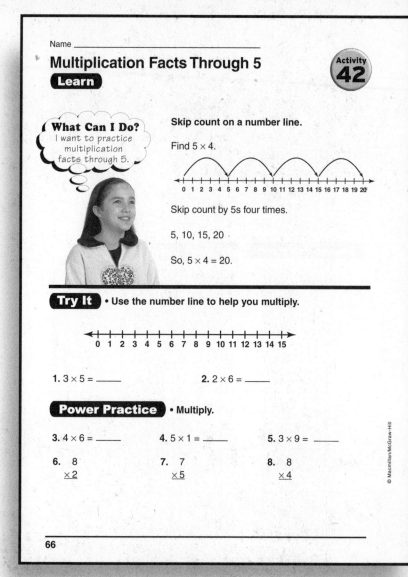

Name _____

Multiplication Facts Through 5

Learn

Activity **42**

What Can I Do?
I want to practice multiplication facts through 5.

Skip count on a number line.

Find 5×4.

Skip count by 5s four times.

5, 10, 15, 20

So, $5 \times 4 = 20$.

Try It • Use the number line to help you multiply.

0 1 2 3 4 5 6 7 8 9 10 11 12 13 14 15

1. $3 \times 5 =$ _____   2. $2 \times 6 =$ _____

Power Practice • Multiply.

3. $4 \times 6 =$ _____   4. $5 \times 1 =$ _____   5. $3 \times 9 =$ _____

6. 8   7. 7   8. 8
   ×2   ×5   ×4

© Macmillan/McGraw-Hill

66

WHAT IF THE STUDENT CAN'T

Understand Skip Counting

- Use counters to form groups for skip counting. Show students that by gathering the counters into groups of, say, 4, they can count 1-2-3-4, then 5-6-7-8, and so on. The last number in each group of 4 becomes the next number in skip counting.
- Practice selected addition facts daily for 5 or 10 minutes: adding equal numbers, such as $4 + 4$, then 4 to the sum of that $(8 + 4)$, and so on. Repeat until the student can recall the sums for these addition facts automatically.

Recognize Which Number to use to Skip Count

- Point out and practice that in a multiplication fact, $a \times b$, b is the number in a group or the number to be skip counted and a is the number of groups or the number of times to skip count. When the multiplication fact is vertical, the top number is the number in a group or the number to be skip counted, and the bottom number is the number of groups or the number of times to skip-count.

Complete the Power Practice

- Discuss each incorrect answer and review the previous points if necessary.

Multiplication Facts Through 8

Learn

Use equal groups.

Find 6×5.

Draw 6 groups of 5 circles.

What Can I Do?
I want to practice multiplication facts through 8.

There are 30 circles in all.

So, $6 \times 5 = 30$.

Use doubling.

Find 8×8.

You can double a 4s fact to find an 8s fact.

$4 \times 8 = 32$

Double the product.

$32 + 32 = 64$

So, $8 \times 8 = 64$.

Try It • Use equal groups or doubling to multiply.

1. $8 \times 5 = $ _____

2. $7 \times 6 = $ _____

Power Practice • Multiply.

3. $8 \times 2 = $ _____

4. $7 \times 5 = $ _____

5. $6 \times 8 = $ _____

6. $7 \times 3 = $ _____

7. $7 \times 7 = $ _____

8. $6 \times 9 = $ _____

67

© Macmillan/McGraw-Hill

WHAT IF THE STUDENT CAN'T

Recall Basic Addition and Multiplication Facts

• Practice addition and multiplication facts 10 to 15 minutes daily until the student can recall the sums for the addition facts and the products for the multiplication facts with ease.

Complete the Power Practice

• Discuss each incorrect answer.

• Have the student model any fact he or she missed.

Activity 43 Lesson Goal

• Use equal groups or doubling to practice multiplication facts through 8s.

What the Student Needs to Know

• Recall basic addition and multiplication facts.

Getting Started

• Ask students to draw and count a group of 3 objects. Then ask:

• *How can you find out how many are in 6 groups?* (Draw the other 5 groups, then count the total number.)

What Can I Do?

Read the question and the response. Then discuss the first example. Ask:

• *In the first example, what would you draw to show equal groups?* (6 groups of 5 circles)

• *How many circles are there in all?* (30)

• *What multiplication sentence shows this?* ($6 \times 5 = 30$)

Read and discuss the second example. Ask:

• *What method are you going to use to solve this?* (doubling a 4s multiplication fact)

• *What multiplication sentence will you use first?* ($4 \times 8 = 32$)

• *How do you double the product?* (by adding 32 + 32)

Try It

• Have students read exercise 1: $8 \times 5 = $ ____. Ask whether to use equal groups or doubling a 4s fact to multiply. (doubling)

• Now, have students read and go through the steps on the second exercise.

Power Practice

• Have students complete the practice items. Then review each answer and method.

Activity 44 Lesson Goal

- Use any multiplication strategy to multiply two numbers through 9.

What the Student Needs to Know

- Double a basic multiplication fact.
- Use repeated addition.
- Skip count by 2s through 9s on a number line.

Getting Started

- Write the multiplication fact 3×7 on the chalkboard. Say:
- *Of the three strategies of doubling a known fact, repeated addition, and skip counting on a number line, which ones can be used for this example?* (repeated addition, skip counting on a number line)
- Explain that it is necessary to have one of the factors be an even number to be able to use the doubling method, because you don't get a whole number when you divide an odd number by 2.

What Can I Do?

Read the question and the response. Then discuss the first example. Ask:

- *Can you use the doubling method to find the answer to this example?* (Yes)
- *What would you double?* ($3 \times 5 = 15$)
- *How would you use repeated addition to solve?* (add 5 six times: $5 + 5 + 5 + 5 + 5 + 5$)

Use an existing number line from 1 to 30 or draw a new one. Demonstrate skip counting 6 groups of 5 by drawing arrows that show "jumps" between 0 and 5, 5 and 10, 10 and 15, 15 and 20, 20 and 25, and 25 and 30.

- Ask: *Which two methods are most alike?* (repeated addition and skip counting)

Name _____

Multiplication Facts Through 9

Learn

What Can I Do?
I want to multiply two numbers.

Use any multiplication strategy.

Find 6×5.

Double a known fact.	Use repeated addition.
Double 3×5 to find 6×5.	Add 5 six times.
$3 \times 5 = 15$ $15 + 15 = 30$	$5 + 5 + 5 + 5 + 5 + 5 = 30$
So, $6 \times 5 = 30$.	So, $6 \times 5 = 30$.

Skip count on a number line.

Skip count by 5s six times.

So, $6 \times 5 = 30$.

Try It • Double a known fact to find each product.

1. $4 \times 9 = $ _____
Double 2×9

2. $8 \times 5 = $ _____
Double 4×5

3. $6 \times 5 = $ _____
Double 3×5.

4. $10 \times 7 = $ _____
Double 5×7

68

WHAT IF THE STUDENT CAN'T

Double a Basic Multiplication Fact

- Have the student keep handy a chart of numbers and their doubles ($2 \times 2 = 4$, $2 \times 3 = 6$, and so on) to refer to.
- Have the student practice these doubling facts daily until he or she knows them.

Use Repeated Addition

- Practice selected addition facts daily for 5 or 10 minutes: adding equal numbers, such as $4 + 4$, then 4 to the sum of that ($8 + 4$), and so on. Repeat until the student can recall the sums for these addition facts automatically.
- If this is still difficult, have the student use counters to form groups for repeated addition.

Name _____

Use repeated addition to find each product.

5. $3 \times 7 =$ _____   **6.** $5 \times 5 =$ _____

Add: _____   Add: _____

Skip count to find each product.

7. $5 \times 3 =$ _____   **8.** $4 \times 6 =$ _____

Count: _____   Count: _____

Power Practice • Find each product. Use any method.

9. $2 \times 6 =$ _____   **10.** $4 \times 4 =$ _____   **11.** $5 \times 7 =$ _____

12. $6 \times 7 =$ _____   **13.** $3 \times 8 =$ _____   **14.** $9 \times 3 =$ _____

15. $7 \times 4 =$ _____   **16.** $8 \times 6 =$ _____   **17.** $5 \times 8 =$ _____

18.	8	19.	3	20.	7	21.	9
	$\times 2$		$\times 6$		$\times 7$		$\times 3$

22.	6	23.	9	24.	8	25.	6
	$\times 6$		$\times 8$		$\times 4$		$\times 9$

26.	9	27.	7	28.	7	29.	9
	$\times 4$		$\times 8$		$\times 9$		$\times 9$

© Macmillan/McGraw-Hill

69

- Have students do Exercises 1–4 using the doubling method. Check that students understand that they must use the even number as their "double." Ask what would happen if both numbers were even. (They would have a choice of which factor to use as the double.)

- Have students do Exercises 5 and 6 using repeated addition. Check to make sure students are clear on which is the number to add and which tells the number of times it gets added.

- Have students do Exercises 7 and 8 by skip counting. Check to make sure students are clear on which is the number to skip count and which tells the number of times it gets counted.

Power Practice

- Have students complete the practice items. Then review each answer.

WHAT IF THE STUDENT CAN'T

Skip Count

- Show the student that by gathering counters into groups of, say, 4, he or she can count 1-2-3-4, then 5-6-7-8, and so on. The last number in each group of 4 becomes the next number in skip counting.

Complete the Power Practice

- Discuss each incorrect answer and review the previous skills if necessary.

Activity 45 Lesson Goal

- Multiply using a multiplication table or repeated addition.

What the Student Needs to Know

- Read a table.
- Add numbers in repetition.

Getting Started

Find out what students know about multiplication. Have them solve the following addition sentence:
$3 + 3 + 3 + 3 =$ _____ (12). Ask:

- *How can this addition sentence be written as a multiplication fact?* ($4 \times 3 = 12$)

What Can I Do?

- Read the question and the response. Then read and discuss the example. Ask:
- *How can the example be written as a multiplication fact?* ($7 \times 8 = 56$)
- *How is a multiplication table like an addition table? How are the two different?* (Both show you the results of performing an operation with two numbers. A multiplication table shows multiplication, while an addition table shows addition.)

Try It

Have students complete Exercises 1–6. Then have them demonstrate on a multiplication table the correct answers to the multiplication sentences.

Power Practice

- Have students complete the practice items. Then review each answer. Be sure that students understand that repeated addition and using the multiplication table should yield the same answer.

Name _____

Multiplication Facts

Learn

What Can I Do?
I want to multiply two numbers.

Use a Multiplication Table.
Example: To find 7 times 8, look across the 7 row until you are under the 8. The product is 56.

×	0	1	2	3	4	5	6	7	8	9	10
0	0	0	0	0	0	0	0	0	0	0	0
1	0	1	2	3	4	5	6	7	8	9	10
2	0	2	4	6	8	10	12	14	16	18	20
3	0	3	6	9	12	15	18	21	24	27	30
4	0	4	8	12	16	20	24	28	32	36	40
5	0	5	10	15	20	25	30	35	40	45	50
6	0	6	12	18	24	30	36	42	48	54	60
7	0	7	14	21	28	35	42	49	56	63	70
8	0	8	16	24	32	40	48	56	64	72	80
9	0	9	18	27	36	45	54	63	72	81	90
10	0	10	20	30	40	50	60	70	80	90	100

row ⟶ 7

Activity 45

Try It • Adding can help you multiply. Complete each pair of problems to see how.

1. $5 + 5 + 5 =$ _____

   $3 \times 5 =$ _____

2. $9 + 9 =$ _____

   $2 \times 9 =$ _____

3. $2 + 2 + 2 + 2 =$ _____

   $4 \times 2 =$ _____

4. $6 + 6 + 6 + 6 =$ _____

   $4 \times 6 =$ _____

5. $7 + 7 + 7 =$ _____

   $3 \times 7 =$ _____

6. $8 + 8 =$ _____

   $2 \times 8 =$ _____

Power Practice • Multiply.

7. $6 \times 9 =$ _____

8. $7 \times 7 =$ _____

9. $8 \times 6 =$ _____

10. $8 \times 9 =$ _____

11. $4 \times 5 =$ _____

12. $4 \times 6 =$ _____

13. $4 \times 9 =$ _____

14. $7 \times 5 =$ _____

70

© Macmillan/McGraw-Hill

WHAT IF THE STUDENT CAN'T

Read a Table

- Use an addition table. Show the student how finding the intersection of a column and a row gives the sum of two numbers. Have the student practice writing addition sentences using the table.

- Illustrate how a multiplication table works on the same principle.

Add Numbers in Repetition

- Use counters to demonstrate repeated addition of a number. Show, for example, that $4 + 4 = 8$, $4 + 4 + 4 = 12$, and so on.

- Show the student how repeated addition can also be written as multiplication, so that $4 + 4 + 4 + 4 + 4 = 20$ becomes $5 \times 4 = 20$. Have the student practice converting examples of repeated addition into multiplication sentences until the student can do so with ease.

Complete the Power Practice

- Discuss each incorrect answer. Have the student show you the correct answer on the multiplication table. Then have the student use repeated addition to demonstrate the correctness of the answer.

Name_____

Patterns

Learn

What Can I Do?
I want to complete a multiplication pattern.

Find the factor.

In this kind of pattern, the numbers 1, 2, 3, and so on are multiplied by the same factor. Find the factor.

60	120	180	240	?
↑	↑	↑	↑	↑
1×60	2×60	3×60	4×60	5×60

The factor is 60.
Since $5 \times 60 = 300$, the ? equals 300.

Try It • Make a pattern starting with each number. Multiply it by 2, 3, 4, 5.

1. 40, _____, _____, _____, _____   2. 90, _____, _____, _____, _____

3. 800; _____; _____; _____; _____

Power Practice • Complete each multiplication pattern.

4. 700; 1,400; 2,100; 2,800; _____   5. 30, 60, 90, 120, _____

6. 900; 1,800; 2,700; 3,600; _____   7. 200, 400, 600, 800, _____

8. 400; 800; 1,200; 1,600; _____   9. 20, 40, 60, 80, _____

© Macmillan/McGraw-Hill

71

WHAT IF THE STUDENT CAN'T

Multiply a Multiple of 10 or 100 by 2, 3, 4, or 5

• Use tens and hundreds models to show the student what happens when he or she multiplies a multiple of 10 or 100 by 2, 3, 4, or 5. Have the student count the ones in 3 sets of 2 tens models. Point out that he or she can use the basic fact $3 \times 2 = 6$ and write a zero after the 6 to get the same product. Have the student repeat the activity to show the product of 2, 3, 4, or 5 and various other multiples of 10 and 100.

Complete a Multiplication Pattern

• Show the student the following pattern: 2, 4, 6, 8. Explain

that each number in the pattern is a multiple of 2, and that each number is 2 greater than the one before it. Have the student predict the next number in the pattern. Continue with patterns for the numbers 3 through 9 until the concept becomes clear.

• Have the student practice writing multiplication patterns for the numbers 2 through 9.

Complete the Power Practice

• Have students state the rule for the patterns. Have the student multiply the factor by 5. Then have the student add the factor to the previous number in the pattern to check that the answer is correct.

Activity 46 Lesson Goal

• Complete multiplication patterns involving multiples of 10 and 100.

What the Student Needs to Know

• Multiply a multiple of 10 and 100 by 2, 3, 4, or 5.
• Complete a multiplication pattern.

Getting Started

Find out what students know about multiplication patterns. Have them complete the following patterns:

4, 8, 12, 16, _____ (20)
3, 6, 9, 12, _____ (15)
7, 14, 21, 28, _____ (35)

What Can I Do?

Read the question and the response. Then read and discuss the example. Ask:

• *How do you know that the factor is 60?* (Because 60 is the greatest number that each number in the pattern can be divided by evenly. Each number in the pattern is 60 greater than the number before it.)

• *How could you use addition to find 5×60?*
($60 + 60 + 60 + 60 + 60$)

Try It

Have students complete Exercises 1–3. Make sure they understand that the numbers in the pattern should increase by the same amount. Ask:

• *If you aren't sure that you have multiplied correctly for a number in the pattern, how can you check it?* (By adding the factor to the number before it in the pattern.)

Power Practice

• Have students complete Exercises 4–9. Then review each answer.

Operations Skill Builder **T71**

Activity 47 Lesson Goals

- Use properties of multiplication to multiply a number by 0 and 1.

What the Student Needs to Know

- Understand the Identity Property of Multiplication.
- Understand the Zero Property of Multiplication.

Getting Started

Be sure students know the meaning of *identity*. (it means "the same")

- By placing objects on a table, demonstrate that if you take an object (say, a counter) and place it on the table a number of times (say, 5), you will wind up with a number of objects equal to the number of times you did the placement.

- Demonstrate by holding nothing in your hand that no matter how many times you look at it, you still have nothing. (0)

What Can I Do?

Read the question and the response. Then discuss the examples. Tell students that in using the Identity Property, it does not matter which factor is 1. Ask:

- *What is 4 x 1?* (4) *What is 1 x 4?* (4)

Tell student that in using the Zero Property, it does not matter which factor is 0. Ask:

- *What is 7 x 0?* (0) *What is 0 x 7?* (0)

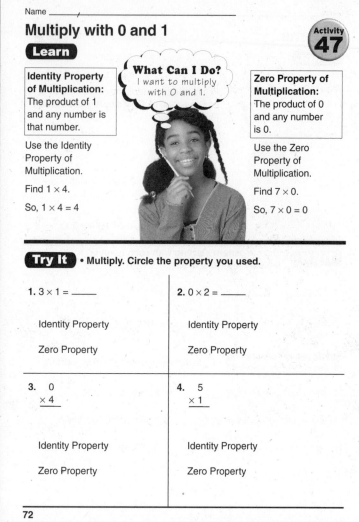

Multiply with 0 and 1

Learn

Identity Property of Multiplication: The product of 1 and any number is that number.

Use the Identity Property of Multiplication.

Find 1×4.

So, $1 \times 4 = 4$

What Can I Do? I want to multiply with 0 and 1.

Zero Property of Multiplication: The product of 0 and any number is 0.

Use the Zero Property of Multiplication.

Find 7×0.

So, $7 \times 0 = 0$

Try It • Multiply. Circle the property you used.

1. $3 \times 1 =$ _____

   Identity Property

   Zero Property

2. $0 \times 2 =$ _____

   Identity Property

   Zero Property

3. $\begin{array}{r} 0 \\ \times\,4 \\ \hline \end{array}$

   Identity Property

   Zero Property

4. $\begin{array}{r} 5 \\ \times\,1 \\ \hline \end{array}$

   Identity Property

   Zero Property

72

© Macmillan/McGraw-Hill

WHAT IF THE STUDENT CAN'T

Understand the Identity Property of Multiplication

- Draw a plate with 5 cookies on the board. Tell students this shows an example of the Identity Property of Multiplication: One group of 5 equals 5, or $1 \times 5 = 5$.

Understand the Zero Property of Multiplication

- Draw five empty plates on the board. Tell students this shows an example of the Zero Property of Multiplication: 5 groups of 0 equals 0, or $5 \times 0 = 0$.

Power Practice • Multiply.

5. $2 \times 0 =$ _____   **6.** $1 \times 6 =$ _____   **7.** $8 \times 1 =$ _____

8. $4 \times 0 =$ _____   **9.** $1 \times 5 =$ _____   **10.** $9 \times 0 =$ _____

11. $7 \times 1 =$ _____   **12.** $2 \times 1 =$ _____   **13.** $0 \times 8 =$ _____

14. $\begin{array}{r} 0 \\ \times\, 3 \\ \hline \end{array}$ **15.** $\begin{array}{r} 6 \\ \times\, 1 \\ \hline \end{array}$ **16.** $\begin{array}{r} 4 \\ \times\, 1 \\ \hline \end{array}$ **17.** $\begin{array}{r} 8 \\ \times\, 0 \\ \hline \end{array}$

18. $\begin{array}{r} 1 \\ \times\, 2 \\ \hline \end{array}$ **19.** $\begin{array}{r} 3 \\ \times\, 0 \\ \hline \end{array}$ **20.** $\begin{array}{r} 0 \\ \times\, 5 \\ \hline \end{array}$ **21.** $\begin{array}{r} 9 \\ \times\, 1 \\ \hline \end{array}$

22. $\begin{array}{r} 0 \\ \times\, 6 \\ \hline \end{array}$ **23.** $\begin{array}{r} 1 \\ \times\, 8 \\ \hline \end{array}$ **24.** $\begin{array}{r} 0 \\ \times\, 7 \\ \hline \end{array}$ **25.** $\begin{array}{r} 0 \\ \times\, 9 \\ \hline \end{array}$

26. $\begin{array}{r} 0 \\ \times\, 0 \\ \hline \end{array}$ **27.** $\begin{array}{r} 0 \\ \times\, 1 \\ \hline \end{array}$ **28.** $\begin{array}{r} 1 \\ \times\, 1 \\ \hline \end{array}$ **29.** $\begin{array}{r} 5 \\ \times\, 0 \\ \hline \end{array}$

30. $\begin{array}{r} 6 \\ \times\, 0 \\ \hline \end{array}$ **31.** $\begin{array}{r} 1 \\ \times\, 1 \\ \hline \end{array}$ **32.** $\begin{array}{r} 1 \\ \times\, 7 \\ \hline \end{array}$ **33.** $\begin{array}{r} 1 \\ \times\, 0 \\ \hline \end{array}$

73

Try It

Have students do Exercises 1–4.
Ask:

- *How did you decide which property to use?* (If one of the factors is 1, use the Identity Property. If one of the factors is 0, use the Zero Property.)
- *Which property would you use if you multiplied 1 x 0 or 0 x 1?* (It would not matter; you are using both.)

Power Practice

Have students complete the practice items. Then review each answer.

WHAT IF THE STUDENT CAN'T

Complete the Power Practice
- Review missed exercises with the student. Explain again the difference between the Identity Property and the Zero Property.

USING THE LESSON

Activity 48 Lesson Goal

- Use the rows and columns in a multiplication table to find patterns in multiplication.

What the Student Needs to Know

- Track accurately across a *row* or down a *column* in a multiplication table.
- Identify *odd* and *even* numbers.

Getting Started

Have students look at the table. Ask:

- *What does the table show about any number multiplied by 0?* (the product is 0)
- *Reading across a row or down a column is like what process?* (skip counting)

What Can I Do?

Read the question and the response. Then examine the exercise. Ask:

- *How can you compare the 2s row and the 4s row?* (Look at the pairs of numbers in the same column to look for relationships.)
- *How do the numbers in the 4s row compare to the numbers in the 2s row?* (The 4s row is 2 times the 2s row.)

Try It

Have students read Exercise 1 and then read the choices—*odd*, *even*, or *odd and even*. Have students look along the row until one of the choices is clear.

Do the same for Exercise 2. Students should see by the 3s row that the numbers are even.

Power Practice

- Have students complete the practice items. Then review each answer.

Name _____

Use a Multiplication Table

Activity 48

Learn

What Can I Do?
I want to find patterns in a multiplication table.

Look at the rows and the columns.

What pattern do you see in the 2s row and the 4s row?

↓**Columns**

x	0	1	2	3	4	5	6	7	8	9	
0	0	0	0	0	0	0	0	0	0	0	
1	0	1	2	3	4	5	6	7	8	9	
2	0	2	4	6	8	10	12	14	16	18	←2s row
3	0	3	6	9	12	15	18	21	24	27	
4	0	4	8	12	16	20	24	28	32	36	←4s row
5	0	5	10	15	20	25	30	35	40	45	

Rows

The numbers in the 4s row are double the numbers in the 2s row.

Try It • Complete. Write *odd*, *even*, or *odd and even*.

1. The numbers in the 3s **row** are _____.

2. The numbers in the 6s **column** are _____.

Power Practice • Use the multiplication table.

3. Which **rows** have only even numbers? _____

4. Which **columns** have both odd and even numbers? _____

_____

5. What do you notice about the first six numbers in the 5s **row** and the 5s **column?** _____

_____

_____

74

WHAT IF THE STUDENT CAN'T

Track Accurately Across a *Row* or Down a *Column* in a Multiplication Table

- Suggest using a 6-inch ruler or a 3 × 5 card to help tracking.

Identify *Odd* and *Even* Numbers

- Point out that all even numbers can be divided by 2; odd numbers cannot. In the multiplication table even and odd numbers alternate in odd-numbered rows and columns.

Complete the Power Practice

- Discuss any incorrect answers.
- Have the student model exercises that were answered incorrectly.

Multiplication Patterns

Name_____

Learn

What Can I Do?
I want to multiply by 10; 100; or 1,000.

Look for a pattern.
The number of zeros in the product is the same as in the power of ten.

1 zero	→	$4 \times 10 = 40$
2 zeros	→	$4 \times 100 = 400$
3 zeros	→	$4 \times 1,000 = 4,000$

Try It • Complete each pattern.

1. $7 \times 10 = $ _____   **2.** $2 \times 10 = $ _____   **3.** $9 \times 10 = $ _____

$7 \times 100 = $ _____ $2 \times 100 = $ _____ $9 \times 100 = $ _____

$7 \times 1,000 = $ _____ $2 \times 1,000 = $ _____ $9 \times 1,000 = $ _____

4. $3 \times 10 = $ _____   **5.** $8 \times 10 = $ _____   **6.** $5 \times 10 = $ _____

$3 \times 100 = $ _____ $8 \times 100 = $ _____ $5 \times 100 = $ _____

$3 \times 1,000 = $ _____ $8 \times 1,000 = $ _____ $5 \times 1,000 = $ _____

Power Practice • Find each product.

7. $9 \times 100 = $ _____   **8.** $3 \times 1,000 = $ _____   **9.** $7 \times 10 = $ _____

10. $6 \times 10 = $ _____   **11.** $5 \times 100 = $ _____   **12.** $3 \times 1,000 = $ _____

13. $8 \times 1,000 = $ _____   **14.** $4 \times 10 = $ _____   **15.** $8 \times 10 = $ _____

16. $4 \times 100 = $ _____   **17.** $6 \times 1,000 = $ _____   **18.** $2 \times 100 = $ _____

© Macmillan/McGraw-Hill

75

WHAT IF THE STUDENT CAN'T

Multiply by One

- Use counters to demonstrate simple multiplication equations, such as 4×2 and 4×3. Then show how multiplying a number by one results in a product of that number.

- Have the student practice multiplying the numbers 1 through 9 by 1 until the concept is clear.

Understand the Relationships between 10, 100, and 1,000

- Use grid strips and grids to model the relationship between the three numbers.

Demonstrate how it takes 10 strips of 10 grid squares to make 100, and 10 grids of 100 squares to make 1,000.

Complete the Power Practice

- Discuss each incorrect answer. Have the student identify the number of zeros in the second factor. Then have the student write the answer by attaching those zeros to the 1-digit factor.

USING THE LESSON

Activity 49 Lesson Goal

- Multiply numbers by 10, 100, and 1,000.

What the Student Needs to Know

- Multiply by one.
- Understand the relationship between 10, 100, and 1,000.

Getting Started

Find out what students know about the relationship between 10, 100, and 1,000. Ask:

- *How many zeros are there in 10? 100? 1,000?* (1, 2, 3)

What Can I Do?

Read the question and the response. Then read and discuss the examples. Ask:

- *What is a simple way of multiplying 4 times 10, 100, or 1,000?* (Possible answer: take the number 4 and write 1, 2, or 3 zeros after it.)

Try It

Have students answer Exercises 1 and 2 aloud. Then have students complete Exercises 3–6. Ask:

- *As you move from multiplying by 10 to multiplying by 100, then by 1,000, what happens to your products?* (They increase by a factor of ten each time.)

Power Practice

- Have students complete the practice items. Then review each answer.

- Compare any incorrect answers with similar exercises on the page that the student has answered correctly. For example, if the student answers 4×100 incorrectly, it can be compared with a correct answer for 4×10 or 9×100.

Activity 50 Lesson Goal

- Use the Associative Property of Addition to add 3 numbers.

What the Student Needs to Know

- Recall basic addition facts through 18.

Getting Started

Ask students to think of using the Associative Property as a way to make addition easier. Say:

- *When adding, look for number combinations that you know well.*
- *Think of this pair of sums. Which one is easier to add, 4 + 2 or 4 + 8? Why?* (4 + 2; you don't have to regroup)
- *In adding 4 + 2 + 8, which two addends would you group? Why?* (2 + 8, because they make 10; and 4 + 10 is easier to add than 6 + 8)

What Can I Do?

Read the question and the response. Then review the exercise: 5 + 1 + 9. Tell students that parentheses are used around the two numbers that are grouped. Ask:

- *Which two numbers will you group? Why?* (1 + 9, because they add up to 10, and 5 + 10 is easier to add than 6 + 9)
- *The Associative Property will not always provide an easier group to add. How would you group 5 + 4 + 7?* (Answers will vary.)

Try It

- Have students do Exercises 1 and 2 by using the groupings suggested. Ask:
- *Would you choose different groupings for either exercise?* (in Exercise 2, some students may think 9 + 2 easier than 7 + 4)

Power Practice

- Have students complete the practice items. Then review each answer. Each student should tell what grouping they used.

Name _____

Associative Property of Addition

Learn

What Can I Do?
I want to add 3 numbers.

> **Associative Property of Addition:** The grouping of the addends does not change the sum.

Use the Associative Property of Addition to find $5 + 1 + 9$.

Group the numbers to make addition easier. Use parentheses.

$5 + (1 + 9) =$ ___?___

$5 + 10 = 15$

So, $5 + 1 + 9 = 15$.

> Look for a ten or a double

Try It • Find each sum. Add the grouped addends first.

1. $(8 + 2) + 3$

____ + 3 = ____

2. $7 + (2 + 2)$

$7 +$ ____ = ____

Power Practice • Find each sum.

3. $6 + 9 + 1 =$ ____

4. $3 + 7 + 3 =$ ____

5. $9 + 5 + 4 =$ ____

6. $3 + 2 + 7 =$ ____

7. $5 + 8 + 2 =$ ____

8. $4 + 6 + 5 =$ ____

9. $8 + 4 + 6 =$ ____

10. $9 + 3 + 7 =$ ____

76

WHAT IF THE STUDENT CAN'T

Recall Basic Addition Facts through 18

- Practice addition facts through 18 for about 10 minutes daily, until the student can recall the sums for the addition facts automatically.

Complete the Power Practice

- Discuss each incorrect answer. Use counters, other physical objects, or pictured objects in groups to reinforce the concept of grouping.

Name_____

Multiplication Properties

Learn

What Can I Do?
I want to use properties of multiplication.

Property	What It Tells You
Commutative	You can multiply two numbers in either order.
Zero	Any number times zero is zero.
Distributive	You can break a product into the sum of two other products.

Try It • Use the Distributive Property to fill in the blanks.

1. $5 \times 43 = (5 \times 40) + (5 \times$ _____ $)$ 2. $4 \times 31 = (4 \times 30) + ($ _____ $\times 1)$

3. $9 \times 27 = (9 \times$ _____ $) + (9 \times 7)$ 4. $8 \times 62 = ($ _____ $\times 60) + (8 \times 2)$

Power Practice • Complete by writing the missing number. Tell which property you used.

5. $5 \times 0 =$ _____ _____ Property

6. $3 \times 26 = (3 \times$ _____ $) + ($ _____ $\times 6)$ _____ Property

7. $6 \times 7 = 7 \times$ _____ _____ Property

8. $7 \times 18 = (7 \times$ _____ $) + (7 \times$ _____ $)$ _____ Property

77

WHAT IF THE STUDENT CAN'T

Multiply a Two-Digit Number by a One-Digit Number

• Check that students have mastered multiplication facts. Use models to demonstrate finding products of greater numbers. Then have the student do the same. Finally, have the student use the algorithm. Check that the student regroups ones if necessary and remembers to add the regrouped ten(s).

Break a Two-Digit Number Down by Place Value

• Use place-value models to illustrate how a two-digit number can be seen as the sum of its tens and its ones.

For each number, have the student identify the number of tens and of ones.

• Have the student practice writing two-digit numbers in expanded form until he or she can do so automatically.

Complete the Power Practice

• For each incorrect property identification, draw the student's attention to the characteristic feature of the mathematics statement: an inversion of order, a zero, or an expansion of the two-digit number as the sum of two products. Then have the student give a new answer based on this feature.

USING THE LESSON

Activity 51 Lesson Goal
• Understand properties of multiplication.

What the Student Needs to Know
• Multiply a two-digit number by a one-digit number.
• Break a two-digit number down by place value.

Getting Started
Write the following on the board:
$7 \times 6 =$ _____ ; $6 \times 7 =$ _____ (42)
$4 \times 0 =$ _____ ; $9 \times 0 =$ _____ (0)
$3 \times 12 =$ _____ ; $(3 \times 10) + (3 \times 2) =$ _____ (36)
Have students complete the exercises. Ask:
• *What do you notice about each pair of exercises?* (Both have the same answer.)

What Can I Do?
• Read the question. Then introduce the three properties being studied. Relate each property to a pair on the board. Then ask:
• *According to the Commutative Property of Multiplication, $9 \times 4 = 4 \times$ ___ ?* (9)
• *According to the Zero Property of Multiplication, does $2 \times 0 = 7{,}292 \times 0$?* (Yes)

Try It
Have students look at Exercises 1 and 2. Ask:
• *According to the Distributive Property, how can you find the number that belongs in the blank in Exercise 1?* (Subtract 40 from 43.) *In Exercise 2?* (Take the number that 31 is being multiplied by.)
Have students complete Exercises 1–4.

Power Practice
• Have students complete the practice items. Then review each answer.

Operations Skill Builder **T77**

Activity 52 Lesson Goal

- Multiply with multiples of 10, 100, or 1,000

What the Student Needs to Know

- Recall basic multiplication facts.
- Understand place value up to thousands.
- Multiply by 10, 100, and 1,000.

Getting Started

Have students solve the following two number sentences:

$8 \times 1 =$ _____ (8)

$8 \times 10 =$ _____ (80)

- Ask: *What is the relationship between the first answer and the second answer?* (Possible answers: The second answer is ten times more than the first answer; The second answer is the first answer with a zero attached.)

What Can I Do?

Read the question and the response. Then read and discuss the example. Ask:

- *Which multiplication fact do you need to know to solve the problem?* ($5 \times 4 = 20$)
- *What do you have to know about place value to solve the problem?* (You have to know that 4,000 is the same as 4 thousands.)
- *What would the answer be if the problem were $5 \times 3,000$?* (15,000) $5 \times 5,000$? (25,000)

Name _____

Multiplying with Multiples of 10, 100, or 1,000

Activity 52

Learn

What Can I Do?
I want to multiply with tens, hundreds, and thousands.

Use place value.

$5 \times 4,000 = 5 \times 4$ thousands

Use the basic fact.

5×4 thousands $= 20$ thousands $= 20,000$

Think :
$5 \times 4 = 20$

Try It • Write each number in standard form.

1. 24 tens = _____
2. 56 hundreds = _____
3. 63 thousands = _____

4. 18 tens = _____
5. 30 hundreds = _____
6. 12 thousands = _____

7. 35 tens = _____
8. 14 hundreds = _____
9. 45 thousands = _____

Complete the steps to find each product.

10. 3×80

= $3 \times$ _____ tens
= _____ tens
= _____

11. 7×400

= $7 \times$ _____ hundreds
= _____ hundreds
= _____

12. $6 \times 3,000$

= $6 \times$ _____ thousands
= _____ thousands
= _____

© Macmillan/McGraw-Hill

78

WHAT IF THE STUDENT CAN'T

Recall Basic Multiplication Facts

- Use counters or models to demonstrate the products of multiplying two 1-digit numbers. Then have the student do the same.
- Have the student write multiplication facts on flash cards and practice until they can be recalled with ease.

Understand Place Value through the Thousands

- Have the student practice writing two-digit through four-digit numbers in a place value chart and reading them aloud until it can be done

with ease. Be sure the student understands that each place value must have a single digit from 0 to 9.

- Have the student write down the following numbers in place value and standard forms: *3 tens* (30); *4 thousands* (4,000); *7 hundreds* (700); *6 tens* (600); *4 hundreds* (400); *8 thousands* (8,000). Be sure the student understands that a place value that isn't specified can be assumed to have a value of 0.

Name _____

Use the basic fact to write each product.

13. $4 \times 6 = 24$

$4 \times 60 =$ _____

14. $7 \times 9 = 63$

$7 \times 900 =$ _____

15. $5 \times 8 = 40$

$5 \times 8,000 =$ _____

16. $3 \times 9 = 27$

$3 \times 90 =$ _____

17. $6 \times 5 = 30$

$6 \times 500 =$ _____

18. $2 \times 6 = 12$

$2 \times 6,000 =$ _____

19. $6 \times 7 =$ _____

$6 \times 70 =$ _____

20. $8 \times 3 =$ _____

$8 \times 300 =$ _____

21. $4 \times 5 =$ _____

$4 \times 5,000 =$ _____

22. $5 \times 3 =$ _____

$5 \times 30 =$ _____

23. $9 \times 2 =$ _____

$9 \times 200 =$ _____

24. $8 \times 8 =$ _____

$8 \times 8,000 =$ _____

Power Practice • Find each product.

25. $\begin{array}{r} 800 \\ \times\ 9 \\ \hline \end{array}$

26. $\begin{array}{r} 70 \\ \times\ 7 \\ \hline \end{array}$

27. $\begin{array}{r} 4,000 \\ \times\ \ \ 3 \\ \hline \end{array}$

28. $\begin{array}{r} 60 \\ \times\ 8 \\ \hline \end{array}$

29. $\begin{array}{r} 50 \\ \times\ 4 \\ \hline \end{array}$

30. $\begin{array}{r} 8,000 \\ \times\ \ \ 4 \\ \hline \end{array}$

31. $\begin{array}{r} 600 \\ \times\ \ 6 \\ \hline \end{array}$

32. $\begin{array}{r} 2,000 \\ \times\ \ \ 6 \\ \hline \end{array}$

33. $\begin{array}{r} 900 \\ \times\ \ 5 \\ \hline \end{array}$

34. $\begin{array}{r} 30 \\ \times\ 4 \\ \hline \end{array}$

35. $\begin{array}{r} 7,000 \\ \times\ \ \ 8 \\ \hline \end{array}$

36. $\begin{array}{r} 90 \\ \times\ 7 \\ \hline \end{array}$

37. $\begin{array}{r} 7,000 \\ \times\ \ \ 6 \\ \hline \end{array}$

38. $\begin{array}{r} 900 \\ \times\ \ 9 \\ \hline \end{array}$

39. $\begin{array}{r} 50 \\ \times\ 2 \\ \hline \end{array}$

40. $\begin{array}{r} 500 \\ \times\ \ 6 \\ \hline \end{array}$

© Macmillan/McGraw-Hill

79

WHAT IF THE STUDENT CAN'T

Multiply by 10, 100, and 1,000

- Use grids, grid strips, and cubes to model multiplication sentences that include these numbers. Show the student how a number may be multiplied by 10, 100, or 1,000 by attaching one, two, or three zeros to the original number. For example, $13 \times 10 = 130$; $13 \times 100 = 1,300$; and $13 \times 1,000 = 13,000$.
- Have the student practice multiplying by 10, 100, and 1,000 until the procedure becomes familiar.

Complete the Power Practice

- Discuss each incorrect answer. Have the student identify the multiplication fact central to the problem. Then have the student describe the first factor in terms of place value. Finally, have the student use words to describe the answer in terms of place value before converting it to standard form.

Try It

Have the students look at Exercises 1–3. Make sure students understand that to write each number in standard form, they must multiply the 2-digit number by its place value. For example, 24 tens = 24 × 10 = 240. If students are not comfortable multiplying, have them write the number out in a place-value chart. For example, 24 tens becomes 2 hundreds, 4 tens, and 0 ones, or 240. Then have the students complete Exercises 1–9. Ask:

- *What is a quick way to write 27 tens in standard form?* (Add a zero to the end of 27 to get 270.) *27 hundreds in standard form?* (Add two zeros to the end of 27 to get 2,700.) *27 thousands in standard form?* (Add three zeros to the end of 27 to get 27,000.)

Have students look at Exercise 10. Be sure they understand how to rewrite 80 as 8 tens to facilitate multiplication. Then have the students complete Exercises 10–15.

Have the students look at Exercises 16–24. Be sure they understand how to name the second factor in the second number sentence in terms of its place values: 90 = 9 tens; 500 = 5 hundreds; and 6,000 = 6 thousands.

Power Practice

- Have students complete the practice exercises. Then review each answer.
- Select several of the exercises and have students identify the multiplication fact central to each problem.

Activity 53 Lesson Goal

- Multiply one-digit numbers by two-digit numbers.

What the Student Needs to Know

- Recall multiplication facts.
- Understand place value and regrouping.

Getting Started

Find out what students know about regrouping. Write the following multiplication on the chalkboard:

$$\begin{array}{r} 6 \\ \times 2 \\ \hline 12 \end{array}$$

- *Why do you write a 1 in the tens column in the answer?* (because 6 × 2 = 12, which is 1 ten and 2 ones)

Write the following multiplication sentences on the board:

$$\begin{array}{r} 10 \\ \times 6 \\ \hline 60 \end{array} \qquad \begin{array}{r} 12 \\ \times 6 \\ \hline 72 \end{array}$$

- Ask: *What number is in the tens column in the answer to the first problem?* (6) *In the answer to the second problem?* (7) *Why is there a change?* (Because in the second problem, the ones need to be regrouped after you multiply. In the answer, you write a 2 in the ones place, and write 1 ten above the tens column and add it after you multiply the tens.)

What Can I Do?

Read the question and the response. Then read and discuss the example. Ask:

- *In what order do you multiply the digits of a two-digit number?* (Start with the ones, then multiply the tens.)
- *When do you need to regroup to the next place value in a multiplication problem?* (when the number in a place value is more than 9)

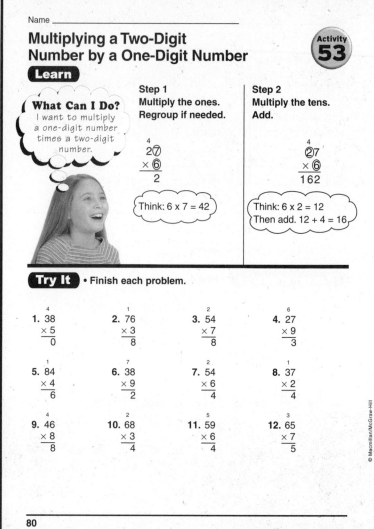

Name _____

Multiplying a Two-Digit Number by a One-Digit Number

Learn

What Can I Do? I want to multiply a one-digit number times a two-digit number.

Step 1 Multiply the ones. Regroup if needed.

$$\begin{array}{r} 4 \\ 2\!\!\!\!/ 7 \\ \times \, 6 \\ \hline 2 \end{array}$$

Think: 6 × 7 = 42

Step 2 Multiply the tens. Add.

$$\begin{array}{r} 4 \\ 2\!\!\!\!/ 7 \\ \times \, 6 \\ \hline 162 \end{array}$$

Think: 6 × 2 = 12
Then add. 12 + 4 = 16

Try It • Finish each problem.

1. $\begin{array}{r}4\\38\\\times 5\\\hline 0\end{array}$	2. $\begin{array}{r}1\\76\\\times 3\\\hline 8\end{array}$	3. $\begin{array}{r}2\\54\\\times 7\\\hline 8\end{array}$	4. $\begin{array}{r}6\\27\\\times 9\\\hline 3\end{array}$
5. $\begin{array}{r}1\\84\\\times 4\\\hline 6\end{array}$	6. $\begin{array}{r}7\\38\\\times 9\\\hline 2\end{array}$	7. $\begin{array}{r}2\\54\\\times 6\\\hline 4\end{array}$	8. $\begin{array}{r}1\\37\\\times 2\\\hline 4\end{array}$
9. $\begin{array}{r}4\\46\\\times 8\\\hline 8\end{array}$	10. $\begin{array}{r}2\\68\\\times 3\\\hline 4\end{array}$	11. $\begin{array}{r}5\\59\\\times 6\\\hline 4\end{array}$	12. $\begin{array}{r}3\\65\\\times 7\\\hline 5\end{array}$

80

WHAT IF THE STUDENT CAN'T

Recall Basic Multiplication Facts

- Use counters or models to demonstrate the products of multiplying 2 one-digit numbers. Then have the student do the same.
- Have the student write out a multiplication table for the numbers 0 through 9.
- Have the student write multiplication facts on flash cards and practice until they can be recalled with ease.

Understand Place Value and Regrouping

- Have the student write a two-digit number and read it aloud. Then have the student tell you how many tens and ones are in the number.
- Have the student practice writing two-digit numbers in a place-value chart until it can be done with ease.

Find each product.

13.	32 × 1	14.	73 × 3	15.	53 × 7	16.	43 × 2

17.	91 × 5	18.	62 × 5	19.	78 × 3	20.	34 × 2

Power Practice • Find each product.

21.	32 × 6	22.	68 × 2	23.	24 × 7	24.	69 × 4

25.	24 × 9	26.	53 × 7	27.	78 × 3	28.	46 × 8

29.	88 × 3	30.	39 × 5

31.	26 × 8	32.	57 × 6

33.	47 × 2	34.	83 × 4

35.	65 × 5	36.	45 × 9

© Macmillan/McGraw-Hill

Learn with Partners & Parents

Greatest Product Game

You will need one set of 0 to 9 digit cards.

- Turn the cards over and mix them up. Each player draws three cards.
- Make a problem like this:

  ☐ × ☐☐

  Find your product.
- The player with the greater product gets one point. Play until one player has 7 points.

81

WHAT IF THE STUDENT CAN'T

- Use grid strips and squares to illustrate a situation where regrouping is required. For example: 1 ten, 7 ones (17) + 2 tens, 8 ones (28) = 3 tens, 15 ones. Since a number in a place value may only be 9 or less, the ones must be regrouped. To get the answer of 45, 10 of the ones are converted to 1 ten, making a total of 4. The 5 ones remain in the ones column.

Complete the Power Practice

- Discuss each incorrect answer. Have the student write out the multiplication of the ones column as a multiplication fact. Then have the student write down the ones digit and regroup the tens. Finally, have the student multiply the tens column and add the results of the regrouping.
- Have the student use the Distributive Property of Multiplication to check the correctness of each revised answer. For example, $32 \times 6 = 192$ can be broken into $(30 \times 6) + (2 \times 6) = 180 + 12 = 192$.

- *How do you regroup?* (After multiplying, write down the digit in the ones place in the product and add the digit in the tens place to the product of the next column.)

Try It

Look at Exercise 1 with students. Ask:

- *How can you complete this problem?* (Multiply 5 by 3, then add 4.)

Be sure students understand that they should first multiply the tens column, and then add any numbers resulting from regrouping. Then have them complete Exercises 1–12.

Have the students look at exercise 15. Check to be sure they understand the order in which they should multiply the digits of the two-digit number. Ask:

- *How can you find the answer to this problem?* (Multiply 3 by 7 to get 21, then write 1 in the ones column. Remember that you need to regroup 2 tens. Multiply 5 by 7 to get 35, then write a 3 in the hundreds column and a 7 in the tens column because you add the 2 tens from regrouping.)

Have the students complete Exercises 16–20.

Power Practice

- Have students complete the practice items. Then review each answer.
- Select a few of the exercises. Have volunteers demonstrate how to get at the correct answer by regrouping.

Learn with Partners & Parents

- Players may enjoy playing a reverse game where they try to get products that are low.

Activity 54 Lesson Goal

• Multiply three-digit numbers by one-digit numbers

What the Student Needs to Know

• Recall basic multiplication facts.
• Understand place value and regrouping.

Getting Started

Find out what students know about regrouping. Write the following multiplications on the board and have students solve:

$$\begin{array}{r} 43 \\ \times 2 \\ \hline 86 \end{array} \qquad \begin{array}{r} 43 \\ \times 4 \\ \hline 172 \end{array}$$

Ask:

• *Is regrouping required in the first problem?* (No) *Why or why not?* (Because the value of the ones place after multiplying is 6, which is not greater than 9.)

• *Why is regrouping required in the second problem?* (Because the value of the ones place after multiplying is 12, which is greater than 9.)

• *How do you regroup?* (You write down the digit in the ones place in the answer. Then you write the digit in the tens place above the tens column and add it after you multiply the column.)

What Can I Do?

• Read the question and the response. Then read and discuss the example. Ask:

• *In what order do you multiply the digits of a three-digit number?* (Start with the ones, then move on to the tens, and then on to the hundreds.)

• *How do you regroup tens to hundreds when multiplying tens?* (Write the ones digit in the tens place of the product. Then write the tens digit of your product above the hundreds column and add it to the product of that column.)

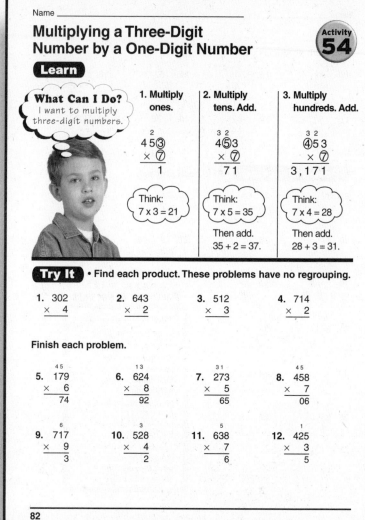

Name _____

Multiplying a Three-Digit Number by a One-Digit Number

Learn

What Can I Do? I want to multiply three-digit numbers.

1. Multiply ones.	2. Multiply tens. Add.	3. Multiply hundreds. Add.
$\begin{array}{r} 2 \\ 45③ \\ \times ⑦ \\ \hline 1 \end{array}$	$\begin{array}{r} 3\,2 \\ 4⑤3 \\ \times ⑦ \\ \hline 71 \end{array}$	$\begin{array}{r} 3\,2 \\ ④53 \\ \times ⑦ \\ \hline 3,171 \end{array}$
Think: 7 x 3 = 21	Think: 7 x 5 = 35 Then add. 35 + 2 = 37.	Think: 7 x 4 = 28 Then add. 28 + 3 = 31.

Try It • Find each product. These problems have no regrouping.

| 1. $\begin{array}{r} 302 \\ \times\ 4 \\ \hline \end{array}$ | 2. $\begin{array}{r} 643 \\ \times\ 2 \\ \hline \end{array}$ | 3. $\begin{array}{r} 512 \\ \times\ 3 \\ \hline \end{array}$ | 4. $\begin{array}{r} 714 \\ \times\ 2 \\ \hline \end{array}$ |

Finish each problem.

| 5. $\begin{array}{r} {}^{45} \\ 179 \\ \times\ 6 \\ \hline 74 \end{array}$ | 6. $\begin{array}{r} {}^{13} \\ 624 \\ \times\ 8 \\ \hline 92 \end{array}$ | 7. $\begin{array}{r} {}^{31} \\ 273 \\ \times\ 5 \\ \hline 65 \end{array}$ | 8. $\begin{array}{r} {}^{45} \\ 458 \\ \times\ 7 \\ \hline 06 \end{array}$ |

| 9. $\begin{array}{r} {}^{6} \\ 717 \\ \times\ 9 \\ \hline 3 \end{array}$ | 10. $\begin{array}{r} {}^{3} \\ 528 \\ \times\ 4 \\ \hline 2 \end{array}$ | 11. $\begin{array}{r} {}^{5} \\ 638 \\ \times\ 7 \\ \hline 6 \end{array}$ | 12. $\begin{array}{r} {}^{1} \\ 425 \\ \times\ 3 \\ \hline 5 \end{array}$ |

82

WHAT IF THE STUDENT CAN'T

Recall Basic Multiplication Facts

• Use counters or models to demonstrate the products of multiplying 2 one-digit numbers. Then have the student do the same.

• Have the student write out a multiplication table for the numbers 0 through 9.

• Have the student write multiplication facts on flash cards and practice until they can be recalled with ease.

Understand Place Value and Regrouping

• Have the student write a three-digit number and read it aloud. Then have the student tell you how many hundreds, tens, and ones are in the number.

• Have the student practice writing three-digit numbers in a place-value chart until it can be done with ease.

Name _____

Find each product. Use a dollar sign and decimal point in each answer.

13. $3.52	14. $1.76	15. $8.04	16. $4.63
× 6	× 5	× 8	× 2

Power Practice • Find each product.

17. 314	18. 261	19. 585	20. 193
× 7	× 3	× 4	× 7

21. 426	22. 619	23. 758	24. 294
× 2	× 9	× 5	× 8

25. $7.24	26. $5.81	27. $2.90	28. $6.35
× 5	× 6	× 4	× 2

29. 8 × 341 = _____ 30. 3 × 826 = _____ 31. 7 × 684 = _____

32. 9 × 256 = _____ 33. 5 × 489 = _____ 34. 9 × 327 = _____

35. 8 × 295 = _____ 36. 6 × 372 = _____ 37. 3 × 898 = _____

38. 5 × $2.43 = _____ 39. 9 × $7.56 = _____ 40. 6 × $4.07 = _____

41. 6 × $7.15 = _____ 42. 5 × $9.49 = _____ 43. 8 × $3.89 = _____

44. 7 × $4.78 = _____ 45. 9 × $6.85 = _____ 46. 4 × $7.79 = _____

83

WHAT IF THE STUDENT CAN'T

- Use grids, grid strips and squares to illustrate multiplication with regrouping. For example: 2 hundreds, 8 tens, and 5 ones (285) + 4 hundreds, 5 tens, and 2 ones (452) = 6 hundreds, 13 tens, and 7 ones. Since a place value may only be 9 or less, the tens column must be regrouped. To get the answer of 737, 10 of the tens are regrouped as 1 hundred, making a total of 7 hundreds. 3 tens remain in the tens column, and there are 7 ones.

Complete the Power Practice

- Discuss each incorrect answer. Have the student write out the multiplication in each place-value column as a multiplication fact, including the addition of any regrouped numbers.
- Have the student use the Distributive Property of Multiplication to check the correctness of each revised answer. For example, 314 × 7 = 2,198 can be broken into (300 × 7) + (10 × 7) + (4 × 7) = 2,100 + 70 + 28 = 2,198.

Try It

Have the students look at Exercise 2. Check to be sure they understand the order in which they should multiply the digits of the 3-digit number. Ask:

- *Which digit should you multiply first?* (3, or the ones) *Second?* (4, or the tens) *Third?* (6, or the hundreds)

Then have students complete Exercises 1–4.

Have students look at Exercise 6. Be sure students understand that any numbers that result from regrouping should only be added after the column has been multiplied. Ask:

- *What is the final step in the multiplication?* (Multiply 6 hundreds by 8, then add 1 hundred.)

Then have students complete Exercises 5–8.

Have students look at Exercise 9. Ask:

- *How many times in all do you have to regroup in this problem?* (2)
- *After you regroup the tens column, how many hundreds will you need to add to the hundreds column?* (1)

Then have students complete Exercises 9–16.

Power Practice

- Have students complete Exercises 17–46. Then review each answer.
- Select a few of the exercises. Have volunteers demonstrate how to arrive at the correct answer by regrouping.

Activity 55 Lesson Goal

- Complete and identify rules for function tables.

What the Student Needs to Know

- Multiply numbers by a given factor.
- Identify the factor by which a number is multiplied.
- Read a function table.

Getting Started

Write the following function table on the board:

Input	Output
1	2
2	4
3	6
4	8

Ask:

- *What is the relationship between the number in the input column and the number in the output column?* (The output number is the input number × 2.)
- *If the number in the input column is 5, what will the number in the output column be?* (10)

What Can I Do?

Read the question and the response. Then discuss the example. Ask:

- *How can you tell what the relationship between the input number and the output number is?* (Use repeated addition or division to determine how many times the input number goes into the output number.)
- *The first input number is 3, and the first output number is 15. How can you be sure that the rule of the table isn't + 12?* (Because the rule doesn't apply to the other numbers.)
- *If the input number is 9, what will the output number be? What if the input number is 7?* (45, 35)

Name_____

Function Tables

Learn

What Can I Do?
I want to find missing numbers in a function table.

Look for the rule.
Look at the number going in, the input. Then look at the number coming out, the output. What number would make this true?.
3 x ? = 15

Input	Output
3	15
4	20
6	30
9	?

Think: 3 times 5 is 15.
The rule is "times 5."
So, 9 × 5 = 45

Try It • Use the rules to complete the tables.

1. Rule: × 6

Input	Output
3	18
4	24
7	

2. Rule: × 3

Input	Output
2	6
6	18
9	

3. Rule: × 4

Input	Output
1	4
5	20
8	

4. Rule: × 8

Input	Output
3	24
6	48
	56

5. Rule: × 2

Input	Output
4	8
6	12
	16

6. Rule: × 7

Input	Output
2	14
4	28
	35

84

WHAT IF THE STUDENT CAN'T

Multiply Numbers by a Given Factor

- Use models to illustrate the pattern that develops when consecutive numbers are multiplied by the same factor.
- Use a multiplication table to demonstrate the products that result when different numbers are multiplied by the same factor.

Identify the Factor by Which a Number Is Multiplied

- Use counters to illustrate the way that division and repeated addition can be used to identify the factor by which a number is multiplied. For example, 3 × ____ = 18 can be solved by using counters to determine that 18 can be divided into 6 groups of 3, or that 3 has to be added 6 times to get 18.

Power Practice • Complete each table.
Then identify the rule.

7. Rule: _____

Input	Output
3	21
5	35
7	49
9	

8. Rule: _____

Input	Output
1	3
3	9
6	18
7	

9. Rule: _____

Input	Output
4	24
5	30
7	42
8	

10. Rule: _____

Input	Output
3	12
5	20
6	24
8	

11. Rule: _____

Input	Output
4	20
6	30
7	35
9	

12. Rule: _____

Input	Output
2	18
4	36
5	45
7	

13. Rule: _____

Input	Output
3	24
5	40
7	56
	64

14. Rule: _____

Input	Output
2	4
4	8
6	12
	18

15. Rule: _____

Input	Output
1	6
3	18
4	24
	36

16. Rule: _____

Input	Output
4	16
6	24
8	32
	40

17. Rule: _____

Input	Output
2	10
4	20
8	40
10	

18. Rule: _____

Input	Output
3	18
5	30
7	42
	54

© Macmillan/McGraw-Hill

85

WHAT IF THE STUDENT CAN'T

Read a Function Table

- Choose one of the function tables from Exercises 1–6. Show how the output column can be treated as an equal sign. For example, an input of 4 and an output of 24 can be read as $4 \times \underline{\quad} = 24$. Have the student interpret the table for you in this way.

- Explain that the rule for the table tells you what to do with the number in the input column to get the number in the output column. Have the student write equations for each of the rows in one of the tables in Exercises 1–6.

Complete the Power Practice

- Discuss each incorrect answer. Have the student use division or repeated addition to identify the rule or missing number in the table.

Try It

Make sure students can complete Exercises 1–6 by applying the rule given for each table. Ask:

- *How can you find the output number if you know the input number?* (multiply)

- *How can you find the input number if you know the output number?* (divide)

Power Practice

- Have students complete Exercises 7–18. Then review each answer. Have students demonstrate how to identify the rule for a table.

Activity 56 Lesson Goal

- Use basic multiplication facts to find a missing factor.

What the Student Needs to Know

- Recall basic multiplication facts from 1 to 5.

Getting Started

Remind students that they usually multiply two factors to get a product. Here they will have the product and one of the factors and have to find the other factor. Say:

- *Let's see how we can find a missing factor. When I see 2 × ___ = 6, and I immediately recognize a missing factor, that's all there is to the problem. If I don't recognize it immediately, there is a simple method to use.*

- *I can set up a list of facts for 2. I write out 2 × 1 = 2, 2 × 2 = 4, 2 × 3 = 6. So 3 is the missing factor.*

What Can I Do?

Read the question and the response. Then discuss the example. Ask:

- *What do we do if we don't recognize the missing factor in 2 × __ = 10?* (Make a list of facts for 2.)

- *How far do you have to go to find the factor?* (2 × 5)

Try It

Have students read each of the exercises and use a list of facts, if necessary, to find each of the missing factors.

Power Practice

- Have students complete the practice items. Then review each answer.

Name _____

Missing Factors

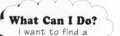

What Can I Do?
I want to find a missing factor.

Use basic multiplication facts.

Write the missing factor.

2 × ___?___ = 10

Think: 2 times what number is equal to 10?

Find the multiplication fact for 2 with a product of 10.

2 × 1 = 2
2 × 2 = 4
2 × 3 = 6
2 × 4 = 8
2 × 5 = 10

So, 5 is the missing factor.

Try It • Write each product. Then write each missing factor.

1. 3 × 4 = _____

   3 × _____ = 12

2. 4 × 5 = _____

   4 × _____ = 20

Power Practice • Write each missing factor.

3. 2 × _____ = 14

4. 5 × _____ = 15

5. 4 × _____ = 16

6. 3 × _____ = 24

7. 6 × _____ = 24

8. 4 × _____ = 36

9. 7 × _____ = 63

10. 5 × _____ = 20

86

© Macmillan/McGraw-Hill

WHAT IF THE STUDENT CAN'T

Recall Basic Multiplication Facts from 1 to 5

- Have the student use physical counters to make groups of objects.

- Have the student write out lists of multiplication facts and keep them handy to use as a reference.

Complete the Power Practice

- Discuss each incorrect answer. Review how the student can check his or her answers by using counters or lists.

Name _____

Closest Multiple

Learn

Activity **57**

What Can I Do?
I want to find multiples close to a given number.

Use a list of multiples.

Example: What multiple of 5 is closest to 27?

Multiples of 5: 5, 10, 15, 20, 25, 30, 35, 40, 45, 50

Answer: 25

Try It • List the first ten multiples of each number.

1. 6 _____

2. 7 _____

3. 8 _____

Power Practice • Write a multiple *less than* each number.

What multiple of 6 is closest to each number?

4. 55 _____ **5.** 20 _____ **6.** 39 _____ **7.** 51 _____ **8.** 25 _____

What multiple of 7 is closest to each number?

9. 45 _____ **10.** 30 _____ **11.** 59 _____ **12.** 23 _____ **13.** 50 _____

What multiple of 8 is closest to each number?

14. 43 _____ **15.** 66 _____ **16.** 73 _____ **17.** 20 _____ **18.** 35 _____

© Macmillan/McGraw-Hill

87

WHAT IF THE STUDENT CAN'T

Recall Basic Multiplication Facts

- Use counters or models to demonstrate the products of multiplying 6, 7, 8, and 9 by the numbers 1 through 10. Then have the student do the same.

- Have the student write multiplication facts for the numbers 6 through 9 on flash cards. Then have the student practice using the flash cards until the facts can be recalled with ease.

Compare Numbers as *Greater Than* and *Less Than*

- Have the student draw a number line from 0 to 10 and point to two numbers. Explain that the number to the right on the line is greater than the one to its left. This means that the number to the left is less than the number to the right.

Complete the Power Practice

- Discuss each incorrect answer with the student, correcting the error.

Activity 57 Lesson Goal

- Find the multiple that is closest to another number.

What the Student Needs to Know

- Recall basic multiplication facts.

- Compare numbers as *greater than* and *less than*.

Getting Started

Write the numbers from 0 to 20 on the board. Then have students tell you the first 5 multiples of 4 (4, 8, 12, 16, 20). Circle these numbers on the board. Ask:

- *What are the numbers between 0 and 4?* (1, 2, 3) *4 and 8?* (5, 6, 7) *8 and 12?* (9, 10, 11) *12 and 16?* (13, 14, 15) *16 and 20?* (17, 18, 19)

What Can I Do?

Read the question and the response. Then discuss the example. Ask:

- *How do you know that 25 is the multiple of 5 closest to 27?* (Because it is only 2 away from 27, but 30 is 3 away from 27.)

Try It

Look at Exercises 1–3 with the students. For each number, have them say the first ten multiples aloud before writing multiples down.

Power Practice

- Be sure students understand that the multiple in each answer must be less than the number given. Then have the students complete the practice items. Review each answer.

Activity 58 Lesson Goal

- Estimate the quotient of a three-digit number and a one-digit number by finding the greatest multiple of 10 and the divisor that is less than the dividend.

What the Student Needs to Know

- Recall multiplication facts through 9×9.
- Multiply one-digit numbers times multiples of 10.
- Compare three-digit numbers.

Getting Started

Find out what students know about multiples of 10 and multiplication facts. Say:

- *Starting at 10, what are the first 10 multiples of 10?* (10, 20, 30, 40, 50, 60, 70, 80, 90, 100) *How can you find the multiples of a number?* (skip count, use repeated addition, or count on by the number)

- *Is 40 a multiple of 4?* (Yes) *Is 40 a multiple of 10?* (Yes) *How do you know that 40 is a multiple of 4 and 10?* (Because $4 \times 10 = 40$.)

- *How can you use the multiplication fact 4×2 to find another multiple of 4 and 10?* (Multiply 4×20; since $4 \times 2 = 8$, $4 \times 20 = 80$.)

What Can I Do?

Read the question and the response. Then discuss the examples. Ask:

- *How do you know that 240 is the closest multiple of 8 and 10 that is less than 255?* (Because $8 \times 30 = 240$, which is less than 255; the next multiple of 10 is 40, and $8 \times 40 = 320$, which is greater than 255.)

- *Explain why 30 is a good estimate for the quotient of $255 \div 8$.* ($8 \times 30 = 240$ and 240 is the greatest multiple of 8 and 10 that is less than 255.)

Name _____

Closest (Three–Digit) Multiple

Learn

What Can I Do?
I want to use closest multiples to help me estimate quotients.

Use multiplication facts to estimate quotients.

To estimate the quotient of $255 \div 8$ look for the closest multiple of 8 and 10 that is less than 255.

Think:

$8 \times 1 = 8$, so $8 \times 10 = 80$ 80 is less than 255.
$8 \times 2 = 16$, so $8 \times 20 = 160$ 160 is less than 255.
$8 \times 3 = 24$, so $8 \times \mathbf{30} = \mathbf{240}$ 240 is less than 255.
$8 \times 4 = 32$, so $8 \times 40 = 320$ 320 is too great.

So, 240 is the closest multiple of 8 and 10 that is less than 255.

Since $8 \times 30 = 240$, the quotient of $255 \div 8$ is about 30.

Try It • Complete.

1. To estimate the quotient of $235 \div 6$, find the closest multiple of _____ and 10 that is less than _____.

2. $6 \times 1 = 6$, so $6 \times 10 =$ _____
   $6 \times 2 = 12$, so $6 \times 20 =$ _____
   $6 \times 3 = 18$, so $6 \times 30 =$ _____
   $6 \times 4 = 24$, so $6 \times 40 =$ _____
   $6 \times 5 = 30$, so $6 \times 50 =$ _____
   $6 \times 6 = 36$, so $6 \times 60 =$ _____
   $6 \times 7 = 42$, so $6 \times 70 =$ _____

3. The closest multiple of 6 and 10 that is less than 235 is 6×30, or _____.

4. So, the quotient of $235 \div 6$ is about _____.

88

WHAT IF THE STUDENT CAN'T

Recall Multiplication Facts Through 9×9

- Use counters or models to demonstrate the products of multiplying 2 one-digit numbers. Then have the student do the same.

- Then have the student write multiplication facts on flash cards and practice until they can be recalled with ease.

Multiply One-Digit Numbers Times Multiples of 10

- Explain that if the student recalls multiplication facts, he or she can use those facts to multiply tens. Use place-value tens rods to illustrate that, for example, 3×2 tens = 6 tens, and 6 tens = 60. Give several examples.

- Then have the student use multiplication facts to find multiples of 10.

Continue the list of multiples. Circle the closest multiple less than the number.

5. 255

Multiples of 7 and 10: 7 × 10 = 70, 7 × 20 = _____, 7 × 30 = _____,

7 × 40 = _____, 7 × 50 = _____, 7 × 60 = _____,

7 × 70 = _____, 7 × 80= _____, 7 × 90 = _____

6. 338

Multiples of 8 and 10: 8 × 10 = 80, 8 × 20 = _____, 8 × 30 = _____,

8 × 40 = _____, 8 × 50 = _____, 8 × 60 = _____,

8 × 70 = _____, 8 × 80= _____, 8 × 90 = _____

Power Practice • **Find the closest multiples that are less than each number. Complete.**

Find the closest multiple of 6 and 10 that is less than each number.

7. 554 _____ So the quotient of 554 ÷ 6 is about _____.
8. 207 _____ So the quotient of 207 ÷ 6 is about _____.

Find the closest multiple of 5 and 10 that is less than each number.

9. 354 _____ So the quotient of 354 ÷ 5 is about _____.
10. 337 _____ So the quotient of 337 ÷ 5 is about _____.

Find the closest multiple of 7 and 10 that is less than each number.

11. 451 _____ So the quotient of 451 ÷ 7 is about _____.
12. 207 _____ So the quotient of 207 ÷ 7 is about _____.

Find the closest multiple of 9 and 10 that is less than each number.

13. 387 _____ So the quotient of 387 ÷ 9 is about _____.
14. 472 _____ So the quotient of 472 ÷ 9 is about _____.

Find the closest multiple of 8 and 10 that is less than each number.

15. 432 _____ So the quotient of 432 ÷ 8 is about _____.
16. 665 _____ So the quotient of 665 ÷ 8 is about _____.

89

Try It

Have the students complete Exercises 1–4. Ask:

- *How will you know that you have found the greatest multiple of 6 and 10 that is less than 235?* (Use place value to compare each multiple of 10 to 235. If 6 × 30 = 180 and 6 × 40 = 240, then 180 must be the greatest multiple of 6 and 10 that is less than 235, since there are no multiples of 10 and 6 that are between 180 and 240.)

- Look at Exercises 5–6 with students. For each exercise, have students say the list of multiples aloud before writing them.

Power Practice

- Be sure that students understand that the multiple in each answer must be less than the given number. Then have students complete the practice items. Review each answer.

WHAT IF THE STUDENT CAN'T

Compare Numbers as *Greater Than* or *Less Than*

- Have the student draw a number line for numbers 120–150. Have the student point to two numbers on the line. Explain that the number to the right on the line is greater than the number to the left on the line. This means that the number to the left is less than the number on the right.

- Then name pairs of numbers on the number line and have the student identify the number that is greater or less than the other number.

Complete the Power Practice

- Discuss each incorrect answer with the student, explaining the correct answer.

Activity 59 Lesson Goal

- Learn the principle of division.

What the Student Needs to Know

- Understand the idea of dividing a large group of items into equal, smaller groups.
- Add numbers in repetition.

Getting Started

Find out what students know about division. Draw 6 diamonds on the board. Say:

- *There are 6 diamonds on the board. How can you divide the diamonds into 2 equal groups?* (2 equal groups of 3)

What Can I Do?

- Read the question and the response. Then read and discuss the examples. Ask:
- *If you want to draw 12 stars and you know that there are 4 stars in each group, how can you find out how many groups there are?* (Find out how many times you have to add 4 to get 12.)
- *If you want to draw 18 circles and you know that there are 3 equal groups, how can you find out how many circles are in each group?* (Find out how many times you have to add 3 to get 18.)

Name_____

Meaning of Division

Learn

What Can I Do? I want to draw pictures for division problems.

Put the same number in each group.

12 stars
4 stars in each group

Count the groups.
3 groups of stars

Make equal groups.

18 circles
3 equal groups of circles

Count the number in each group.
6 circles in each group

Try It • Use counters or small objects.

1. Use 20 counters. Put 4 counters in each group. How many groups do you get?

   _____ groups of counters

2. Use 18 counters. Make 2 equal groups. How many counters are there in each group?

   _____ counters in each group

3. Use 15 counters. Put 3 counters in each group. How many groups do you get?

   _____ groups of counters

4. Use 24 counters. Make 4 equal groups. How many counters are there in each group?

   _____ counters in each group

90

WHAT IF THE STUDENT CAN'T

Understand the Idea of Dividing a Larger Group into Smaller Groups

- Use counters to demonstrate how to divide even numbers into 2 equal parts. Have the student practice doing this with the numbers 2 through 18 until the student can do so easily.

- From here, move on to the idea of 3, 4, 5, 6, 7, 8, and 9 equal groups.

- Demonstrate how repeated addition or multiplication can be used to be sure that a number has been divided correctly.

Name_____

Power Practice • Draw each picture. Then tell how many equal groups, or how many are in each group.

5. 8 squares

    4 squares in each group

_____ groups of squares

6. 10 triangles

    2 equal groups of triangles

_____ triangles in each group

7. 6 stars

    3 stars in each group

_____ groups of stars

8. 9 circles

    3 equal groups of circles

_____ circles in each group

9. 16 triangles

    8 triangles in each group

_____ groups of triangles

10. 12 squares

    3 equal groups of squares

_____ squares in each group

91

Try It

Have students look at Exercises 1–4. Make sure they understand that the same operation can be used to determine both the number of groups into which a greater number is broken down and to find how many items are in each group.

Power Practice

• Have students complete the practice items. Then review each answer. For any incorrect answers, have students use counters to model the correct number of groups and items.

WHAT IF THE STUDENT CAN'T

Add Numbers in Repetition

• Use counters to demonstrate how a number may be added to itself repeatedly and that the sum increases each time the number is added. For example: $3 + 3 = 6$; $3 + 3 + 3 = 9$; $3 + 3 + 3 + 3 = 12$; and so on.

• Have the student practice adding the numbers 1 through 9 in repetition until the student can do so with ease.

Complete the Power Practice

• Discuss each incorrect answer. Have the student use counting, serial addition, or multiplication to show why the answer is incorrect.

Activity 60 Lesson Goal

- Use any division strategy to divide using basic facts through 9.

What the Student Needs to Know

- Use a related multiplication fact.
- Use an array.
- Use repeated subtraction.
- Skip count backward by 2s through 9s on a number line.

Getting Started

Find out what students know about division strategies. Write the division fact 36 ÷ 9 on the board. Say:

- *Of the four strategies, using a related multiplication fact, an array, repeated subtraction, or skip counting backwards on a number line, which ones would be easiest to use for this example?* (related multiplication fact and repeated subtraction)

- *What related multiplication fact can you name to solve this division fact?* (9 × 4 = 36 or 4 × 9 = 36) *How can you use the related multiplication fact to solve the division 36 ÷ 9?* (If 4 × 9 = 36, then 36 ÷ 9 must be 4) *So 36 ÷ 4 =* ? . (9)

- *How can you use repeated subtraction to solve this division?* (Start at 36 and subtract 9 to get 27. Then subtract 9 again to get 18. Subtract 9 from 18 to get 9, and then subtract 9 from 9 to get 0.) *So what is the quotient of 36 ÷ 9?* (4)

What Can I Do?

Read the question and the response. Then discuss each example. Ask:

- *Can you use a related multiplication fact to find the answer to this example?* (Yes.)

- *Which fact do you know that will help you solve this division?* (6 × 4 = 24 and 4 × 6 = 24)

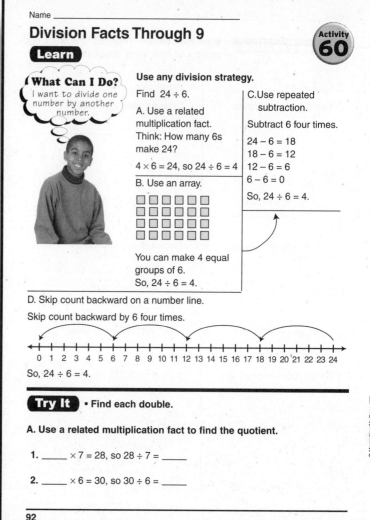

Name _____

Division Facts Through 9

Activity 60

Learn

What Can I Do? I want to divide one number by another number.

Use any division strategy.

Find 24 ÷ 6.

A. Use a related multiplication fact.
Think: How many 6s make 24?

4 × 6 = 24, so 24 ÷ 6 = 4

B. Use an array.

You can make 4 equal groups of 6.
So, 24 ÷ 6 = 4.

C. Use repeated subtraction.
Subtract 6 four times.

24 − 6 = 18
18 − 6 = 12
12 − 6 = 6
6 − 6 = 0

So, 24 ÷ 6 = 4.

D. Skip count backward on a number line.
Skip count backward by 6 four times.

0 1 2 3 4 5 6 7 8 9 10 11 12 13 14 15 16 17 18 19 20 21 22 23 24

So, 24 ÷ 6 = 4.

Try It • Find each double.

A. Use a related multiplication fact to find the quotient.

1. _____ × 7 = 28, so 28 ÷ 7 = _____

2. _____ × 6 = 30, so 30 ÷ 6 = _____

92

WHAT IF THE STUDENT CAN'T

Use Multiplication Facts

- Have the student use a multiplication table to create related multiplication and division facts on note cards. Have the students choose facts that are troublesome for him or her and write a related pair of facts on each card.

- Have the student practice these facts daily until he or she can recall them with ease.

Use Repeated Subtraction

- Have the student use counters to perform repeated addition such as 3 + 3 + 3 + 3 + 3 = 15

- Then have the student "undo" the repeated addition with repeated subtraction. For the example above, subtract 15 − 3 = 12; 12 − 3 = 9; 9 − 3 = 6; 6 − 3 = 3; and 3 − 3 = 0.

Name _____

A. Use an array to find each quotient.

3. $27 \div 9 =$ _____

▢▢▢▢▢▢▢▢▢
▢▢▢▢▢▢▢▢▢
▢▢▢▢▢▢▢▢▢

4. $5 \div 3 =$ _____

▢▢▢▢▢
▢▢▢▢▢
▢▢▢▢▢

B. Use repeated subtraction to find each quotient.

5. $9 \div 3 =$ _____

Subtract: _____

_____

6. $30 \div 5 =$ _____

Subtract: _____

_____

_____

C. Skip count backward to find each quotient.

7. $45 \div 5 =$ _____

Count backward: _____

_____

8. $42 \div 6 =$ _____

Count backward: _____

_____

Power Practice • Find each quotient. Use any method.

9. $8 \div 4 =$ _____   **10.** $20 \div 4 =$ _____   **11.** $48 \div 8 =$ _____

12. $35 \div 5 =$ _____   **13.** $36 \div 6 =$ _____   **14.** $40 \div 5 =$ _____

15. $28 \div 4 =$ _____   **16.** $12 \div 6 =$ _____   **17.** $49 \div 7 =$ _____

18. $8\overline{)64}$ **19.** $9\overline{)81}$ **20.** $7\overline{)21}$ **21.** $4\overline{)16}$

22. $4\overline{)24}$ **23.** $7\overline{)42}$ **24.** $8\overline{)32}$ **25.** $4\overline{)36}$

-93

WHAT IF THE STUDENT CAN'T

Skip Count Backward

- Have the student put 3 counters into each of 8 groups. Then have the student skip count to find the total. (3, 6, 9, 12, 15, 18, 21, 24)
- Then have the student start with the total and skip count backward by 3 (24, 21, 18, 15, 12, 9, 6, 3, 0)
- Repeat with other numbers of counters and groups.

Complete the Power Practice

- Discuss each incorrect answer. Have the student model any exercise he or she missed using counters or a number line.

- How would you use repeated subtraction to solve? Start with 24 and subtract 6 four times: $24 - 6 = 18$; $18 - 6 = 12$; $12 - 6 = 6$; $6 - 6 = 0$)

Use an existing number line from 0 to 24 or draw a new one. Demonstrate skip counting backwards 4 groups of 6 by drawing arrows that show the "jumps" between 24 and 18, 18 and 12, 12 and 6, and 6 and 0.

Try It

- Have students complete Exercises 1 and 2 using related multiplication and division facts. Check that students understand that the same three numbers are used in each pair of related facts. Once they know one fact, they can write all four related facts. Ask:

- *How much is 1×7? (7) How much is 2×7? (14) How much is 3×7? (21) How much is 4×7? (28) So what number times 4 is 28? (7) How can I use the fact $4 \times 7 = 28$ to find the quotient?* (The numbers in the related facts are the same, so $4 \times 7 = 28$ and $28 \div 7 = 4$.)

- Have the students do Exercises 3 and 4 using the arrays. Check that students understand that they separate the elements of the array into equal groups.

- Have the students do Exercises 5 and 6 using the arrays. Check to make sure that students understand which number they begin subtracting with and that they continue subtracting the same number from the difference until they reach 0.

- Have students do Exercises 7 and 8 using skip counting backwards. Check that students understand where they begin counting, the number that they skip count backwards, and how to count the number of skips.

Power Practice

- Have students complete the practice items. Then review each answer.

Activity 61 Lesson Goal
• Practice division facts.

What the Student Needs to Know
• Use a multiplication table.
• Understand how multiplication and division are related.

Getting Started
Find out what students know about the relationship between multiplication and division. Write the following number sentences on the board and have students complete them:

$3 \times 9 =$ _____ (27); $27 \div 3 =$ _____ (9)

$5 \times 4 =$ _____ (20); $20 \div 4 =$ _____ (5)

$8 \times 6 =$ _____ (48); $48 \div 6 =$ _____ (8)

• Say: *Each pair of number sentences uses only 3 numbers. The first number sentence uses the numbers for multiplication and the second uses them for division.*

• Ask: *If you divide the product of a multiplication sentence by one of its factors, what will the quotient be?* (the other factor)

What Can I Do?
Read the question and the response. Then read and discuss the example. Ask:

• *How do you find the answer to $56 \div 8$?* (Look across the 8-row until I find 56. Then I look to see the number at the top of the column containing 56.)

• *How is using a multiplication table to find the answer to a division problem different from using it to find the answer to a multiplication problem?* (In a multiplication problem, you know the row and column and look to see where they meet. In a division problem, you know the row and the number in the table, and look to see what column the number is under.)

Name _____

Division Facts

Learn

Use a related multiplication fact.

To find $56 \div 8$, think:
What number times 8 equals 56?

Since 7×8 is 56, $56 \div 8 = 7$.

Use a Multiplication Table.

What Can I Do?
I want to practice the division facts.

×	0	1	2	3	4	5	6	7	8	9	10
0	0	0	0	0	0	0	0	0	0	0	0
1	0	1	2	3	4	5	6	7	8	9	10
2	0	2	4	6	8	10	12	14	16	18	20
3	0	3	6	9	12	15	18	21	24	27	30
4	0	4	8	12	16	20	24	28	32	36	40
5	0	5	10	15	20	25	30	35	40	45	50
6	0	6	12	18	24	30	36	42	48	54	60
7	0	7	14	21	28	35	42	49	56	63	70
row → 8	0	8	16	24	32	40	48	56	64	72	80
9	0	9	18	27	36	45	54	63	72	81	90
10	0	10	20	30	40	50	60	70	80	90	100

Example: To find $56 \div 8$, look across the 8 row until you get to 56. The answer, 7, is directly above the 56.

Try It • Use the related multiplication fact to write each quotient.

1. $6 \times 8 = 48$	**2.** $6 \times 9 = 54$	**3.** $7 \times 7 = 49$
$48 \div 6 =$ _____	$54 \div 9 =$ _____	$49 \div 7 =$ _____
4. $4 \times 8 = 32$	**5.** $9 \times 8 = 72$	**6.** $5 \times 9 = 45$
$32 \div 8 =$ _____	$72 \div 8 =$ _____	$45 \div 5 =$ _____
7. $7 \times 9 = 63$	**8.** $5 \times 7 = 35$	**9.** $8 \times 8 = 64$
$63 \div 7 =$ _____	$35 \div 5 =$ _____	$64 \div 8 =$ _____

94

WHAT IF THE STUDENT CAN'T

Use a Multiplication Table
• Have the student write a multiplication fact. On a multiplication table, highlight the two factors in the corresponding row and column. Then illustrate how finding the square where the row and column intersect gives their product.

• Have the student practice writing multiplication sentences using the table until the procedure becomes familiar and the student memorizes multiplication facts.

Understand How Multiplication and Division are Related
• Use counters to demonstrated how multiplication may be used to arrive at a certain product. For example, 8 groups of 4 will give you a product of 32. Then show how this operation may be turned around, so that 32 may be divided into 8 groups of 4.

• Have the student use counters to illustrate multiplication sentences and their division counterparts.

Use the multiplication table if you need help.
Practice dividing by 7.

10. $49 \div 7 =$ _____   11. $35 \div 7 =$ _____   12. $28 \div 7 =$ _____

13. $14 \div 7 =$ _____   14. $70 \div 7 =$ _____   15. $56 \div 7 =$ _____

16. $63 \div 7 =$ _____   17. $21 \div 7 =$ _____   18. $42 \div 7 =$ _____

Practice dividing by 8.

19. $72 \div 8 =$ _____   20. $32 \div 8 =$ _____   21. $16 \div 8 =$ _____

22. $40 \div 8 =$ _____   23. $24 \div 8 =$ _____   24. $56 \div 8 =$ _____

25. $8 \div 8 =$ _____   26. $64 \div 8 =$ _____   27. $48 \div 8 =$ _____

Practice dividing by 9.

28. $45 \div 9 =$ _____   29. $18 \div 9 =$ _____   30. $63 \div 9 =$ _____

31. $27 \div 9 =$ _____   32. $90 \div 9 =$ _____   33. $72 \div 9 =$ _____

34. $81 \div 9 =$ _____   35. $54 \div 9 =$ _____   36. $36 \div 9 =$ _____

Power Practice • **Find each quotient.**

37. $64 \div 8 =$ _____   38. $56 \div 7 =$ _____   39. $24 \div 4 =$ _____

40. $35 \div 5 =$ _____   41. $32 \div 8 =$ _____   42. $63 \div 7 =$ _____

43. $21 \div 7 =$ _____   44. $8 \div 1 =$ _____   45. $48 \div 8 =$ _____

46. $72 \div 9 =$ _____   47. $28 \div 4 =$ _____   48. $24 \div 6 =$ _____

49. $16 \div 2 =$ _____   50. $36 \div 9 =$ _____   51. $81 \div 9 =$ _____

© Macmillan/McGraw-Hill

95

WHAT IF THE STUDENT CAN'T

- Have the student practice turning multiplication sentences into division sentences, and division sentences into multiplication sentences, until the student can do so with ease.

Complete the Power Practice

- Discuss each incorrect answer. Have the student identify the row in the times table where the correct answer may be found. Then have the student find the correct answer.

- For each incorrect answer, have the student write a multiplication sentence using the same numbers.

Try It

Have the students look at Exercise 1. Read the multiplication sentence aloud. Ask:

- *Which three numbers should appear in the division sentence for Exercise 1?* (6, 8, 48)

Then have the students complete Exercises 1–9.

Have the students look at Exercises 10–18. Ask:

- *In a multiplication times table, which row would you use to find the answer to each of these problems?* (the 7-row)

Then have the students complete the exercises.

Have the students look at Exercises 19–27. Ask:

- *In a multiplication table, which row would you use to find the answer to each of these problems?* (the 8-row)

Then have the students complete the exercises.

Have the students look at Exercises 28–36. Ask:

- *In a multiplication table, which row would you use to find the answer to each of these problems?* (the 9-row)

Then have the students complete the problems.

Power Practice

- Have the students complete the practice items. Then review each answer.

Activity 62 Lesson Goal

- Divide a two-digit number by a one-digit number when the quotient includes a remainder.

What the Student Needs to Know

- Recall basic division facts.
- Understand how multiplication and division are related.

Getting Started

Find out what the students know about division. Write the following division sentences on the board:

8 ÷ 2   9 ÷ 2   10 ÷ 2

Ask:

- *Which of these division sentences will give you a whole number as a quotient?* (8 ÷ 2; 10 ÷ 2)
- *Which of these division sentences will not give you a whole number as a quotient?* (9 ÷ 2)
- *What do you call the number that is left after the division?* (the remainder)

What Can I Do?

Read the question and the response. Then read and discuss the example. Ask:

- *What does "the greatest possible quotient" mean?* (It means the greatest number of times that the divisor can go into the number being divided.)
- *How do you know that 7 is the greatest possible quotient?* (Because 7 × 6 = 42, which is less than 45, but 8 × 6 = 48, which is greater than 45.)
- *Why do you have to make sure that the remainder is less than the divisor?* (Because if the remainder is greater than the divisor, it means that the divisor can go into the number being divided at least one more time, and that you haven't found the greatest possible quotient.)

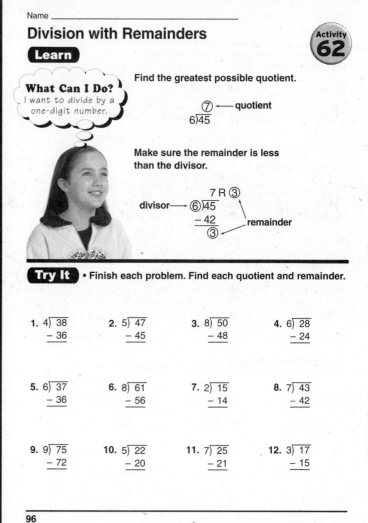

Name _____

Division with Remainders

Learn

What Can I Do?
I want to divide by a one-digit number.

Find the greatest possible quotient.

⑦ ← quotient
6)45

Make sure the remainder is less than the divisor.

```
          7 R ③
divisor → 6)45
          −42      ← remainder
          ③
```

Try It • Finish each problem. Find each quotient and remainder.

1. 4)38
   − 36

2. 5)47
   − 45

3. 8)50
   − 48

4. 6)28
   − 24

5. 6)37
   − 36

6. 8)61
   − 56

7. 2)15
   − 14

8. 7)43
   − 42

9. 9)75
   − 72

10. 5)22
    − 20

11. 7)25
    − 21

12. 3)17
    − 15

96

WHAT IF THE STUDENT CAN'T

Recall Basic Division Facts

- Use counters to demonstrate how one number may be divided into equal groups. For example, 14 may be divided into 2 groups of 7, and 20 may be divided into 2 groups of 10 or 4 groups of 5. Then have the student use counters to illustrate the division of other two-digit numbers.
- Have the student practice completing division number sentences with one-digit divisors until this can be done with ease.

Understand How Multiplication and Division Are Related

- Use counters to demonstrate how multiplication may be used to arrive at a certain product. For example, 6 groups of 7 will give you a product of 42. Then show how this operation may be turned around, so that 42 may be divided into 6 groups of 7.
- Have the student use counters to illustrate multiplication sentences and their division counterparts.

Name _____

13. $37 \div 7 =$ _____ R _____   **14.** $26 \div 3 =$ _____ R _____

15. $34 \div 5 =$ _____ R _____   **16.** $62 \div 9 =$ _____ R _____

17. $11 \div 2 =$ _____ R _____

18. $40 \div 6 =$ _____ R _____

19. $44 \div 8 =$ _____ R _____

20. $29 \div 4 =$ _____ R _____

© Macmillan/McGraw-Hill

Learn with Partners & Parents

Division Roll

You will need three 1–6 number cubes.

- Toss the cubes. Use the numbers to make two different division problems like this:

  [ ] [ ] ÷ [ ]

- Find the quotient and remainder for each problem you make.

- Toss again. Find the problems with the greatest and least quotients.

- Toss to get three different digits. Write all six division problems you can make with these digits.

97

WHAT IF THE STUDENT CAN'T

- Have the student practice turning multiplication sentences into division sentences, and division sentences into multiplication sentences, until the student can do so with ease.

Complete the Power Practice

- Discuss each incorrect answer. Have the student demonstrate why the quotient given is the largest possible and identify the remainder. Then have the student check the correctness of the remainder by multiplying the divisor by the quotient and adding the remainder to it. The result should be the number being divided.

Try It

- Have the students look at Exercise 1. Ask:
- *What should the number be in the quotient?* (9)
- *Why is it the greatest possible quotient?* (because $9 \times 4 = 36$, which is less than 38, but $10 \times 4 = 40$, which is greater than 38)
- *What is the remainder?* (2)
- *How can you check that this is the correct remainder?* (Check to be sure it is less than the divisor. Then multiply the quotient by the divisor and add the remainder. The number should be equal to the number being divided.)
- Have the students complete Exercises 2–12.

Power Practice

- Have a volunteer write Exercise 13 on the chalkboard as a long division equation. Then have students complete the equation, demonstrating why the quotient is the largest possible and that the remainder is the correct one.
- Have students complete Exercises 14–20. Then review each answer.

Learn with Partners & Parents

- Partners should experiment with many different pairs of numbers for the dividends. If they toss a 3, 4, and 7, they should see how many different dividends they can make from any two of the three.
- Ask: *To get a greater quotient, what must you have for the divisor?* (a very low divisor) *To get a very low quotient, what must be true of the divisor?* (It must be a very high number.)

USING THE LESSON

Activity 63 Lesson Goal
- Recall multiplication and division facts with the aid of arrays.

What the Student Needs to Know
- Make an array.
- Understand multiplication.
- Understand division.

Getting Started
Find out what students know about arrays. Draw an array of 3 rows of 7 counters on the board. Ask:

- *How many counters are in this figure?* (21)
- *How can you tell how many counters are in the figure without counting each one or using addition?* (Multiply the number of rows by the number of counters in each row.)
- *What multiplication fact does this figure illustrate?* (3 × 7 = 21)

What Can I Do?
- Read the question and the response. Then read and discuss the first example. Ask:
- *If there were one less row, what multiplication fact would the array show?* (3 × 6 = 18)
- *If there were one less counter in each row, but the number of rows remained the same, what multiplication fact would the array show?* (4 × 5 = 20)
- Read and discuss the second example. Ask:
- *If the problem asked you to solve 24 ÷ 6, how many counters would you put in each group in the array?* (6)
- *When you use an array to show a division fact, how can you check to be sure the array is correct?* (Multiply the number of groups in the array by the number of counters in each group.)

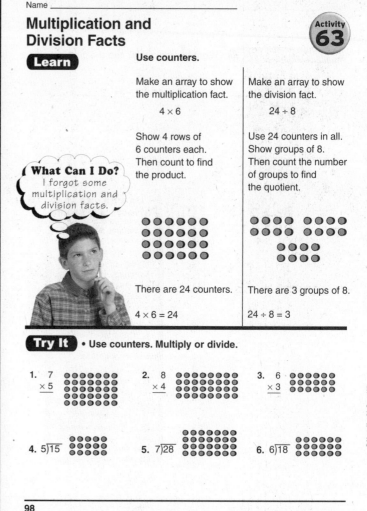

WHAT IF THE STUDENT CAN'T

Make an Array
- Draw a 3 × 4 array. Have the student write down how many rows are in the array (3), how many counters are in each row (4), and how many counters there are in all (12). Then explain to the student that the array represents the multiplication fact 3 × 4 = 12. Point out that the number of rows is one factor, and the number of counters in each row is the other factor.
- Explain how it also represents the division fact 12 ÷ 4 = 3. Point out that the number of counters in each row is the divisor, and that the number of rows is the quotient.

- Have the student practice drawing arrays for multiplication and division facts until he or she can do so easily.

Understand Multiplication
- Have the student complete the following number sentence: 8 + 8 + 8 = _____ (24). Explain that this sentence can also be written 3 × 8, where the first number (3) tells you how many times you need to add the second number (8).
- Have the student convert multiplication facts into addition sentences and vice versa until the concept of multiplication becomes clear.

Name_____

7. $\begin{array}{r} 3 \\ \times 2 \\ \hline \end{array}$	**8.** $\begin{array}{r} 4 \\ \times 6 \\ \hline \end{array}$	**9.** $\begin{array}{r} 2 \\ \times 7 \\ \hline \end{array}$	**10.** $\begin{array}{r} 0 \\ \times 4 \\ \hline \end{array}$
11. $6\overline{)30}$	**12.** $3\overline{)27}$	**13.** $7\overline{)42}$	**14.** $9\overline{)36}$
15. $\begin{array}{r} 9 \\ \times 4 \\ \hline \end{array}$	**16.** $\begin{array}{r} 8 \\ \times 8 \\ \hline \end{array}$	**17.** $\begin{array}{r} 7 \\ \times 5 \\ \hline \end{array}$	**18.** $\begin{array}{r} 2 \\ \times 9 \\ \hline \end{array}$
19. $5\overline{)40}$	**20.** $1\overline{)6}$	**21.** $4\overline{)8}$	**22.** $7\overline{)56}$
23. $\begin{array}{r} 8 \\ \times 0 \\ \hline \end{array}$	**24.** $\begin{array}{r} 7 \\ \times 9 \\ \hline \end{array}$	**25.** $\begin{array}{r} 4 \\ \times 4 \\ \hline \end{array}$	**26.** $\begin{array}{r} 7 \\ \times 2 \\ \hline \end{array}$
27. $8\overline{)72}$	**28.** $9\overline{)54}$	**29.** $9\overline{)72}$	**30.** $5\overline{)20}$
31. $\begin{array}{r} 9 \\ \times 9 \\ \hline \end{array}$	**32.** $\begin{array}{r} 1 \\ \times 3 \\ \hline \end{array}$	**33.** $\begin{array}{r} 7 \\ \times 8 \\ \hline \end{array}$	**34.** $\begin{array}{r} 9 \\ \times 3 \\ \hline \end{array}$
35. $8\overline{)48}$	**36.** $2\overline{)16}$	**37.** $5\overline{)45}$	**38.** $4\overline{)32}$

99

Try It

Have students look at Exercise 1. Ask:

- *How many rows will be in your array?* (5) *How many counters will be in each row?* (7)

Then have students complete Exercises 1–3.

Have students look at Exercise 4. Ask:

- *How many counters in all will be in your array?* (15) *How many will be in each group?* (5)

Then have students complete Exercises 4–6.

Power Practice

- Have students complete the practice items. Then review each answer.

WHAT IF THE STUDENT CAN'T

Understand Division

- Use counters to illustrate how a larger number may be broken down into a smaller number of equal groups. Write the relevant division fact. For example, 15 may be broken into 3 groups of 5, and labeled $15 \div 5 = 3$. Explain that the first number is the number being divided, that the second number tells how many will be in each group, and the third tells how many groups there will be.

- Have the student practice writing and illustrating division sentences until it can be done with ease.

Complete the Power Practice

- For each incorrect multiplication fact, have the student circle how many rows should be in the array, and underline how many counters should be in each row. Then have the student draw the array, and count or use repeated addition to arrive at the correct answer.

- For each incorrect division fact, have the student circle how many counters should be in the array in all, and underline how many counters should be in each group. Then have the student draw an array and count groups to arrive at the correct answer.

Activity 64 Lesson Goal

- Multiply and divide by 10, 100, and 1,000.

What the Student Needs to Know

- Multiply by 1.
- Divide by 1.
- Understand the relationship between 10, 100, and 1,000.

Getting Started

Find out what students know about multiplication facts involving 1. Write the following multiplication sentence on the board and have students solve:

$4 \times 1 =$ ___ (4)

Ask:

- *If you change the first factor to 5, what is the answer? (5) What is the answer if you change the first factor to 23? (23)*

- *If you multiply any number by 1, what will the product be? (the number you are multiplying)*

Write the following division sentence on the board and have students solve:

$4 \div 1 =$ ____ (4)

Ask:

- *If you change the number being divided to 9, what will the quotient be? (9) What is the quotient if you change the number being divided to 41? (41)*

- *If you divide any number by one, what will the quotient be? (the number you are dividing)*

What Can I Do?

- Read the question and the response. Then read and discuss the multiplication sentences. Ask:

- *What multiplication fact do you need to know to solve these problems? ($7 \times 1 = 7$)*

Name _____

Multiply and Divide by 10, 100, and 1,000

Activity 64

Learn

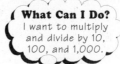
What Can I Do?
I want to multiply and divide by 10, 100, and 1,000.

Use basic facts.

To multiply by 10, 100, or 1,000, use basic facts to write the first digit.

$7 \times 10 = ?$
$7 \times 100 = ?$
$7 \times 1,000 = ?$

Use the basic fact $7 \times 1 = 7$.

Then count the number of zeros in 10, 100, or 1,000. Write the number of zeros in the product.

10 has 1 zero, so $7 \times 10 = 70$.
100 has 2 zeros, so $7 \times 100 = 700$.
1,000 has 3 zeros, so $7 \times 1,000 = 7,000$.

Use multiplication to divide.

To divide by 10, 100, or 1,000, use what you know about multiplication.

You know that multiplication and division are related operations.

$60 \div 10 = ?$ ⟶ $6 \times 10 = 60$, so $60 \div 10 = 6$.

$600 \div 100 = ?$ ⟶ $6 \times 100 = 600$, so $600 \div 100 = 6$.

$6,000 \div 1,000 = ?$ ⟶ $6 \times 1,000 = 6,000$, so $6,000 \div 1,000 = 6$.

100

© Macmillan/McGraw-Hill

WHAT IF THE STUDENT CAN'T

Multiply by 1

- Use counters to illustrate multiplication facts involving the numbers 2 through 9. Then introduce facts for multiplying by 1. Demonstrate that, just as 2×5 is represented by 2 groups of 5, 1×5 is represented by 1 group of 5. Be sure the student understands that any number multiplied by 1 is equal to itself.

- Have the student use counters to illustrate and solve the multiplication facts for 1 until he or she can do so with ease.

Divide by 1

- Use counters to illustrate division facts for the number 1. Explain that in each fact, the original number is broken down into "groups" of 1, and that this means the quotient will be equal to the number being divided.

- Have the student use counters to illustrate and solve the division facts for 1 until he or she can do so with ease.

Name_____

Try It • Use basic facts. Find each product.

1. $10 \times 9 =$ _____   2. $8 \times 100 =$ _____   3. $4 \times 1,000 =$ _____

Use multiplication to complete each division sentence.

4. $4 \times 100 = 400$ so $400 \div 100 =$ _____

5. $1,000 \times 8 = 8,000$ so $8,000 \div 1,000 =$ _____

6. $7 \times 10 = 70$ so $70 \div 10 =$ _____

Power Practice • Find each product or quotient.

7. $1,000 \times 5 =$ _____   8. $400 \div 100 =$ _____

9. $7,000 \div 1,000 =$ _____   10. $2 \times 100 =$ _____

11. $30 \div 10 =$ _____   12. $100 \times 8 =$ _____

13. $\begin{array}{r} 1,000 \\ \times\ \ 2 \\ \hline \end{array}$ 14. $100\overline{)800}$ 15. $\begin{array}{r} 100 \\ \times 3 \\ \hline \end{array}$ 16. $1,000\overline{)9,000}$

17. $\begin{array}{r} 1,000 \\ \times\ \ 3 \\ \hline \end{array}$ 18. $1,000\overline{)4,000}$ 19. $\begin{array}{r} 1,000 \\ \times\ \ 5 \\ \hline \end{array}$ 20. $10\overline{)90}$

21. $1,000 \times 3 =$ _____   22. $6,000 \div 1,000 =$ _____

23. $50 \div 10 =$ _____   24. $100 \times 4 =$ _____

25. $1,000 \times 8 =$ _____   26. $40 \div 10 =$ _____

© Macmillan/McGraw-Hill

101

WHAT IF THE STUDENT CAN'T

Understand the Relationship Between 10, 100, and 1,000

- Use grid strips and grids to model the relationship between the three numbers. Demonstrate how it takes 10 strips of 10 grid squares to make 100, and 10 grids of 100 squares to make 1,000.

- Have the student practice regrouping tens into hundreds and hundreds into thousands, as well as thousands into hundreds and hundreds into tens, until it can be done with ease.

Complete the Power Practice

- For each incorrect multiplication exercise, have the student identify the multiplication fact relevant to the problem. Then have the student explain how many zeros should be added to the product to arrive at the correct answer.

- For each incorrect division exercise, have the student write a related multiplication sentence. Then have the student identify the number in the multiplication sentence that is the quotient of the division sentence.

- *If you multiply by 10, how many zeros do you write in the product? (1) If you multiply by 100? (2) If you multiply by 1,000? (3)*

- Read and discuss the division sentences. Ask:

- *How do you use multiplication sentences to solve these problems?* (You figure out what number × 10 = 60, what number × 100 = 600, and what number × 1,000 = 6,000. The missing factor in the multiplication sentence is the quotient in the division sentence.)

- *What division fact will also help you solve these problems?* (6 ÷ 1 = 6)

- *If you divide by 10, how many zeros do you take off the number being divided to get the quotient? (1) If you divide by 100? (2) If you divide by 1,000? (3)*

Try It

Have students look at Exercise 1. Ask:

- *What multiplication fact do you need to know to solve this problem?* (1 × 9 = 9)

- *How many zeros will you write at the end of the product?* (1)

Then have students complete Exercises 1–3.

Have students look at Exercise 4. Ask:

- *Which number in the multiplication sentence is the quotient for the division sentence?* (the first factor, 4)

Then have students complete Exercises 4–6.

Power Practice

- Have students complete the practice items. Then review each answer.

Activity 65 Lesson Goal

- Represent fractions as parts of a whole.

What the Student Needs to Know

- Identify *numerators* and *denominators*.
- Model fractions as parts of a whole.
- Understand different models of the same fraction.

Getting Started

- Write 1, 2, and $\frac{1}{2}$ on the board. Ask: *Which of these numbers is a fraction?* ($\frac{1}{2}$) *How do you know?* (It has two numbers, stacked one on top of the other, with a horizontal line between them.) Have students write other fractions on the board. Discuss what all fractions have in common. (two numbers and a horizontal line)

- Draw a circle or square on the chalkboard. Ask a volunteer to divide the drawing in half. After the student correctly divides the shape, label it with $\frac{1}{2}$. Tell students that they can use drawings to show many different fractions.

What Can I Do?

Read the question and the response. Then read and discuss the examples. Ask:

- *What is the number above the line in a fraction called?* (the numerator) *What is the number below the line called?* (the denominator)
- Have students count the number of parts in the rectangle (8). Explain that the rectangle is divided into eighths. After exploring $\frac{7}{8}$ on the page, you may wish to have students model $\frac{1}{8}$, $\frac{4}{8}$, $\frac{5}{8}$, and $\frac{8}{8}$. Point out that to model $\frac{8}{8}$ you need to color the entire rectangle. Write: $\frac{8}{8} = 1$.

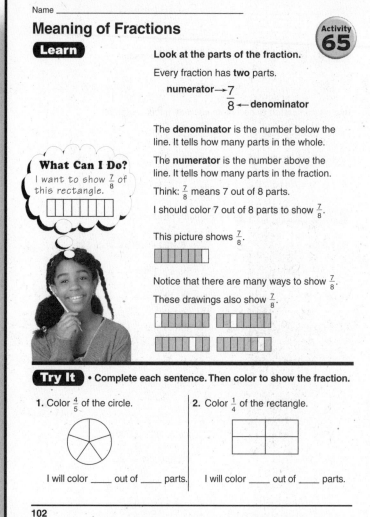

Meaning of Fractions

Learn

Activity **65**

Look at the parts of the fraction.

Every fraction has **two** parts.

numerator→$\dfrac{7}{8}$←denominator

The **denominator** is the number below the line. It tells how many parts in the whole.

The **numerator** is the number above the line. It tells how many parts in the fraction.

Think: $\frac{7}{8}$ means 7 out of 8 parts.

I should color 7 out of 8 parts to show $\frac{7}{8}$.

This picture shows $\frac{7}{8}$.

Notice that there are many ways to show $\frac{7}{8}$.

These drawings also show $\frac{7}{8}$.

What Can I Do?
I want to show $\frac{7}{8}$ of this rectangle.

Try It • Complete each sentence. Then color to show the fraction.

1. Color $\frac{4}{5}$ of the circle.

I will color ____ out of ____ parts.

2. Color $\frac{1}{4}$ of the rectangle.

I will color ____ out of ____ parts.

102

WHAT IF THE STUDENT CAN'T

Identify *Numerators* and *Denominators*

- If the student gets confused when using unfamiliar fractions, remind him or her it really helps to draw a quick sketch of a familiar fraction, such as $\frac{1}{2}$ or $\frac{3}{4}$. Looking at the sketch can help the student remember that the numerator is the number of parts in the fraction and the denominator is the number of parts in the whole.

- You may wish to help the student remember the terms "numerator" and "denominator" by pointing out that both "denominator" and "down" begin with the letter *d*. This fact can help the student remember which number is which in a fraction.

Model Fractions as Parts of a Whole

- Suggest that the student use fraction manipulatives to practice modeling fractions. Encourage the student to write down each fraction he or she models.

Name _____

3. Color $\frac{5}{12}$ of the square.

I will color ____ out of ____ parts.

4. Color $\frac{3}{10}$ of the rectangle.

I will color ____ out of ____ parts.

Power Practice • Show the fraction.

5. Color $\frac{5}{6}$ of the rectangle.

6. Color $\frac{7}{10}$ of the circle.

7. Color $\frac{1}{8}$ of the square.

8. Color $\frac{2}{3}$ of the square.

9. Color $\frac{3}{16}$ of the rectangle.

10. Color $\frac{1}{2}$ of the circle.

11. Color $\frac{11}{12}$ of the circle.

12. Color $\frac{7}{20}$ of the rectangle.

© Macmillan/McGraw-Hill

103

WHAT IF THE STUDENT CAN'T

Understand Different Models of the Same Fraction

- Draw a circle divided into thirds and color in one third. Ask: *How many parts does this circle have?* (3) *How many parts are shaded?* (1) *What fraction does this circle show?* ($\frac{1}{3}$) Draw another circle divided into thirds. Shade a different third. *How are these two models different?* (Different parts are shaded.) *How are they the same?* (They both show $\frac{1}{3}$.) Show students additional examples of fraction models that are shaded differently but show the same fraction.

Complete the Power Practice

- Have the student work with a partner to complete each drawing. Encourage partners to take turns shading in the drawings. Suggest that students begin by saying: *"I will shade ____ out of ____ parts,"* substituting the correct numbers from the fraction they are planning to show.

- Students may want to find all of the possible models for $\frac{7}{8}$. Explain that there are 8 different ways to color in the rectangle to show $\frac{7}{8}$. In each, one part out of the eight equal parts in each drawing is left unshaded.

- For each fraction model, emphasize that there is more than one correct model.

Try It

- Have students read each fraction aloud to solve Exercises 1–4. Help them understand that to complete each sentence, they can write the numerator in the first blank and the denominator in the second blank. Then they can follow the directions to decide how to color the drawing.

- Allow students to compare their drawings. Remind students that different drawings can represent the same fraction.

Power Practice

- You may wish to allow students to use colored pencils or crayons to complete the exercises.

- Remind students that if they get confused, they can fill in a sentence like the ones in Exercises 1–4: "I will shade ____ out of ____ parts."

Activity 66 Lesson Goal

- Model and write mixed numbers.

What the Student Needs to Know

- Model whole numbers and fractions.
- Understand that mixed numbers combine a whole number and a fraction.

Getting Started

- Review fractions with students. Draw a square on the board and divide it into four equal parts. Write $\frac{3}{4}$ on the board. Ask: *How can I shade $\frac{3}{4}$ of this square?* (Shade 3 out of the 4 parts.) *Is $\frac{3}{4}$ more or less than 1?* (less) *Is $\frac{3}{4}$ more or less than 0?* (more)
- Draw a number line on the board. Label 0, 1, 2, 3, and 4. Ask: *Where do you think $2\frac{1}{2}$ is on this number line?* (Students should indicate halfway between 2 and 3.) *Where is $3\frac{1}{2}$?* (halfway between 3 and 4)

What Can I Do?

Read the question and the response. Then read and discuss the example. Ask:

- *What is a mixed number?* (A mixed number is a number that includes a whole number and a fraction.) *Are all mixed numbers greater than 1?* (Yes) *Why?* (Because they all have a whole number, which is 1 or greater, plus a fraction.)
- Have students look at the model of $2\frac{1}{4}$. *How does this model show the whole number 2?* (Two whole rectangles are shaded.) *How does the model show the fraction $\frac{1}{4}$?* (One quarter, or one fourth, of the third rectangle is shaded.)

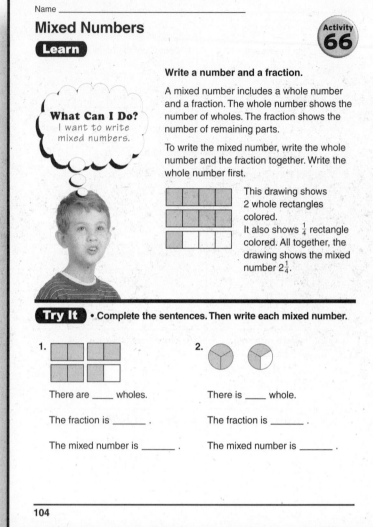

Name _____

Mixed Numbers

Learn

What Can I Do?
I want to write mixed numbers.

Write a number and a fraction.

A mixed number includes a whole number and a fraction. The whole number shows the number of wholes. The fraction shows the number of remaining parts.

To write the mixed number, write the whole number and the fraction together. Write the whole number first.

This drawing shows 2 whole rectangles colored. It also shows $\frac{1}{4}$ rectangle colored. All together, the drawing shows the mixed number $2\frac{1}{4}$.

Try It • Complete the sentences. Then write each mixed number.

1.
There are ____ wholes.

The fraction is _____ .

The mixed number is _____ .

2.
There is ____ whole.

The fraction is _____ .

The mixed number is _____ .

104

© Macmillan/McGraw-Hill

WHAT IF THE STUDENT CAN'T

Model Whole Numbers and Fractions

- Have the student practice modeling whole numbers. Write the fraction $\frac{4}{4}$ on the board and draw a circle divided into four parts. Ask: *How can you shade this circle to show $\frac{4}{4}$?* (Color all four parts.) Write $\frac{4}{4} = 1$ on the board. Explain that when you shade an entire shape, it can represent one whole number. Add another circle divided into four parts and shade all four parts. Ask: *What whole number do these circles show?* (2) Repeat with other whole numbers, such as $\frac{5}{5}$, $\frac{3}{3}$, and $\frac{8}{8}$.

- Review modeling fractions. Write these fractions on the board: $\frac{1}{2}$, $\frac{3}{5}$, $\frac{5}{8}$, $\frac{3}{10}$ and have the student describe how to show each fraction. Remind the student that the denominator of a fraction tells how many parts are in the whole. The numerator tells how many of the parts are in the fraction.

Name _____

3.

There are ____ wholes.

The fraction is _____ .

The mixed number is _____ .

4.

There are ____ wholes.

The fraction is _____ .

The mixed number is _____ .

Power Practice • Write each mixed number.

5.

_____

6.

_____

7.

_____

8.

_____

9.

_____

10.

_____

11.

_____

12.

_____

105

• Review the meaning of mixed numbers by writing these numbers on the board: 5, $4\frac{1}{2}$, 6, and $3\frac{5}{6}$. Have students identify the mixed numbers ($4\frac{1}{2}$, $3\frac{5}{6}$) and explain why they are mixed numbers.

Try It

• Ask a volunteer to read each exercise aloud and complete the sentences below the models.

• You may wish to have students use fraction manipulatives to model each mixed number in Exercises 1–4.

Power Practice

• Help students answer Exercises 5–12 by following this strategy. First, count the number of wholes shown. Write that number as the first part of the mixed number. Then, look at the shape that is only partly shaded. Write the fraction that names the shaded area. Put the whole number and the fraction together to write the answer.

WHAT IF THE STUDENT CAN'T

Understand That Mixed Numbers Combine a Whole Number and a Fraction

• Help the student visualize mixed numbers by creating concrete models. Cut three identical squares out of construction paper. Ask: *How many squares do I have?* (3) Fold one square in half and cut along the fold. Discard one half and show the remaining half with the other squares. *How many squares do I have now?* ($2\frac{1}{2}$) Have students name the parts of the mixed number. (the whole number 2 and the fraction $\frac{1}{2}$) Have students create paper models to show and write other mixed numbers.

Complete the Power Practice

• Encourage the student to use fraction manipulatives to model the mixed numbers in the exercises.

• Emphasize that different models can show the same mixed number. Have the student draw four circles divided into quarters and four squares divided into quarters. Ask him or her to shade $3\frac{1}{4}$ of the circles. Then have the student shade $3\frac{1}{4}$ of the squares in a different way.

Activity 67 Lesson Goal

- Find the number of ones, tens, and hundreds in whole numbers.

What the Student Needs To Know

- Use place-value models to identify the place value of digits.
- Recognize the place value of digits in two- and three-digit numbers.

Getting Started

Find out what students know about using place-value models. Display 1 ones model, 1 tens model, and 1 hundreds model in scrambled order. Call on volunteers to count and read the models and order them from largest to smallest. Say:

- *How many hundreds are in 1 hundreds model?* (1 hundred in all)
- *How many tens are in 1 tens model?* (1 ten in all)
- *How many ones are in 1 ones model?* (1 one in all)

What Can I Do?

- Read the question and the response. Then read and discuss the examples. Ask:
- *How can you figure out how many ones are in a whole number?* (Use the ones models, then count the ones.)
- *How can you figure out how many tens are in a whole number?* (Use the tens models, then count the tens.)
- *How can you figure out how many hundreds are in a whole number?* (Use the hundreds models, then count the hundreds.)
- Display 5 tens models. Say: *Count the tens.* (5 tens) *What whole number equals 5 tens?* (50)
- Display 7 ones models. Say: *Count the ones.* (7 ones) *What whole number equals 7 ones?* (7)
- Display 2 hundreds models. Say: *Count the hundreds.* (2 hundreds) *What whole number equals 2 hundreds?* (200)

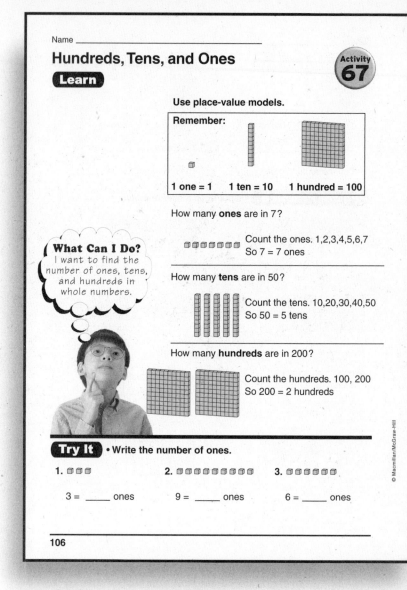

Name _____

Hundreds, Tens, and Ones

Learn

Activity **67**

Use place-value models.

Remember:

1 one = 1   1 ten = 10   1 hundred = 100

What Can I Do?
I want to find the number of ones, tens, and hundreds in whole numbers.

How many **ones** are in 7?

Count the ones. 1,2,3,4,5,6,7
So 7 = 7 ones

How many **tens** are in 50?

Count the tens. 10,20,30,40,50
So 50 = 5 tens

How many **hundreds** are in 200?

Count the hundreds. 100, 200
So 200 = 2 hundreds

Try It • Write the number of ones.

1. 3 = _____ ones

2. 9 = _____ ones

3. 6 = _____ ones

106

© Macmillan/McGraw-Hill

WHAT IF THE STUDENT CAN'T

Use Place-Value Models to Identify the Place Value of Digits

- Have students use place-value charts to write the digits for numbers shown by hundreds, tens, and ones models. Have them point to each group of ones, tens, or hundreds as they count the models and write the appropriate digit.
- Have the student draw in a math journal a ones, tens, and hundreds model and label each model.

- Put 7 tens on a place-value mat. Help the student determine the number by counting the tens models first, then the ones. (7 tens, 0 ones, so there are 7 tens in 70)
- Ask the student to draw place-value models for 4, 30, and 600. Then have him or her tell the numbers of ones, tens, or hundreds in each.

Name _____

Write the number of tens.

4. 40 = _____ tens

5. 70 = _____ tens

6. 30 = _____ tens

Write the number of hundreds.

7. 100 = _____ hundred

8. 800 = _____ hundreds

Power Practice • Write each missing number.

9. 2 = _____ ones

10. 50 = _____ tens

11. 300 = _____ hundreds

12. 60 = _____ tens

13. 500 = _____ hundreds

14. 80 = _____ tens

15. 900 = _____ hundreds

16. 20 = _____ tens

17. 5 = _____ ones

18. 90 = _____ tens

19. 400 = _____ hundreds

20. 10 = _____ ten

© Macmillan/McGraw-Hill

107

Try It

• Have students read their answers aloud. Remind them to say "ones," "tens," or "hundreds," as appropriate.

• Ask students to show their answers on place-value charts. Have them work in pairs to reorder the numbers from least to greatest so they can see the models increase in size.

Power Practice

• Select several of the exercises and have volunteers show the numbers on place-value charts.

WHAT IF THE STUDENT CAN'T

Recognize the Place Value of Digits in Two- and Three-Digit Numbers

• Show the student a two- or three-digit number. Point to a digit and have the student tell the value of the digit as so many ones, tens, or hundreds. Include some examples where the answer will be 0 ones, 0 tens, or 0 hundreds.

Complete the Power Practice

• Discuss each incorrect answer. Have the student model any exercise he or she missed using a place-value chart or drawing. Then ask the student to write the correct answer.

Activity 68 Lesson Goal

- Compare one-digit numbers and two-digit numbers using >, <, and =.

What the Student Needs To Know

- Recognize the symbols >, <, and =.
- Use place-value models to compare two numbers.
- Identify the digit in the tens place and ones place.

Getting Started

Find out what students know about comparing two numbers. Say:

- *Let's compare 10 and 20. I'll start: There is 1 ten in 10, and 2 tens in 20. 1 ten is less than 2 tens, so 10 is less than 20.*
- *Now, you compare 60 and 70.*

What Can I Do?

- Read the question and the response. Then read and discuss the examples. Ask students to write and label the symbols >, <, and = on separate pieces of paper. Ask:
- *What are three ways to compare one number to another?* (See if it is greater than, less than, or equal to another.) *Hold up each symbol after I say its meaning: "is greater than," "equal to," " is less than."*
- *How can you use place-value models to compare 2-digit numbers?* (Use tens models to compare the tens first. If the tens are the same, compare the ones.)
- *Compare 43 and 51. What is in the tens place in 43?* (4 tens) *What is in the tens place in 51?* (5 tens) *Are these numbers the same?* (no) *How are they different?* (4 tens is less than 5 tens) *So, how can you compare 43 and 51?* (43 is less than 51) *Hold up the "less than" symbol.*

Name _____

Compare Numbers

68

Learn

What Can I Do?
I want to compare two numbers.

Use place-value models to compare numbers.

Remember: You can compare numbers using >, <, and =.

> means **greater than**	< means **less than**	= means **equal to**
3 is greater than 1.	2 is less than 4.	5 is equal to 5.
3 > 1	2 < 4	5 = 5

Compare 23 and 19.

Compare the tens first. If the tens are the same, compare the ones.

2 tens are greater than 1 ten.
2 tens > 1 ten
So, 23 > 19

Compare 52 and 55.

Compare the tens first. If the tens are the same, compare the ones.

5 tens = 5 tens, so compare the ones.
2 ones < 5 ones
So, 52 < 55

Try It • Compare. Write >, <, or =.
Use place-value models to help.

1.

   8 ◯ 7

2.

   30 ◯ 40

© Macmillan/McGraw-Hill

WHAT IF THE STUDENT CAN'T

Recognize the Symbols >, <, and =

- Help the student remember the difference between > and < by explaining that the open end of each symbol faces the number that is greater. Have the student choose pairs of numbers and use the symbols correctly to compare the numbers.
- Have the student write >, <, and = and the definition of each symbol in a math journal.

Use Place-Value Models to Compare Two Numbers

- Put tens blocks and ones blocks equal to 47 in a place-value mat. Help the student determine the number by counting the tens blocks first, then the ones.
- Ask the student to draw place-value models for 21 and 34. Then have them compare the numbers.

Name _____

Compare. Write >, <, or =. Use place-value models to help.

3.

18 ◯ 18

4.

45 ◯ 26

5.

27 ◯ 31

6.

53 ◯ 53

7.

76 ◯ 66

8.

80 ◯ 84

Power Practice • Compare. Write >, <, or =.

9. 9 ◯ 5 **10.** 12 ◯ 17 **11.** 20 ◯ 40

12. 22 ◯ 22 **13.** 14 ◯ 32 **14.** 18 ◯ 16

15. 45 ◯ 34 **16.** 59 ◯ 62 **17.** 67 ◯ 37

18. 23 ◯ 32 **19.** 71 ◯ 76 **20.** 98 ◯ 98

109

© Macmillan/McGraw-Hill

WHAT IF THE STUDENT CAN'T

Identify the Digit in the Tens Place and Ones Place

- Stress that in a two-digit whole number, the digit on the left is in the tens place, and the digit on the right is in the ones place.

- Have the student read each number in the Power Practice and identify the digit in the tens place and in the ones place.

Complete the Power Practice

- Discuss each incorrect answer. Have the student use a place-value mat or make a drawing to illustrate the comparison. Then ask the student to write the correct answer.

- Have the student identify the correct symbol that compares the two numbers.

- Compare 64 and 62. What is in the tens place in 64? (6 tens) What is in the tens place in 62? (6 tens) These digits are the same. What is in the ones place in 64? (4 ones) What is in the ones place in 62? (2 ones) Are these digits the same? (no) How are they different? (4 ones is greater than 2 ones) So, how can you compare 64 and 62? (64 is greater than 62) Hold up the "is greater than" symbol.

- Compare 78 and 78. What is in the tens place in 78? (7 tens) What is in the tens place in 78? (7 tens) These digits are the same. What is in the ones place in 78? (8 ones) What is in the ones place in 78? (8 ones) Are these digits the same? (yes) So, how can you compare 78 and 78? (78 is equal to 78) Hold up the "equal to" symbol.

Try It

Have students say each number to be compared and explain the corresponding place-value model. Ask them to identify whether the number on the left is greater than, less than, or equal to the number on the right. Have them write the appropriate symbol. Say:

- If the numbers have a tens place, compare the tens first. If not, compare the ones. Use the place-value models to help you.

Power Practice

- Select several of the exercises and have volunteers model their comparisons on place-value mats.

- Ask students to review the steps to compare two-digit numbers: compare the tens first; if the tens are the same, compare the ones.

Activity 69 Lesson Goal

• Regroup ones as tens and ones.

What the Student Needs to Know

• Understand that 10 ones equal 1 ten.

• Connect place-value models with numerals.

• Identify ones and tens places in a numeral.

Getting Started

Show students 11 loose connecting cubes. Have a volunteer count the cubes. Ask how many tens and ones students think are in 11 cubes. For example, ask:

• *How can you find out how many tens are in 11 cubes?* (Connect cubes until you have a train of 10.)

• *How many 10-cube trains can you make?* (1) *How many cubes are left over?* (1)

• *How many tens and ones are in 11?* (1 ten and 1 one)

What Can I Do?

Read the question and the response. Then read and discuss the examples. Ask:

• *How many groups of 10 can you make from 25 ones blocks?* (2 groups)

• *Why can't you make 3 groups?* (There are only 5 ones blocks left over after making 2 groups of 10. You can't make another group of 10 from only 5 ones blocks.)

• *What does each tens block equal, or stand for?* (10 ones blocks)

• *So how many tens and ones are there in 25?* (2 tens and 5 ones)

• *How could you figure out the number of tens and ones without using blocks?* (The digit in the ones place—the column on the right—shows how many ones. The digit in the tens place—to the left of the ones place—shows how many tens.)

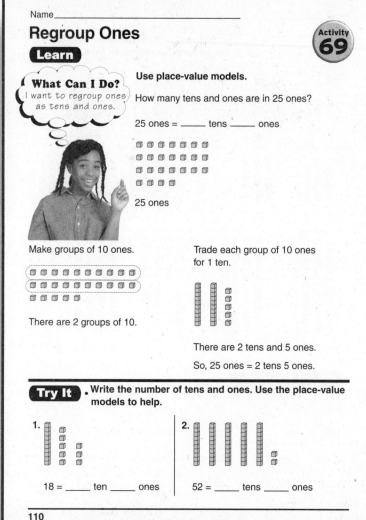

Name_____

Regroup Ones

Learn

What Can I Do?
I want to regroup ones as tens and ones.

Use place-value models.

How many tens and ones are in 25 ones?

25 ones = _____ tens _____ ones

25 ones

Make groups of 10 ones.

There are 2 groups of 10.

Trade each group of 10 ones for 1 ten.

There are 2 tens and 5 ones.

So, 25 ones = 2 tens 5 ones.

Try It • Write the number of tens and ones. Use the place-value models to help.

1. 18 = _____ ten _____ ones

2. 52 = _____ tens _____ ones

110

© Macmillan/McGraw-Hill

WHAT IF THE STUDENT CAN'T

Understand that 10 Ones Equal 1 Ten

• Provide more practice counting connecting cubes and forming them into 10-cube trains with some cubes left over. For example, give the student 27 cubes and have him or her form two 10-cube trains with 7 cubes left over.

• Then have the student model the same number using tens and ones blocks.

Connect Place-Value Models with Numerals

• After the student uses connecting cubes to model the number of tens and ones in a number, have the student write, for example:

27 has 2 tens and 7 ones.

• Next, have the student model the same number using tens and ones blocks.

Name_____

Circle groups of 10 ones.
Write the number of tens and ones.

3. ▫▫▫▫▫▫▫▫▫▫▫▫
▫▫▫▫▫▫▫▫

16 ones = __ ten __ ones

4. ▫▫▫▫▫▫▫▫▫▫▫▫▫
▫▫▫▫▫▫▫▫▫▫▫▫
▫▫▫▫▫

31 ones = __ tens __ one

5. ▫▫▫▫▫▫▫▫▫▫▫▫
▫▫▫▫▫▫▫▫▫▫▫
▫▫▫▫▫▫▫▫

29 ones = __ tens __ ones

6. ▫▫▫▫▫▫▫▫▫▫▫▫▫
▫▫▫▫▫▫▫▫▫▫▫▫
▫▫▫▫

43 ones = __ tens __ ones

Power Practice • Write the number of tens and ones.

7. 11 = _____ ten _____ one

8. 17 = _____ ten _____ ones

9. 34 = _____ tens _____ ones

10. 55 = _____ tens _____ ones

11. 67 = _____ tens _____ ones

12. 82 = _____ tens _____ ones

13. 78 = _____ tens _____ ones

14. 96 = _____ tens _____ ones

15. 23 = _____ tens _____ ones

16. 19 = _____ ten _____ ones

17. 41 = _____ tens _____ one

18. 92 = _____ tens _____ ones

111

WHAT IF THE STUDENT CAN'T

Identify Ones and Tens Places in a Numeral

- Have the student look at two-digit numbers and practice pointing to the digits in the tens and ones places and saying, for example: *There are 2 tens in 27. There are 7 ones in 27.*

- Have the student use a place-value mat to model two-digit numbers using connecting cubes and/or tens and ones blocks. Then he or she can write each number in a place-value chart as follows:

Tens	Ones
2	7

Complete the Power Practice

- Discuss each incorrect answer. Have the student model any exercise he or she missed using connecting cubes or tens and ones blocks. Help him or her point to the tens place and the ones place in each number.

Try It

- Make sure students recognize tens blocks and ones blocks, and that they understand the value of each tens block (10 ones blocks).

- Students might begin by modeling the exercises using connecting cubes. For example, for Exercise 1, they might set out 18 cubes, connect cubes to make a 10-cube train, and count the 8 cubes left over.

- For Exercises 3–4, students might count by placing a finger on each pictured ones block as they count silently or aloud.

Power Practice

- Review with students the different methods they have learned to help them figure out how many tens and ones in a number. Tell them they may use tens and ones blocks or connecting cubes if they need to. If they complete the exercises by simply copying the digits in the tens and ones places, suggest that they picture tens and ones blocks in their minds.

- Select several of the exercises and have volunteers explain which methods they can use to show that the numbers they have written are correct. For example, they might model the exercises using tens and ones blocks or connecting cubes. Alternatively, they might point to the digits in the tens and ones places and then point to the numbers they wrote.

Activity 70 Lesson Goal

- Write whole numbers for hundreds and tens.

What the Student Needs to Know

- Skip count by tens and hundreds.
- Use a place-value chart to understand place value.

Getting Started

Find out what students know about tens and hundreds. Say:

- *Let's count to 100 by tens. I'll start: 10, 20, 30… . Now you continue to count to 100.*
- *Let's count to 900 by hundreds. I'll start: 100, 200, 300… . Now you continue to count to 900.*

What Can I Do?

Read the question and the response. Draw a place-value chart on the board. Ask:

- *I want to write 70 in my place-value chart. Where should I write the 0?* (the ones column) *Where should I write the 7?* (the tens column)
- *What do 3 hundreds equal?* (300) *How can I write 300 in my place-value chart?* (Write 3 in the hundreds column, 0 in the tens column, and 0 in the ones column.)

Name _____

Hundreds and Tens

Learn

What Can I Do?
I want to write whole numbers for hundreds and tens.

Use a place-value chart.

Write the number.

7 tens = _____

hundreds	tens	ones
	7	0

7 tens is the same as 70.

So, 7 tens = 70.

3 hundreds = _____

hundreds	tens	ones
3	0	0

3 hundreds is the same as 300.

So, 3 hundreds = 300.

Try It • Fill in the place-value chart. Write each number.

1. | hundreds | tens | ones |
   |----------|------|------|
   | | | |

   2 tens = _____

2. | hundreds | tens | ones |
   |----------|------|------|
   | | | |

   5 hundreds = _____

3. | hundreds | tens | ones |
   |----------|------|------|
   | | | |

   6 hundreds = _____

4. | hundreds | tens | ones |
   |----------|------|------|
   | | | |

   6 tens = _____

5. | hundreds | tens | ones |
   |----------|------|------|
   | | | |

   4 tens = _____

6. | hundreds | tens | ones |
   |----------|------|------|
   | | | |

   9 hundreds = _____

© Macmillan/McGraw-Hill

112

WHAT IF THE STUDENT CAN'T

Skip Count by Tens and by Hundreds

- Provide more practice skip counting by tens using tens blocks. The student can set down one tens block at a time saying "10, 20, 30… ," and so on.
- Follow a similar procedure for skip counting by hundreds using hundreds models.

Use a Place-Value Chart to Understand Place Value

- Have the student use connecting cubes and a place-value mat to model numbers such as 11, 27, and 35. The student can connect cubes to create 10–cube trains, place the left-over cubes in the ones column.
- Then the student can write each number in a place value chart as follows:

tens	ones
1	1

Fill in the place-value chart. Write the number of tens or hundreds.

7. | hundreds | tens | ones |
   |----------|------|------|
   | | | |

_____ hundreds = 300

8. | hundreds | tens | ones |
   |----------|------|------|
   | | | |

_____ tens = 80

9. | hundreds | tens | ones |
   |----------|------|------|
   | | | |

_____ tens = 20

10. | hundreds | tens | ones |
    |----------|------|------|
    | | | |

_____ hundreds = 700

11. | hundreds | tens | ones |
    |----------|------|------|
    | | | |

_____ hundreds = 800

12. | hundreds | tens | ones |
    |----------|------|------|
    | | | |

_____ tens = 70

Power Practice • Write each number.

13. 4 tens = _____

14. 2 hundreds = _____

15. 3 tens = _____

16. 1 hundred = _____

17. 6 hundreds = _____

18. 9 tens = _____

19. 8 tens = _____

20. 8 hundreds = _____

21. 5 tens = _____

22. 4 hundreds = _____

23. 7 hundreds = _____

24. 6 tens = _____

25. _____ tens = 50

26. _____ hundreds = 900

27. _____ hundreds = 400

28. _____ ten = 10

29. _____ tens = 80

30. _____ hundreds = 500

113

WHAT IF THE STUDENT CAN'T

Complete the Power Practice

- Discuss each incorrect answer. Have the student model any exercise he or she missed using tens or hundreds models.

- Help the student point to the hundreds place, tens place, and ones place in each number.

Try It

Have students write the numbers in the place-value charts. Ask:

- *What do 5 hundreds equal?* (500) *Why did you write 0 in the tens place, and 0 in the ones place?* (to show 5 hundreds with no tens and no ones left over)

- *Does the number 40 have 4 tens or 4 hundreds?* (4 tens) *Does the number 600 have 6 tens or 6 hundreds?* (6 hundreds) *How many tens are in 90?* (9) *How many hundreds are in 700?* (7)

Power Practice

- Have students complete the practice items. Then review each answer.

Activity 71 Lesson Goal

- Write whole numbers for ten thousands, thousands, and hundreds.

What the Student Needs to Know

- Skip count by hundreds, thousands, and ten thousands.
- Use a place-value chart to understand place value.

Getting Started

Find out what students know about ten thousands, thousands, and hundreds. Say:

- *Let's count to 900 by hundreds. I'll start: 100, 200, 300... . Now you continue to count to 900.*
- *Let's count to 9,000 by thousands. I'll start: 1,000, 2,000, 3,000... . Now you continue to count to 9,000.*
- *Let's count to 90,000 by ten thousands. I'll start: 10,000, 20,000, 30,000... . Now you continue to count to 90,000.*

What Can I Do?

Read the question and the response. Draw a place-value chart on the board. Ask:

- *I want to write the number that shows what 4 ten thousands is. Where should I write the 4?* (in the ten thousands column) *What do I write in the thousands column?* (0) *What do I write in the hundreds column?* (0) *What do I write in the tens column?* (0), *What do I write in the ones column?* (0) *What number is the same as 4 ten thousands?* (40,000)

Name_____

Ten Thousands, Thousands, and Hundreds

Learn

What Can I Do?
I want to write whole numbers for ten thousands, thousands, and hundreds.

Use a place-value chart.

Write the number.

4 ten thousands = _____

ten-thousands	thousands	,	hundreds	tens	ones
4	0		0	0	0

4 ten thousands is the same as 40,000.

Always write a comma between the thousands and hundreds places.

So, 4 ten thousands = 40,000.

8 thousands = _____

ten-thousands	thousands	,	hundreds	tens	ones
	8		0	0	0

8 thousands is the same as 8,000.

So, 8 thousands = 8,000.

2 hundreds = _____

ten-thousands	thousands	,	hundreds	tens	ones
			2	0	0

2 hundreds is the same as 200.

So, 2 hundreds = 200.

114

WHAT IF THE STUDENT CAN'T

Skip Count by Hundreds, Thousands, and Ten Thousands

- Provide more practice skip counting by hundreds and thousands by first writing the numbers from 1–9 on a sheet of paper. As the student points to the numbers in order, he or she reads the number as a hundred: 100, 200, 300, and so on. Then the students can repeat for thousands: 1,000; 2,000; 3,000, and so on.

- For ten thousands, have the student write the skip counting numbers from 10–90 on a paper. Then have him or her follow a similar procedure as above, saying 10,000; 20,000; 30,000, and so on.

Use a Place-Value Chart to Understand Place Value

- Have the student use base ten models and a place-value mat to model numbers such as 90 or 900. The student can add an additional tens or hundreds model to force regrouping.

- Then the student can write each number in a place-value chart as follows:

ten thousands	thousands	,	hundreds	tens	ones
			9	0	0
	1	,	0	0	0

Try It • Fill in the place-value chart. Write each number.

1.

ten-thousands	thousands	,	hundreds	tens	ones

5 ten thousands = _____

2.

ten-thousands	thousands	,	hundreds	tens	ones

6 thousands = _____

3.

ten-thousands	thousands	,	hundreds	tens	ones

4 hundreds = _____

4.

ten-thousands	thousands	,	hundreds	tens	ones

8 ten thousands = _____

Power Practice • Write each number.

5. 2 thousands = _____　　6. 6 hundreds = _____

7. 3 ten thousands = _____　　8. 1 ten thousand = _____

9. 5 thousands = _____　　10. 7 hundreds = _____

11. 9 ten thousands = _____　　12. 2 ten thousands = _____

13. 7 thousands = _____　　14. 9 hundreds = _____

15. 8 hundreds = _____　　16. 2 thousands = _____

17. 5 ten thousands = _____　　18. 1 hundred = _____

115

- *What do 8 thousands equal?*
  (8,000) *How can I write 8,000 in my place-value chart?* (Write 8 in the thousands column, 0 in the hundreds column, 0 in the tens column, and 0 in the ones column.)

- *What do 2 hundreds equal?* (200) *Where do I write the 2 in the place-value chart?* (in the hundreds column) *What number do I write in the tens and ones columns?* (0)

Try It

Have students write the numbers in the place-value charts. Ask:

- *What do 5 tens equal?* (50) *What do 5 thousands equal?* (5,000) *What do 5 ten thousands equal?* (50,000) *Why must you write 0 in each place to the right of the ten thousands place when you write 50,000?* (to show that there are no thousands, hundreds, tens, or ones) *Where do you write the comma in 50,000?* (after the 0 in the thousands place)

- *When you write 6 thousands, where do you write the 6?* (in the thousands place) *Where do you write zeros?* (in the hundreds, tens, and ones places) *Where do you write the comma?* (after the 6)

Power Practice

- Have students complete the practice items. Then review each answer.

WHAT IF THE STUDENT CAN'T

Write Zeros in the Correct Places

- Have the student use base-ten blocks to represent numbers. First have him or her put a rubber band or a sticker on several ones cubes and tens rods. Tell the student that the marked ones cubes represent thousands, and that the marked tens rods are ten thousands rods.

- Then have the student use the base-ten blocks to model related numbers to the ten thousands such as 200; 2,000; and 20,000.

- After modeling, have the student write each number in a place-value chart and say the number aloud.

Complete the Power Practice

- Discuss each incorrect answer. Help the student match the ten thousands, thousands, hundreds, tens, and ones places in each number to the same places in a place-value chart.

Activity 72 Lesson Goal

- Use place-value models to find the number of tens in two-digit numbers ending in 0.

What the Student Needs to Know

- Recognize the ones and tens digits in a number.

Getting Started

Ask students to count by 1s from 10 to 20. Say:

- *When you get to 20, how many 1s have you counted?* (10)
- *Ten 1s is the same as how many 10s?* (1)
- *So if you started with one 10 and now you have another 10, how many 10s do you have?* (2)
- *20 is the same as how many 10s?* (2)
- *What does the 2 in the number 20 show?* (that there are two 10s)

What Can I Do?

Read the question and the response. Then follow the steps of the example by using the place-value models. Ask:

- *What does it mean to "trade" each group of ten 1s for one 10?* (to exchange equal amounts)

Try It

- Have students use place-value models to help do Exercises 1 and 2. Note that Example 1 uses 20 = 2 tens, the same as you used in the "Getting Started" section.

Power Practice

- Have students complete practice items. Then review each answer.

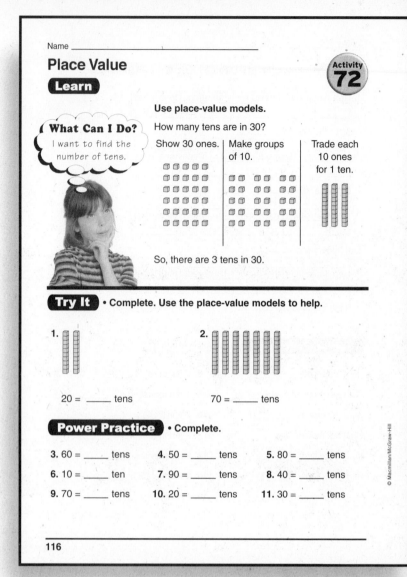

Name _____

Place Value

Learn

Activity **72**

What Can I Do?
I want to find the number of tens.

Use place-value models.

How many tens are in 30?

Show 30 ones.	Make groups of 10.	Trade each 10 ones for 1 ten.

So, there are 3 tens in 30.

Try It • Complete. Use the place-value models to help.

1.

20 = _____ tens

2.

70 = _____ tens

Power Practice • Complete.

3. 60 = _____ tens   4. 50 = _____ tens   5. 80 = _____ tens

6. 10 = _____ ten   7. 90 = _____ tens   8. 40 = _____ tens

9. 70 = _____ tens   10. 20 = _____ tens   11. 30 = _____ tens

116

© Macmillan/McGraw-Hill

WHAT IF THE STUDENT CAN'T

Recognize the Ones and the Tens Digits in a Number

- Stress that in a whole number the last digit is in the 1s column.
- The 10s column is the digit before the 1s.
- Have students practice reading two-digit numbers and identifying the 1s and the 10s.

Complete the Power Practice

- Discuss each incorrect answer. Make sure the student knows that the non-zero digit names the number of tens.

Name_____

Expanded Notation or Expanded Form **Learn**

What Can I Do?
I want to show the expanded form for a number.

Use a place-value chart.

thousands	hundreds	tens	ones
6	3	0	7

Write the value of each digit.

6,307 = 6,000 + 300 + 0 + 7
        thousands hundreds tens ones

Try It • Write each number in expanded notation.

1. 1,208 = _____ + _____ + _____ + _____
      thousands   hundreds   tens   ones

2. 9,422 = _____ + _____ + _____ + _____
      thousands   hundreds   tens   ones

3. 7,320 = _____ + 300 + 20 + _____

Power Practice • Write each number in expanded notation.

4. 8,437 = _____ + _____ + _____ + _____

5. 2,954 = _____ + _____ + _____ + _____

6. 6,015 = _____ + _____ + _____ + _____

117

© Macmillan/McGraw-Hill

WHAT IF THE STUDENT CAN'T

Understand Place Value Through Thousands

- Have the student write the number 2,936 and then read it aloud. Explain that each digit can be seen as one place in a place-value chart. Then have the student tell you how many thousands, hundreds, tens, and ones are in the number. Be sure the student understands that each place can hold only one of the 10 digits 0–9.

- Have the student practice writing four-digit numbers in a place-value chart until it can be done with ease.

Add One-Digit through Four-Digit Numbers

- Have the student write and solve the following equation vertically: 5,000 + 800 + 30 + 6. Be sure the student aligns the numbers properly, and adds only the numbers in a given column. Have the student practice addition in both vertical and horizontal formats.

Complete the Power Practice

- For each incorrect part of the expanded form, have the student underline the corresponding digit in the original number and write the place value underneath the blank.

Activity 73 Lesson Goal

- Write four-digit numbers in expanded notation (or expanded form).

What the Student Needs to Know

- Understand place value through thousands.

- Add one-digit through four-digit numbers.

Getting Started

Write the following addition sentence on the board: 4,000 + 300 + 70 + 1 = ____ (4,371)

Have students complete the exercise. Then ask:

- *In your answer, what digit is in the thousands place? hundreds? tens? ones?* (4, 3, 7, 1)

What Can I Do?

- Read the question and the response. Then read and discuss the example. Ask:

- *What does it mean to write the expanded notation of a number?* (Possible answer: To write it as an addition, with each addend representing the place value of one digit in the original number.)

Try It

Have the student write each number in expanded notation. Ask:

- *What is a rule you can follow when you write the value of any digit in a number?* (Multiply the digit by its place value, so that, for example, a 6 in the hundreds place becomes 600.)

Power Practice

Have students complete the exercises. Then review each answer.

Activity 74 Lesson Goal

• Rename tens and ones as ones.

What the Student Needs to Know

• Understand that 1 ten equals 10 ones.

• Count by tens.

• Add one-digit numbers to multiples of 10 through 90.

Getting Started

Show students one 10-train of connecting cubes and 2 loose cubes. Ask:

• *How many tens and ones do I have?* (1 ten and 2 ones) *If I take apart the 10-train and add the cubes to the 2 ones, how many ones will I have?* (12)

• *How can you find out how many ones are in 1 ten and 2 ones?* (Add 10 + 2 for a sum of 12.)

What Can I Do?

Read the question and the response. Then read and discuss the example. Ask:

• *How many ones are in each tens block?* (10) *How can you find out how many ones are in 3 tens blocks?* (Count by tens: 10, 20, 30. There are 30 ones in 3 tens.)

• *What does 30 ones + 4 ones equal?* (34 ones)

Try It

Students might begin by modeling the exercises using connecting cubes. For example, for Exercise 1 they might set out a 10-train and 6 loose cubes. Then they can take apart the train and count all of the cubes for a total of 16.

Power Practice

• Review with students the steps they have learned to help them rename tens and ones as ones. Allow them to use tens and ones blocks or connecting cubes if they need to.

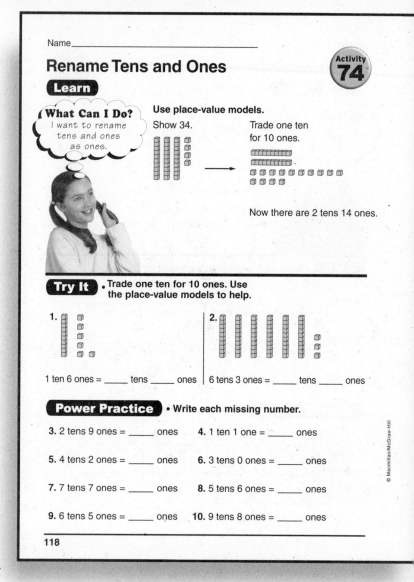

Name_____

Rename Tens and Ones

Learn

What Can I Do? I want to rename tens and ones as ones.

Use place-value models.

Show 34.

Trade one ten for 10 ones.

Now there are 2 tens 14 ones.

Try It • Trade one ten for 10 ones. Use the place-value models to help.

1.

1 ten 6 ones = _____ tens _____ ones

2.

6 tens 3 ones = _____ tens _____ ones

Power Practice • Write each missing number.

3. 2 tens 9 ones = _____ ones   4. 1 ten 1 one = _____ ones

5. 4 tens 2 ones = _____ ones   6. 3 tens 0 ones = _____ ones

7. 7 tens 7 ones = _____ ones   8. 5 tens 6 ones = _____ ones

9. 6 tens 5 ones = _____ ones   10. 9 tens 8 ones = _____ ones

118

© Macmillan/McGraw-Hill

WHAT IF THE STUDENT CAN'T

Understand That 1 Ten Equals 10 Ones

• Make sure the student recognizes tens blocks and ones blocks, and that he or she understands the value of each tens block (10 ones blocks).

• Provide more practice connecting cubes into 10-cube trains and using the trains along with loose cubes to model various two-digit numbers.

Count by Tens

• Provide daily practice counting by tens from 10 through 100 until the student can do so with ease.

Add One-Digit Numbers to Multiples of 10 through 90

• Write multiples of 10 on the board and have the student mentally add 1-digit numbers to each. For example, ask:

• What does 10 + 1 equal? (11) What does 50 + 6 equal? (56)

• Continue such practice until the student can complete the addition sentences with ease.

Complete the Power Practice

• Discuss each incorrect answer. Have the student model any exercise he or she missed using connecting cubes or tens and ones blocks.

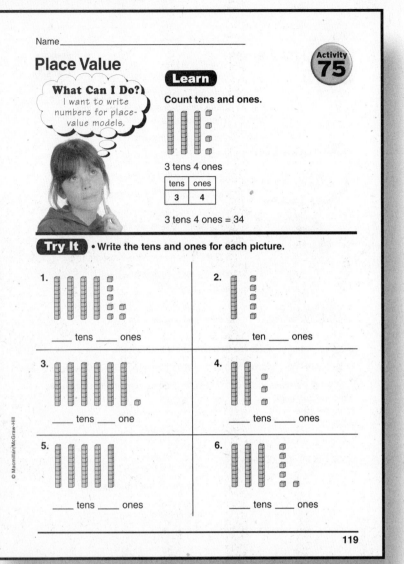

Name_____

Place Value

What Can I Do?
I want to write numbers for place-value models.

Learn

Count tens and ones.

3 tens 4 ones

tens	ones
3	4

3 tens 4 ones = 34

Try It • Write the tens and ones for each picture.

1. _____ tens _____ ones

2. _____ ten _____ ones

3. _____ tens _____ one

4. _____ tens _____ ones

5. _____ tens _____ ones

6. _____ tens _____ ones

© Macmillan/McGraw-Hill

119

WHAT IF THE STUDENT CAN'T

Recognize Tens and Ones Models

• Use tens and ones models to illustrate a two-digit number such as 25. Have the student count the ones and write down the number counted. Point out that the number consists of two numbers written together to show a greater number. Note that the left-hand digit shows how many tens are in the model and that the right-hand digit shows how many ones are used.

• Have the student draw models for two-digit numbers using tens strips and squares. Each drawing should be labeled with the number, as well as a description of the number of tens and ones in each drawing.

USING THE LESSON

Activity 75 Lesson Goal

• Write the standard form of a number represented by place-value models.

What the Student Needs to Know

• Recognize tens and ones models.

• Recognize tens and ones digits in two-digit numbers.

Getting Started

Ask students to think of a two-digit number. Then ask:

• How can you break this number into two addends, so that one number is a multiple of ten and the other one is a single digit? (Possible answer: 53 can be broken down into 50 + 3.)

Have students use place-value models to show the two addends.

What Can I Do?

Read the question and the response. Then read and discuss the example. Ask:

• How can you write 3 tens as a number? (30)

• How can you write 3 tens and 4 ones as an addition sentence? (30 + 4 = 34)

• If there were 3 more ones in the model, how would you write the number? (37) How many tens would there be? (3) How many ones? (7)

Activity 76 Lesson Goal

- Compare numbers written in standard and expanded notation.

What the Student Needs to Know

- Recognize place value in numbers written in standard notation (or expanded form).
- Write a number in expanded notation (or form).
- Use a place-value chart.

Getting Started

Remind students that the same number can be written in different ways. For example, 30 and 3 tens are different names for the same number. You may wish to introduce the term equivalent. Say: *Two names are equivalent if they name the same number.*

- Write the numbers 23, 538, 7,399, and 3,687 on the board. Have students identify the 3 in each number. Ask: *Which number shows 3 ones?* (23) *Which number shows 3 thousands?* (3,687) *What does the 3 in 538 show?* (3 tens or 30) *What does the 3 in 7,399 show?* (3 hundreds or 300)
- Write "2 hundreds and 5 ones" on the board. Then write 250 and 205. Ask: *Which number matches "2 hundreds and 5 ones"?* (205)

What Can I Do?

- Read the question and the response. Then read and discuss the examples. Have students read the labels on the place-value chart. Then ask:
- *What does the 5 in 5,428 show?* (5 thousands; 5,000) *What does the 4 show?* (4 hundreds, 400) *What does the 2 show?* (2 tens; 20) *What does the 8 show?* (8 ones; 8)
- Help students relate numbers in expanded notation with numbers written in a place-value chart. After students read the expanded notation for 9,366, have them write the number in a place-value chart.

Name _____

Equivalent Names

Learn

Use a place-value chart.

Is 5,428 equal to 5 thousands, 4 hundreds, 2 tens, and 8 ones? Write 5,428 in a place-value chart.

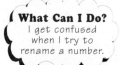

What Can I Do?
I get confused when I try to rename a number.

thousands	hundreds	tens	ones
5	4	2	8

Read the numbers and their place value.

5 thousands 4 hundreds 2 tens 8 ones

Yes, 5,428 is equal to 5 thousands, 4 hundreds, 2 tens, and 8 ones.

Is 5,428 equal to 54 hundreds, 2 tens, and 8 ones? Read the place-value chart.

Think: 5 thousands 4 hundreds is the same as 54 hundreds.

So 5,428 is also equal to 54 hundreds, 2 tens, and 8 ones.

Write a number in expanded notation or expanded form.

Write 9,366 in expanded notation.	Is 5,612 equal to 5,000 + 100 + 60 + 2?
First, write the thousands. 9,000 Write the hundreds. 300 Write the tens. 60 Write the ones. 6 Add the numbers together. 9,366 = 9,000 + 300 + 60 + 6	To answer, combine the expanded number. 5,000 100 60 + 2 ‾‾‾‾‾ 5,162 5,162 is **not** equal to 5,612. 5,612 is equal to 5,000 + 600 + 10 + 2.

120

WHAT IF THE STUDENT CAN'T

Recognize Place Value in Numbers Written in Standard Notation

- Have the student use place-value charts to complete each activity. Review the organization of the chart, reinforcing the fact that each place value is ten times greater than the place value to its right.
- Encourage the student to add labels to several numbers written in standard notation. Write 4,572 and then have the student label each digit with its correct place value.

Write a Number in Expanded Notation (or Form)

- Have the student look at numbers written in expanded notation and look for patterns. The student should notice that each number usually has one less zero than the number to its left. Have the student add several numbers in expanded notation to find the equivalent number in standard notation. Then demonstrate how to do the same steps "backwards" to rewrite the standard number in expanded notation.

Try It • Use the place-value chart to help you answer each question.

1. Is 6,938 equal to 6 thousands, 3 hundreds, 9 tens, and 8 ones?

thousands	hundreds	tens	ones

_____

Complete each expanded notation.

2. 1,502 = _____ + 500 + _____

3. 9,911 = 9,000 + _____ + _____ + _____

4. 8,067 = _____ + _____ + _____

5. 2,821 = _____ + _____ + _____ + _____

Power Practice • Circle the numbers in each row that are equal.

6. 668   6 hundreds 6 tens 8 ones   600 + 80 + 6

7. 7,283   7 thousands 2 tens 3 ones   7,000 + 200 + 80 + 3

8. 6,594   65 hundreds 9 tens 4 ones   6,000 + 5,000 + 9,000 + 4,000

Write the number in the box that is equal to each number below.

628	6,208	6,882

9. 600 + 20 + 8   **10.** 6,000 + 800 + 80 + 2   **11.** 62 hundreds 8 ones

_____   _____   _____

121

© Macmillan/McGraw-Hill

WHAT IF THE STUDENT CAN'T

Use a Place-Value Chart

- Allow the student to use manipulatives to model numbers in the lesson. Review the terms thousands, hundreds, tens, and ones to make sure the student is comfortable with place-value vocabulary.

Complete the Power Practice

- Review incorrect answers. Have the student vocalize the thinking processes to identify errors in logic. Encourage the student to read confusing numbers aloud. Point out that when you read a number, such as 6,882, you are using place-value words (6 thousand, 8 hundred, eighty-two).

- When students identify two numbers that are not equal, such as 5,612 and 5,162, ask them to identify which number is greater than the other. Reinforce the understanding of equivalence by pointing out that if one number is larger than another number, the two numbers are not equal.

Try It

- Help students complete the place-value chart. Remind students that only one digit can go in each square of the place-value chart. In Exercise 1, students might try to write 69 in the hundreds column. Help them understand that only the 9 goes in the hundreds column; the 6 should be written in the thousands column.

- To complete Exercises 2–5, have students begin by counting the number of digits in each number. Explain: *If there are four digits in a number, the expanded number will usually have four addends. Why are there only three addends in Exercises 2 and 4?* (Because one of the digits in each number is a zero.)

Power Practice

- Students can compare numbers by writing them all in the same notation. Suggest that students use place-value charts to help them compare the numbers.

- For Exercises 9–11, remind students that numbers in the box may look similar even if they are not equal. Have them read each of the numbers in the box to help them understand why each number is different from the others.

Activity 77 Lesson Goal

- Find the value of a set of coins.

What the Student Needs To Know

- Identify the value of a quarter, dime, nickel, and penny.
- Skip count by 5s, 10s, and 25s.
- Keep track of the coins counted.

Getting Started

Determine what students know about the value of a set of coins. Display this set of play coins: 1 quarter, 1 nickel, and 2 pennies. Say:

- *Let's find the total amount. Start with the quarter. (25¢). Now skip count by 1 five. (30¢) Count on by 2 ones. (31¢, 32¢) What is the total amount? (32¢)*

What Can I Do?

Read the question and the response. Then read and discuss the examples. Ask:

- *By what amount do you skip count with dimes? (by 10s) Skip count to find the value of 3 dimes. (10¢, 20¢, 30¢)*
- *By what amount do you skip count with nickels? (by 5s) Skip count to find the value of 4 nickels. (5¢, 10¢, 15¢, 20¢)*
- *By what amount do you count on with pennies? (by ones) Count on to find the value of 6 pennies. (1¢, 2¢, 3¢, 4¢, 5¢, 6¢)*
- Draw and label on the chalk board the coins shown in the first example: Ask: *What coin do you see first? (the penny) Then what? (the nickel) Then what? (the dime) What comes next? (the quarter)*
- *When you count coins, group coins with the same value and start with the coins of greatest value.*
- Circle each coin as it is counted. Say: *Let's count these coins. We'll start at 1 quarter, 25¢. What do we do next? (count the nickels) Say: 30¢, 35¢, 40¢. What do we count next? (the pennies) What is the total value? (43¢)*

Name _____

Counting Coins

Learn

Activity **77**

What Can I Do?
I want to find the value of a set of coins.

You can skip count and count on to count coins.

Remember:

penny	nickel	dime	quarter
1¢ one cent	5¢ five cents	10¢ ten cents	25¢ twenty-five cents

Find the total amount.

Start with the coins that have the greatest value.

Start at 25¢. Skip count by 5s and say, 25¢, 30¢, 35¢, 40¢.

Then count on and say, 41¢, 42¢, 43¢.

25¢,   30¢,   35¢,   40¢,   41¢,   42¢,   43¢

So, the total amount is 43¢.

122

© Macmillan/McGraw-Hill

WHAT IF THE STUDENT CAN'T

Identify the Value of a Quarter, Dime, Nickel, and Penny

- Hand out a quarter, dime, nickel, and penny to the student. Have the student read each coin and order the set by value from most to least. Review each coin's name and value daily until the student can recognize it easily.

Skip Count by 5s, 10s, and 25s

- Have the student practice skip counting by 5s, 10s, and 25s a few times a day until the student can do so easily.

Try It • Skip count or count on to fill in the blanks. Then write each amount.

1. _____¢ _____¢ _____¢ _____¢ _____¢

   Total amount: _____¢

2. _____¢ _____¢ _____¢ _____¢ _____¢ _____¢

   Total amount: _____¢

3. _____¢ _____¢ _____¢ _____¢ _____¢ _____¢

   Total amount: _____¢

Power Practice • Write each amount.

4. _____¢

5. _____¢

6. _____¢

7. _____¢

8. _____¢

123

WHAT IF THE STUDENT CAN'T

Keep Track of the Coins Counted

• Help the student correct any errors. Have the student draw pictures of the coins they are counting, then circle each coin as they skip count or count on. Make sure the student understands from which amount to start counting.

Complete the Power Practice

• Discuss each incorrect answer. Use play coins to help the student find the correct amount.

• *Why is it important to say "cents" when you are finding the value of a set of coins?* (to show that the numbers refer to coins and not some other unit)

• *Why is it easy to skip count with a set of nickels and dimes?* (It is faster to count by 5s or 10s than to count on by ones.)

• *Why should you count the coins in groups, according to their value?* (It is faster and easier to count in groups of quarters, dimes, nickels, and pennies.)

Try It

• Have students name each coin and its value, and count how many there are of each. Ask students to skip count or count on and have them fill in the blanks to show the increasing value. To review, ask:

• *How many nickels are in Exercise 1?* (2) *How do you skip count 2 nickels?* (5¢, 10¢)

• *How many pennies are there?* (2) *Count on 2 pennies to find the total amount. Start at 20¢.* (20¢, 21¢, 22¢) *What is the total amount of 1 dime, 2 nickels, and 2 pennies?* (22¢)

• Continue the procedure for Exercises 2–3.

Power Practice

• Review students' answers and have them make corrections as needed. Call on volunteers to model their answers with play coins.

• Have students make a chart in their math journal showing a picture of each coin, its name, and its value.

Activity 78 Lesson Goal

• Tell time on an analog clock.

What the Student Needs to Know

• Identify the *hour hand* and *minute hand* on an analog clock.
• Count by 5s.
• Understand how to write times.

Getting Started

Use an analog clock. Ask:

• *Which is the hour hand?* (the shorter one) *What is the longer hand called?* (the minute hand)

• *In one hour, how far does the minute hand move?* (all the way around the clock) *How far does the hour hand move in one hour?* (from one numeral to the next)

• *If the minute hand is on the 3, how many minutes after the hour does it show?* (15 minutes) *What part of an hour is 15 minutes?* (a quarter of an hour)

• *If it is 30 minutes, or half an hour after the hour, where will the minute hand be?* (on the 6)

What Can I Do?

• Read the question and the response. Then read and discuss the examples. Ask:

• *Where is the hour hand on the first clock?* (on 5) *Where is the minute hand?* (on 12) *How would you read this time?* (five o'clock) *How would you write it?* (5:00)

• *Where is the minute hand on the second clock?* (on the 6) *How many minutes after the hour does it show?* (30 minutes)

• *On the third clock, where are the hour and minute hands?* (The hour hand is a little past the 7, and the minute hand is on the 3.) *How many minutes after seven o'clock does it show?* (15 minutes) *Why do we put a colon between the 7 and the 15?* (to separate the hour from the minutes after the hour)

Name_____

Time to the Hour, Half Hour, and Quarter Hour

Activity **78**

Learn

What Can I Do?
I want to tell time on a clock.

Look at the hour hand and the minute hand.

The **hour hand** is the *short* hand.
The **minute hand** is the *long* hand.

Read:	Read:	Read:
five o'clock	ten-thirty	seven-fifteen
Write:	Write:	Write:
5:00	10:30	7:15

Try It • Complete. Write each time.

1.

The **hour hand** is on the _____.

The **minute hand** is on the _____.

The time is __:__.

2.

The hour hand is on the _____.

The minute hand is on the _____.

The time is __:__.

© Macmillan/McGraw-Hill

124

WHAT IF THE STUDENT CAN'T

Identify the *Hour Hand* and *Minute Hand* on an Analog Clock

• Use an analog clock. Have the student observe how its hands move during the course of the school day. Ask, for example:

• *It's 9 o'clock—where is the hour hand?* (on the 9) *Where is the minute hand?* (on the 12)

• *It's 10:30—where is the minute hand?* (on the 6) *What does the minute hand on the 6 show?* (that it is 30 minutes after the hour)

Count by 5s

• Use a number line from 0 to 60. Have the student practice jumping his or her finger from 0 to 5 to 10 to 15, and so on, counting aloud by fives: "five, ten, fifteen, twenty," and so on. Repeat a few times a day until the student can count by fives with ease.

• Next, have the student count by fives on an analog clock, starting at 12 and counting by fives while jumping his or her finger clockwise from numeral to numeral: "five, ten, fifteen, ... sixty."

Name_____

Complete. Write each time.

3.

The hour hand is past the _____.

The minute hand is on the _____.

The time is ____:____.

4.

The hour hand is past the _____.

The minute hand is on the _____.

The time is ____:____.

Power Practice

Write each time.

5.

____:____

6.

____:____

7.

____:____

8.

____:____

Learn with Partners & Parents

How Long?

You need one set of alphabet cards, paper, and pencils.

- Each player marks a paper with 3 columns titled *15 Minutes, Half Hour,* and *Hour.*
- Shuffle the cards and place them facedown. One player turns over the top card and lets every player see the letter.
- All players have 5 minutes to think of as many activities as they can for each column. Each activity must start with the letter that was drawn. For example, for the letter G, the player might write "Go to the store" in the hour column.
- The player with the most activities wins 5 points.

125

WHAT IF THE STUDENT CAN'T

Understand How to Write Times

- Draw on the board several clock faces showing different times. Write the times beneath the clocks. Show the student that the number before the colon corresponds to the number the hour hand is on or the lesser number it is between.
- Next, show the student that the number following the colon corresponds to the number of minutes after the hour.
- Erase the times under the clocks you drew, and have the student rewrite them.

Complete the Power Practice

- Discuss each incorrect answer. Have the student tell what hour each clock face shows, and how many minutes after the hour it shows. Then have him or her rewrite the answer with your prompting.

Try It

Check students' understanding of how to write times.

- Make sure students know that the hour goes before the colon, and the number of minutes after the hour follow the colon.
- If students need help counting minutes after the hour, show them how to place their finger on the 12 and jump it from numeral to numeral, clockwise, while counting by fives.
- For example, for Exercise 4, they should count "five, ten, fifteen" as they jump their finger from the 12 to the 1, 2, and 3. Since the minute hand is on the 3, students can conclude that it is 15 minutes after the hour.

Power Practice

- Review with students the steps they can follow to help them write times.
- Select several of the exercises and have volunteers describe the steps they followed to find the times and write them.

Learn with Partners & Parents

- Players should check to see if the activities written for each column make sense. For example, it is not appropriate to write "Brush teeth" for the hour column.

Activity 79 Lesson Goal

- Measure length using paper clips.

What the Student Needs to Know

- Understand length.
- Understand the concept of a unit of measurement.

Getting Started

Draw a line segment on the board. Ask:

- *If I measure this line segment from beginning to end, what am I measuring?* (its length)

Then draw a triangle on the chalkboard. The sides of the triangle should each have a different measure. Point to the side of the triangle. Ask:

- *If you measure this side of the triangle, what are you measuring?* (the length of the side)

Do the same for each of the other sides of the triangle.

What Can I Do?

Read the question and the response. Then read and discuss the example. Ask:

- *What is the unit of measurement used in the example?* (paper clip)
- *Is each paper clip in the example the same length?* (Yes)
- *In measuring, can there be any space between paper clips, or do they need to be end to end to give an accurate answer?* (They should be end to end.)

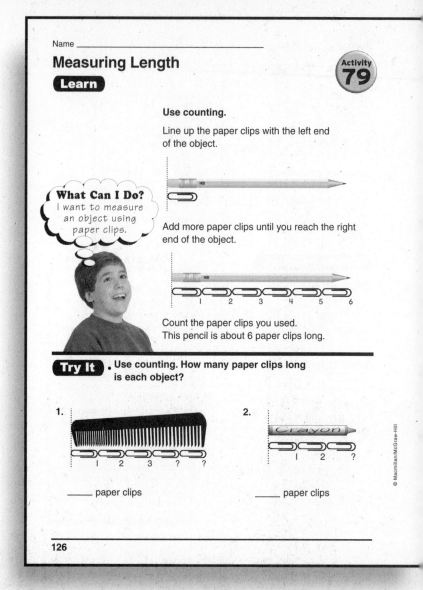

Name _____

Measuring Length

Learn

Activity 79

Use counting.

Line up the paper clips with the left end of the object.

What Can I Do?
I want to measure an object using paper clips.

Add more paper clips until you reach the right end of the object.

1 2 3 4 5 6

Count the paper clips you used.
This pencil is about 6 paper clips long.

Try It . Use counting. How many paper clips long is each object?

1.

1 2 3 ? ?

_____ paper clips

2.

Crayon

1 2 ?

_____ paper clips

© Macmillan/McGraw-Hill

126

WHAT IF THE STUDENT CAN'T

Understand Length

- Draw a line segment on the board. Explain that the length of the segment tells how far it runs from beginning to end. Note that different segments will have different lengths.
- Explain that, just as a line segment can be measured for length, shapes and objects may be measured for length. Have the student draw various shapes and objects, drawing a line for each one that represents the length of the figure.

Understand the Concept of a Unit of Measurement

- Explain that to measure the length of something, you need to have a unit of measurement. A unit of measurement can be an agreed-upon length, such as a foot or a meter. In addition, a unit of measurement can be an object such as a paper clip or eraser.

Name _____

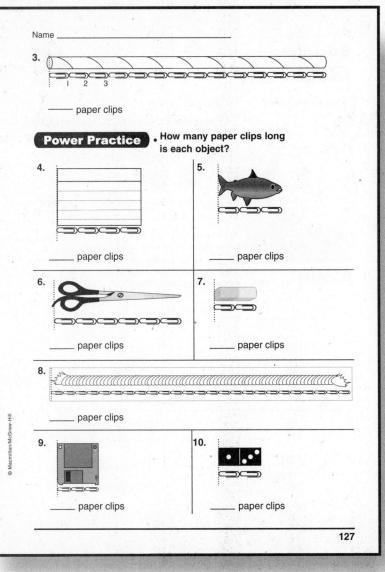

3.

_____ paper clips

Power Practice • How many paper clips long is each object?

4.

_____ paper clips

5.

_____ paper clips

6.

_____ paper clips

7.

_____ paper clips

8.

_____ paper clips

9.

_____ paper clips

10.

_____ paper clips

© Macmillan/McGraw-Hill

127

Try It

Look at Exercises 1–3. Have students count off the number of paper clips in each exercise. Ask:

- *Why should you mark the number at the end of each paper clip instead of at the beginning?* (Because until you reach the end of the paper clip, you haven't reached that number of paper clips in length.)

Power Practice

- Have students complete the practice items. Then review each answer.

WHAT IF THE STUDENT CAN'T

- Use an object in the classroom to demonstrate how different units of measurement can be used to measure the same object. For example, a stapler can be measured in inches, centimeters, or paper clips. Then have the student use various units of measurement to measure other items.

Complete the Power Practice

- Discuss each incorrect answer. Have the student count off the paper clips to arrive at the correct answer.

Measurement and Geometry Skill Builder **T127**

Activity 80 Lesson Goal
- Compare the capacity of objects.

What the Student Needs to Know
- Compare the size of real-life objects based on non-scale drawings.

Getting Started
Find out what students know about capacity. Ask:
- *What are some objects that can hold a tiny amount of liquid?* (Possible answers: an eyedropper, a teaspoon, a thimble)
- *What are some objects that can hold a huge amount of liquid?* (Possible answers: a water tower, a swimming pool, an oil tanker)
- *Which two objects of different sizes can usually hold more liquid—the larger object or the smaller object?*

What Can I Do?
Read the question and the response. Then read and discuss the example. Ask:
- *If the drawing of the drinking glass were larger than the drawing of the pool, what would the correct answer to the problem be?* (It would still be the pool.) *Why?* (Because it is the size of the object in real life that matters, not how large it is drawn.)

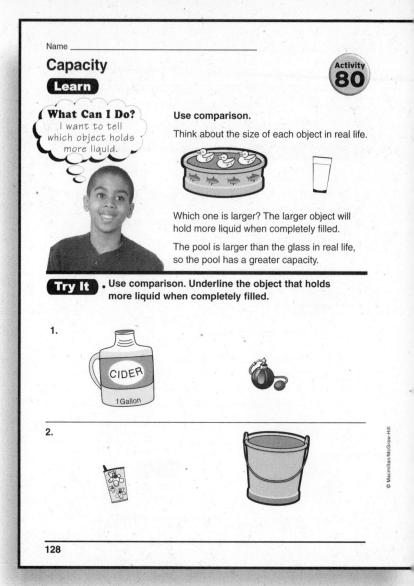

Name _____

Capacity

Learn

What Can I Do?
I want to tell which object holds more liquid.

Use comparison.

Think about the size of each object in real life.

Which one is larger? The larger object will hold more liquid when completely filled.

The pool is larger than the glass in real life, so the pool has a greater capacity.

Try It . Use comparison. Underline the object that holds more liquid when completely filled.

1.

CIDER
1 Gallon

2.

128

© Macmillan/McGraw-Hill

WHAT IF THE STUDENT CAN'T

Compare the Size of Real-Life Objects Based on Non-Scale Drawings
- Draw a truck and a television so that both drawings are about the same size. Ask the student to identify both drawings. Explain that the drawings don't really show how big the objects are compared to one another. Make it clear that the student has to form a picture of how big both objects are in real life.

- Encourage the student to draw the objects as they might look if they were sitting next to each other. Be sure the student is able to draw one object as noticeably larger than the other.

- Explain that another way of testing which of two objects is larger is to figure out whether one object will fit into another. For example, a television can fit into a truck, but a truck can't fit into a television set.

Name_____

Power Practice • Underline the object that holds more liquid when completely filled.

3.

4.

FIDO

5.

6.

7.

8.

Cola

9.

MILK
Pint

10.

129

© Macmillan/McGraw-Hill

Try It
Have students look at Exercises 1 and 2. Be sure it is clear to students what each object is. Then have students complete the exercises. Review the answers. Have volunteers describe how one object is larger than the other.

Power Practice
• Have students complete the practice items. Then review each answer.
• Select a few of the exercises and have a volunteer identify both objects. Then have the volunteer describe the relative sizes of both objects.

WHAT IF THE STUDENT CAN'T

• Have the student practice comparing the sizes of objects represented in words or pictures until it can be done easily.

Complete the Power Practice
• Discuss each incorrect answer. Have the student identify both objects in the exercise. Ask the student to envision both objects next to one another, and to tell you which is larger and able to hold more liquid.

• If the student is unable to visualize the correct answer, have the student draw both objects as they might appear sitting side by side. Then have the student identify which object is able to hold more liquid.

Activity 81 Lesson Goal

• Identify what a group of shapes has in common.

What the Student Needs to Know

• Identify sides and angles.

Getting Started

First find out what students know about a shape's sides and angles. Draw a square on the board. Point out the square's four sides. Point out the square's angle. Have students count with you the square's four angles.

Now draw a rectangle. Point out to students that both the rectangle and the square have four sides and four angles.

Draw a triangle on the board. Ask students to explain how the triangle is different from the square and the rectangle. (The triangle has three sides and three angles.)

Now draw a circle on the board. Ask students to explain how the circle is different from the other shapes they've explored. (The circle has no sides or angles)

What Can I Do?

Read the first example. Then ask: *Why are the shapes alike?* (They all have four sides and four angles)

Read the second example. Then ask: *Why are these shapes alike?* (They all have 3 sides and 3 angles)

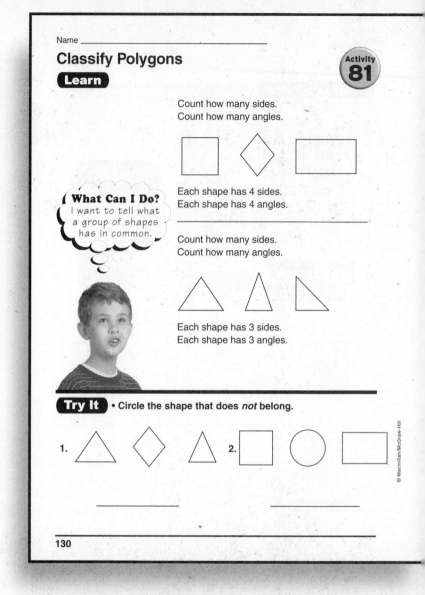

Name _____

Classify Polygons

Learn

Count how many sides.
Count how many angles.

Each shape has 4 sides.
Each shape has 4 angles.

What Can I Do?
I want to tell what a group of shapes has in common.

Count how many sides.
Count how many angles.

Each shape has 3 sides.
Each shape has 3 angles.

Try It • Circle the shape that does *not* belong.

1.

2.

_____   _____

130

© Macmillan/McGraw-Hill

WHAT IF THE STUDENT CAN'T

Draw a Picture

• Have students listen as you give them instructions to draw a shape. Say, "The shape has 3 sides and 3 angles." Review students' drawings. Encourage students to draw another shape that also has 3 sides and 3 angles.

• Have students work in pairs, taking turns giving each other instructions to draw their shapes.

Sort Shapes

• Prepare various shapes having 3–8 sides and a few circles and ovals. Have students explore the shapes. Ask them to sort the shapes into groups that have the same number of sides and angles. Ask them to also put aside any shapes that do not belong.

• Have students work with a partner. Students take turns making groups of three shapes with two like shapes and one shape that does not belong in the group. The partner then identifies the shape that does not belong in the group.

Name _____

3.

4.

5.

6.

© Macmillan/McGraw-Hill

131

WHAT IF THE STUDENT CAN'T

Complete the Power Practice

- Discuss each incorrect answer. For each group of shapes have the student count and write down the number of sides and angles of each shape. Then have them cross out the shape that does not match the number of sides and angles of the other shapes in the group.

- Remind students that circles have no sides or angles.

Try It

Have students look at Exercise 1. Ask:
Which of these shapes does not belong? (the square) *Why not?* (It has 4 sides and 4 angles and the other shapes have 3 sides and 3 angles)

Have students complete Exercise 2. Have volunteers explain why the shape does not belong in the group.

Complete the Power Practice

Discuss each incorrect answer. For each group of shapes have the student count and write down the number of sides and angles of each shape. Then have them cross out the shape that does not match the number of sides and angles of the other shapes in the group.
Remind students that circles have no sides or angles.

Power Practice

- Have students complete the practice exercises. Review each answer.

- Select several of the exercises. Have volunteers explain why the shape does not belong.

Measurement and Geometry Skill Builder **T131**

Activity 82 Lesson Goal
- Identify the number of sides and angles of a figure.

What the Student Needs to Know
- Identify a *line segment*.
- Identify an *angle*.

Getting Started
Find out whether students can recognize the sides and angles in a closed plane figure. Draw a triangle on the board. Ask:
- *How many sides does this figure have?* (3)
- *How many corners does this figure have?* (3)

What Can I Do?
- Read the question and the response. Then read and discuss the example. Be sure students understand that "angle" is the word used in mathematics for a corner. Ask:
- *Is the number of sides the same as the number of angles?* (Yes)
- *Do you have to know the name of the figure to tell how many sides and angles it has?* (No)

Name_____

Identify Sides and Angles

Learn

What Can I Do?
I want to tell the number of sides and angles of a figure.

Use counting.

Count the number of sides of the figure. A side is a straight line segment.

Count the number of angles. An angle is formed where two line segments meet.

This figure has 6 sides and 6 angles.

Try It · Continue numbering sides and angles.
Write the number of sides and angles for each figure.

1.
_____ sides

_____ angles

2.
_____ sides

_____ angles

© Macmillan/McGraw-Hill

132

WHAT IF THE STUDENT CAN'T

Identify a *Line Segment*
- Explain that a line segment is part of a straight line. On the board, illustrate that a line segment can stand on its own, or it can join with other line segments to form a closed figure.
- Be sure that the student understands that a line segment must be straight, and that a curved line is not a line segment.
- Have the student use a ruler to practice drawing closed figures with line segments.

Identify an *Angle*
- Explain that an angle is formed where the ends of two line segments meet. Draw several examples of line segments that meet to form different-sized angles.
- Then draw several closed figures, such as triangles, rectangles, and parallelograms. Ask students to identify the points at which the sides meet to form an angle.

Name_____

3.

_____ sides

_____ angles

4.

_____ sides

_____ angles

5.

_____ sides

_____ angles

6.

_____ sides

_____ angles

7.

_____ sides

_____ angles

8.

_____ sides

_____ angles

9.

_____ sides

_____ angles

10.

_____ sides

_____ angles

11.

_____ sides

_____ angles

12.

_____ sides

_____ angles

13.

_____ sides

_____ angles

14.

_____ sides

_____ angles

© Macmillan/McGraw-Hill

133

Try It

Have students look at Exercise 1. Ask:

- *How many sides does the figure have?* (4)
- *How many angles does it have?* (4)

Then have students complete Exercise 2.

Power Practice

- Have students complete the practice items. Then review each answer. Students should discover that the number of sides in a figure will always be the same as the number of angles.

WHAT IF THE STUDENT CAN'T

Complete the Power Practice

- Discuss each incorrect answer. Have the student number each side of the figure. Then have the student predict the number of angles in the figure before numbering them. Then have the student identify the correct answer.

Activity 83 Lesson Goal
• Compare the size of angles.

What the Student Needs to Know
• Recognize an angle.
• Use the > and < signs.

Getting Started
Find out what students know about comparing. Write the following problem on the board:

32 ◯ 67

Ask:
• *Which of these two numbers is greater?* (67)
• *Which sign should go in the blank?* (the "is less than" sign, or <)

Then write the following problem on the board.

93 ◯ 74

Ask:
• *What should go in the blank?* (the "is greater than" sign, or >)

What Can I Do?
Read the question and the response. Then read and discuss the example. Explain that, just as you can compare two numbers, you can compare two angles. Ask:
• *How can you compare angle A and angle B using the "less than" sign?* (angle A < angle B)

Draw the following angles on the board:

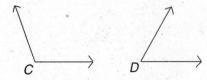

• *Which angle has the greater opening, angle C or angle D?* (angle C)
• *How would you use a symbol to show the relationship between the two angles?* (angle C > angle D; angle D < angle C)

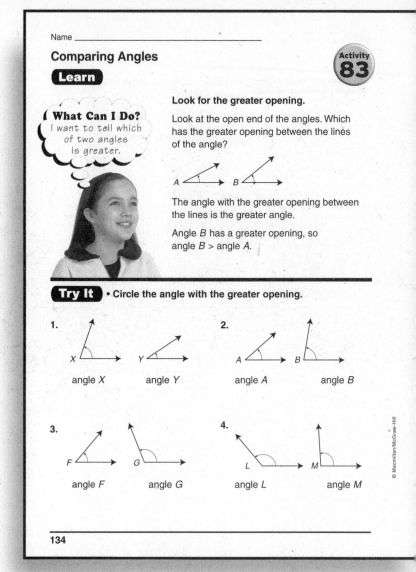

Name _____

Comparing Angles

Learn

What Can I Do?
I want to tell which of two angles is greater.

Look for the greater opening.
Look at the open end of the angles. Which has the greater opening between the lines of the angle?

A ——→   B ——→

The angle with the greater opening between the lines is the greater angle.

Angle B has a greater opening, so angle B > angle A.

Try It • Circle the angle with the greater opening.

1.
angle X   angle Y

2.
angle A   angle B

3.
angle F   angle G

4.
angle L   angle M

134

© Macmillan/McGraw-Hill

WHAT IF THE STUDENT CAN'T

Recognize an Angle
• Explain that an angle is created where two lines or line segments meet. Illustrate how the size of the angle depends on the directions in which the lines run. Show several examples of angles on the board, such as a 20° angle, a 60° angle, a 90° angle, and a 100° angle. Have the student tell you which angle has the smallest opening and which has the greatest.

• Have the student use a ruler to practice drawing angles until the concept becomes clear.

Use the > and < Signs
• Explain that these signs are used to compare two numbers or figures. In a comparison like 9 > 2, the > sign means that 9 is greater than 2. The comparison can also be written 2 < 9, where the < sign means that 2 is less than 9.

Name _____

Compare each pair of angles. Circle the angle with the greater opening. Write > or <.

5.

angle P ◯ angle Q

6.

angle S ◯ angle T

Power Practice • Compare each set of angles. Write > or <.

7.

angle J ◯ angle K

8.

angle C ◯ angle D

9.

angle A ◯ angle B

10.

angle N ◯ angle O

11.

angle R ◯ angle S

12.

angle V ◯ angle W

© Macmillan/McGraw-Hill

135

WHAT IF THE STUDENT CAN'T

- If the student has difficulty writing the signs correctly, mention that the opening in the sign should point to the greater of the two numbers or figures. For example, angle F in Try It is less than angle G. So the open end of the sign will face angle G, and the comparison will either read angle G > angle F or angle F < angle G.

- Have the student practice using the < and > signs to compare single-digit numbers until the concept becomes clear.

Complete the Power Practice

- Discuss each incorrect answer. Have the student look at each angle in the exercise, and identify which has a greater opening. Then have the student use the > and < signs to write two comparisons of the angles.

Try It
Have students complete Exercises 1–4. Ask:

- *Which of the four angles appears to have the greatest opening?* (angle G)

- *Which of the four angles appears to have the smallest opening?* (angle Y)

Power Practice

- Be sure students understand how to use the > and < signs. Have them complete the practice exercises. Then review each answer.

Activity 84 Lesson Goal

- Measure line segments to the nearest half-inch.

What the Student Needs to Know

- Read a ruler.
- Round a measurement to the nearest half-inch.

Getting Started

Find out how familiar students are with using rulers. Ask:

- *What does each number on an inch ruler stand for?* (the number of inches from 0 at the left of the ruler to that point on the ruler.)
- *How do you use a ruler to measure an object?* (Possible answer: You line up one end of the object with the beginning of the ruler. Then you check to see the measure on the ruler at the point where the end of the object is.)
- *What are the little marks on the ruler for?* (They mark $\frac{1}{2}$-inches, $\frac{1}{4}$-inches, $\frac{1}{8}$-inches, and $\frac{1}{16}$-inches on the ruler.)

What Can I Do?

Read the question and the response. Then read and discuss the example. Ask:

- *If you don't line up the left end of the line segment with the edge of the ruler, will your measurement still be correct?* (No.) *Why or why not?* (The measurement won't start from zero.)
- *Why was the measurement rounded to $2\frac{1}{2}$ inches instead of 2 inches?* (Because it was only $\frac{1}{8}$ of an inch to $2\frac{1}{2}$ inches, but $\frac{3}{8}$ of an inch to 2 inches.)

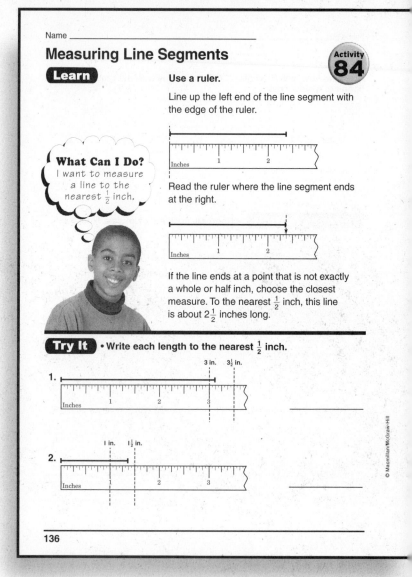

Name _____

Measuring Line Segments

Learn

Activity 84

Use a ruler.

Line up the left end of the line segment with the edge of the ruler.

What Can I Do?
I want to measure a line to the nearest $\frac{1}{2}$ inch.

Read the ruler where the line segment ends at the right.

If the line ends at a point that is not exactly a whole or half inch, choose the closest measure. To the nearest $\frac{1}{2}$ inch, this line is about $2\frac{1}{2}$ inches long.

Try It • Write each length to the nearest $\frac{1}{2}$ inch.

1.   3 in. $3\frac{1}{2}$ in.

2.   1 in. $1\frac{1}{2}$ in.

136

© Macmillan/McGraw-Hill

WHAT IF THE STUDENT CAN'T

Read a Ruler

- Draw a simplified ruler, using the numbers 1 through 5. Explain to the student that each of the large marks next to the numbers represents 1 inch. Then add half-inch marks to the ruler. Explain to the student that even though the half-inch marks don't have a number next to them, you can tell what they represent by going back to the last number and adding $\frac{1}{2}$.

- Have the student look at a ruler and identify the inch marks and half-inch marks. Then give the student several line segments to measure. Be sure that each line segment ends exactly at an inch or half-inch mark.

Round a Measurement to the Nearest Half-inch

- Have the student use a ruler to count from 0 inches to 10 inches by $\frac{1}{2}$s (0, $\frac{1}{2}$, 1, $1\frac{1}{2}$ ...). Explain that when you round a measurement to the nearest half-inch, you can round it to any number that you can reach by counting by $\frac{1}{2}$s.

Name _____

Power Practice
Use an inch ruler. Measure the length of each line segment to the nearest $\frac{1}{2}$ inch.

3. |————————————————| _____

4. |————————————————————| _____

5. |————————————————| _____

6. |——————————| _____

7. |————| _____

8. |——————————————| _____

9. |————————————————| _____

10. |——————————————| _____

11. |————————| _____

137

© Macmillan/McGraw-Hill

Try It

Have students look at Exercises 1 and 2. Be sure that they are able to distinguish between an inch mark and a half-inch mark on the rulers. Ask:

• *How can you use the smaller marks between the inch mark and the half-inch mark to round to the nearest measure?* (Possible answer: Find the mark where the segment ends. Then count the small marks back to the previous inch and forward to the next inch. Compare to see which inch is closer to the end of the segment. Round up or down to that inch.)

Then have students complete the exercises.

Power Practice

• Have the students complete the practice items. Then review each answer.

WHAT IF THE STUDENT CAN'T

• Have the student measure a line segment that measures somewhere between $3\frac{1}{2}$ and 4 inches. Explain that when a measurement doesn't come out exactly at an inch or half-inch mark, you can round the measurement to the nearest half-inch. Mention that if you can't tell which is closer just by looking, you can use the smaller marks on the ruler to count which is closer. Then have the student round the measurement of the line segment to the closest measure.

Complete the Power Practice

• Discuss each incorrect answer. Have the student carefully line up the edge of the ruler with the left end of the line segment. Then have the student measure the segment, using a piece of tape to mark the end of the segment on the ruler. The student should then round to the nearest measure to arrive at the correct answer.

Measurement and Geometry Skill Builder **T137**

Activity 85 Lesson Goal
- Identify equal and unequal fractional parts.

What the Student Needs to Know
- Compare shapes.
- Compare sizes.
- Understand the terms *equal* and *not equal*.

Getting Started
Draw a square on the board. Tell students that it shows a sandwich. *Suppose you were sharing this sandwich with a friend. How could you cut it into two equal parts?* (Students might describe cutting it in half with a horizontal or vertical line or cutting it in half with a diagonal line.)

- To review the terms *equal* and *not equal*, ask: *What does it mean if two numbers are equal?* (They are the same amount.) *Write 2 and 2 on the chalkboard. Are these numbers equal?* (Yes) *Erase one 2 and change it to a 6. Are these numbers equal?* (No)

- *Draw two squares that are the same size. Are these squares equal?* (Yes) *How do you know?* (They are the same size and shape.) *Erase one and draw another square that is much larger or smaller. Are these squares equal?* (No) *Why not?* (They are not the same size.)

What Can I Do?
- Read the question and the response. Then review the examples with the students.

Have students look at the circle on the left. Ask: *How many parts are in the circle?* (3) *Are they all the same size and shape?* (No) *Are the three parts equal?* (No)

- Next look at the second circle. *Imagine this circle is a pizza four friends are sharing. Are the slices equal?* (Yes) *Is this a fair way to share the pizza for 4 people?* (Yes)

Name _____

Identify Equal Parts

Learn

What Can I Do?
How can I tell if the parts are equal?

Compare sizes of the parts.

Which circle shows equal parts?

Look at the first circle. The three parts do not have the same shape and size. They are not equal.

Look at the second circle. The four parts have the same shape and size. They are equal.

The second circle shows equal parts.

Use a mental picture.

Does this square show equal parts?

Think about cutting the square along the lines. You can cut it into these four parts.

Imagine stacking the parts. You can see they have the same size and shape. These four parts are equal.

So, the square shows equal parts.

138

© Macmillan/McGraw-Hill

WHAT IF THE STUDENT CAN'T

Name Equal Shapes
- Review the shapes rectangle, square, and triangle. Remind the student that rectangles can look very different from one another. Draw three or four different rectangles, very wide or very tall. Help the student recognize that they are all rectangles, but they are not equal. Then draw two equal rectangles. Repeat with squares and triangles.

Compare Sizes
- Have the student use construction paper and safety scissors to model the drawings shown in the exercises. Remind the student that the models may not be exactly the same as the drawings, but can help in finding an answer. Demonstrate by copying Exercise 5 on paper and cutting it out. Show that the three rectangles are not the same size. They do not form an equal stack. The parts shown are not equal.

Name _____

Try It • Tell whether or not each rectangle shows equal parts. Write *equal* or *not equal*. Use the drawings to help you compare parts.

1.

2.

3.

_____   _____   _____

Power Practice • Tell whether or not each shape shows equal parts. Write *equal* or *not equal*.

4.   5.   6.   7.

8.   9.   10.   11.

12.   13.   14.   15.

16.   17.   18.   19.

© Macmillan/McGraw-Hill

139

WHAT IF THE STUDENT CAN'T

Use the Terms *Equal* and *Not Equal*
• Allow partners to practice the words *equal* and *not equal* in a brief activity. First, have students create note cards that read *equal* and *not equal*. To begin, one student writes a number or draws a shape. The other student mixes up the two note cards and draws one. If the card says equal, the student writes an equal number or draws an equal shape. If the cards says not equal, the student writes a number or draws a shape that is not equal.

Complete the Power Practice
• Discuss each incorrect answer. Have the student count the number of parts shown and talk about their sizes and shapes.

• Draw students' attention to the divided square. Ask: *What is a mental picture?* (a picture in your mind) *How does thinking of cutting this square help you decide if the pieces are equal?* (Answers will vary.)

• Students might practice identifying equal parts by copying drawings from the lesson, cutting the parts, and trying to stack them, as shown in "Use a Mental Picture."

Try It
• For Exercises 1–3, have students tell how many parts are in each drawing. Then have them compare the sizes and shapes of the parts to see if they are equal.

• Encourage students to use the drawings showing the parts separated. Ask: *In Exercise 1, what do the two drawings show?* (The first drawing shows a rectangle divided by a line; the second drawing shows the two parts separated.) *Are the two parts the same size and shape?* (No) *What is the answer for Exercise 1?* (not equal)

Power Practice
• You may wish to allow partners to work together to solve Exercises 4–19. Suggest that students start each exercise by counting the number of parts. Then have them look at each part to see whether or not they are equal.

• When students find a shape that shows equal parts, have students describe both the shape and the part.

• After students have finished the exercises, ask these questions to help them review their work: *Which drawing shows a rectangle divided into equal squares?* (15) *Which drawing shows a rectangle divided into equal triangles?* (13)

Activity 86 Lesson Goal
- Read a tally chart.

What the Student Needs to Know
- Count on from a given number.
- Count by 5s.

Getting Started
Write on the board tally marks showing the number of students in the group. Ask:

- *How many marks did I make for each student?* (1) *What did I draw to show 5 students?* (4 tally marks with 1 tally mark across them)

- *How many students are in our group?* (Answers will vary.)

What Can I Do?
Read the question and the response. Then read and discuss the example. Ask:

- *What does the chart show?* (numbers of oranges and pears in a box) *How many tally marks are next to the word oranges?* (8)

- *How can you tell there are 8 tally marks?* (There are 5 marks in one group and 3 marks in another group.)

- *Why should we start with 5 when we count the marks?* (to add the group of 3 to the group of 5)

Try It
Have students describe their thinking. To prompt them, ask:

- *For Exercise 2, how can you count on to find the answer?* (Begin at 5, and count 2 more: 6, 7 — there are 7 tally marks.)

- *For Exercise 3, what is the quickest way to count the tally marks?* (Count by 5s: 5, 10, 15.)

Power Practice
- Have the student complete the practice items. Then review each answer.

Name _____

Tally Marks and Charts

Learn Count the tallies.

What Can I Do? I want to read a tally chart.

Fruit in a Box	
Oranges	ЖЖ |||
Pears	ЖЖ ЖЖ	

How many oranges are in the box?

Count the tally marks for oranges.

| = a count of 1

ЖЖ = a count of 5

Count 5, 6, 7, 8.

So, there are 8 oranges in the box.

Try It • Write each number.

1. |||| _____   2. ЖЖ || _____   3. ЖЖ ЖЖ ЖЖ _____

Power Practice • Use the tally chart.

Mr. Quintero's Class	
boys	ЖЖ ЖЖ ||||
girls	ЖЖ ЖЖ

4. How many boys are in the class? _____

5. How many girls are in the class? _____

6. How many total students are in the class? _____

140

© Macmillan/McGraw-Hill

WHAT IF THE STUDENT CAN'T

Count on from a Given Number
- Have the student use a number line to practice counting on from 5 or 10. For example, draw on the board tally marks showing 8. Say:

- *Place your finger on 5. How many times will you need to jump to the right to find the number of tally marks?* (3 times)

- Have the student count aloud as he or she jumps a finger 3 numbers to the right: *6, 7, 8.* Then ask: *what number do the tally marks show?* (8)

- Repeat with numbers shown with tally marks such as 9, 12 (count on from 10), and 17 (count on from 15).

Count by 5s
- Use a number line from 0 to 60. Have the student practice jumping his or her finger from 0 to 5 to 10 to 15, and so on, counting aloud by fives: "five, ten, fifteen, twenty," and so on. Repeat a few times a day until the student can count by fives with ease.

Complete the Power Practice
- Discuss each incorrect answer. Have the student model any exercise he or she missed using loose connecting cubes and 5-cube trains.

Read Pictographs

Learn

Activity **87**

What Can I Do?

I want to compare information in a pictograph.

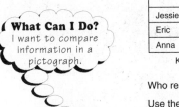

Use the key and count the symbols.

Books Read	
Jessie	📕📕📕
Eric	📕📕
Anna	📕📕📕📕📕

Key: 📕 = 3 books

Who read the most books?

Use the key to find how many books each student read.

Jessie: 3 + 3 + 3 = 9 books

Eric: 3 + 3 = 6 books

Anna: 3 + 3 + 3 + 3 + 3 = 15 books

15 books > 9 books > 6 books

So, Anna read the most books.

Try It • Use the pictograph above.

1. Who read the least number of books? _____

2. How many more books did Anna read than Jessie? _____

3. How many books did Eric and Anna read? _____

4. How many books did the students read in all? _____

141

WHAT IF THE STUDENT CAN'T

Connect Symbols with Numerical Values

• Talk with the student about the words "stands for." For example, if you were making a pictograph showing favorite kinds of fruit, you could use red sticky dots to stand for apples, orange sticky dots to stand for oranges, and yellow sticky dots to stand for bananas.

• Have the student use attribute blocks to invent symbols for various objects. For example, a group of red squares might stand for the number of red cars in a parking lot.

Understand Information Presented in Chart Form

• Talk with the student about the charts shown in the lesson. Ask what each shows, and point out its title.

• Make sure the student understands that a "Key" shows what symbols stand for.

• Have the student point to the symbols that stand for the number of books Jessie read and the number of pink roses in Mr. Finch's flower shop. Make sure he or she knows that the symbols appear in the same row as the words that tell what they stand for.

Activity 87 Lesson Goal

• Compare information in a pictograph.

What the Student Needs to Know

• Connect symbols with numerical values.

• Understand information presented in chart form.

• Compare, add, and subtract numbers from 2 to 11.

Getting Started

Create on the board a simple pictograph showing favorite ice-cream flavors of students in the group. Your chart should resemble the ones in the lesson. Include one row for each ice-cream flavor; draw 1 small ice-cream cone for each student who prefers that flavor. Ask:

• *What does this chart show?* (our favorite ice-cream flavors) *What does each ice-cream cone stand for?* (1 student) *How many students like chocolate ice cream best?* (Answers will vary.)

What Can I Do?

Read the question and the response. Then read and discuss the examples. Ask:

• *What does this chart show?* (how many books Jessie, Eric, and Anna read) *What does the Key show?* (that each 📕 stands for 3 books)

• *How many books did Eric read?* (6) *How many did Jessie read?* (19) *How about Anna?* (She read 15.) *So who read the greatest number?* (Anna)

Try It

Have students explain their thinking. To prompt them, ask:

• *What is the quickest way to answer Question 1?* (Look quickly at the chart. The line of books next to Eric's name is shortest.)

• *What do you need to do to answer Question 2?* (Count the number of books next to Anna's and Jessie's names. Subtract 5 – 3.)

Activity 88 Lesson Goal

- Compare information in a bar graph.

What the Student Needs to Know

- Understand information presented on a bar graph.
- Compare numbers shown on a bar graph.
- Compare, add, and subtract numbers from 1 to 7.

Getting Started

Create on the board a simple bar graph showing kinds of pets owned by students' families. Your bar graph should resemble the ones in the lesson. Include one bar for each type of pet. Ask:

- *What does this bar graph show?* (kinds of pets we own; how many of each kind we own) *What do the words on the side tell?* (kinds of pets) *What do the numbers on the bottom tell?* (numbers of each type) *How many dogs do we own?* (Answers will vary.)
- Ask other questions as appropriate.

What Can I Do?

Read the question and the response. Then read and discuss the example. Ask:

- *What does this bar graph show?* (favorite colors of Kate's friends) *What colors are shown in the graph?* (red, blue, and yellow)
- *What is the greatest number of friends who have the same favorite color?* (5) *What is the smallest number who like a certain color best?* (1)
- *How many friends like yellow best?* (2) *How can you tell?* (The bar for yellow reaches to the 2.)

Name_____

Read Bar Graphs

Learn

What Can I Do?
I want to compare information.

Read a bar graph.

How many of the friends chose yellow as their favorite color?

Favorite Colors of Kate's Friends

Color: red, blue, yellow
Number of Friends: 0 1 2 3 4 5

Look at the bar for yellow.
The bar ends at 2.
So, 2 friends chose yellow.

Try It • Use the bar graph above.

1. How many friends chose red? _____

2. How many friends chose blue? _____

3. Does the graph show that the friends liked

   blue or yellow better? _____

4. How many more friends chose blue than

   chose yellow? _____

5. Which color do the friends like least? _____

6. How many more friends chose yellow than red? _____

142

© Macmillan/McGraw-Hill

Activity 88

WHAT IF THE STUDENT CAN'T

Understand Information Presented on a Bar Graph

- Talk with the student about the bar graphs shown in the lesson. Ask what each shows, and point out its title.
- Have the student point to the bars that stand for the number of friends who like red best and the number of students who like crackers best.

Compare Numbers Shown on a Bar Graph

- Make sure the student knows that a bar graph is a good way to compare amounts. Point out that you can see which is the longest and shortest bar without even looking at the numbers on the bottom of the graph.
- Work with the student to create his or her own bar graph comparing hair colors of students in the group or class. Show the student how to use the numbers at the bottom of the graph to create each bar.

Name_____

Favorite Snacks of Justin's Class

Snack: fruit, crackers, popcorn

Number of Students: 0 1 2 3 4 5 6 7 8

7. What is the title of the bar graph? _____

_____

8. Which snack is the class favorite? _____

9. How many students chose fruit as their

favorite snack?_____

10. How many more students like popcorn better than

crackers? _____

11. How many students voted in all? _____

12. Which was the least favorite snack? _____

13. How many more students voted for
popcorn over fruit? _____

© Macmillan/McGraw-Hill

Try It

Have students explain their thinking. To prompt them, ask:

- *What is the quickest way to answer Question 3?* (Look quickly at the graph. The bar for blue is much longer than the one for yellow.)
- *What is another way to answer Question 3?* (The blue bar reaches to 5; the yellow one reaches to 2; 5 is greater than 2.)
- *What is the quickest way to answer Question 5?* (Look quickly at the bar graph. The shortest bar is the one for red.)

Power Practice

- Select several of the exercises and have volunteers describe what they did to answer the questions. To prompt them, ask:
- *Which is the longest bar?* (the one for popcorn) *Which is the shortest bar?* (the one for crackers)
- *How can you find the answer to Question 10 without subtracting?* (count on from 3 to 7)
- *For Question 11, what addition sentence do you need to complete?* $(6 + 3 + 7 = 16)$

WHAT IF THE STUDENT CAN'T

Compare, Add, and Subtract Numbers from 1 to 7

- Have the student compare on a number line pairs of numbers from 1 to 7. Ask him or her to tell which number is greater and which is smaller.
- Students might practice simple addition and subtraction sentences using a number line, counters, and/or mental math. Practice completing sentences such as $2 + 3$; $7 - 5$; $2 + 3 + 1$; and so on until students can do so with ease.

Complete the Power Practice

- Discuss each incorrect answer. Have the student model any exercise he or she answered incorrectly using connecting cubes to stand for the bars shown in the graphs.

Data Collecting and Probability Skill Builder **T143**

USING THE LESSON

Activity 89 Lesson Goal
- Create and read tally charts.

What the Student Needs to Know
- Mark tallies in groups of five.
- Read chart labels.
- Compare quantities in charts.

Getting Started
- Ask the class a question, such as: *How many of you have a cat at home?* or *How many of you are wearing blue today?* Count raised hands and mark a tally for each student. Mark each fifth tally as a slanting horizontal line over four vertical lines.
- After tallying the answer, count the number of tallies. Demonstrate how you can use skip counting to count groups of fives.

What Can I Do?
- Read the question and the response. Then read and discuss the example. Ask: *What do the numbers in the box show?* (test scores for one class) *What does the tally chart show?* (How many of the scores are below 80, between 80 and 90, and above 90.) *If there was one more test score and it was 73, where would you mark a tally?* (under Below 80)
- *How does the tally chart help you compare the test scores?* (Answers include the fact that the tally chart groups test scores together; students may find it less confusing than the large list of numbers.)
- *How does skip counting help you count tallies?* (You can skip count by fives and then count on to find the total.) *How would you write tallies for the number 28?* (You would mark five groups of five and three ones.) *If a chart shows 6 groups of 5 and 2 ones, what is the number shown?* (32)

Name _____

Frequency Tables

Learn

Make a Tally Chart
This box shows the test scores for one class.

| 87 | 76 | 91 | 92 | 95 | 87 | 96 | 68 | 87 | 89 | 97 | 76 | 69 | 70 |
| 82 | 93 | 65 | 91 | 80 | 79 | 86 | 75 | 82 | 95 | 90 | 91 | 89 | 82 |

Are more test scores below 80 or above 90?

What Can I Do? I want to organize a lot of information.

Use a chart to keep track. Add one tally mark for each test score. Cross off the scores you have tallied.

Below 80	80 to 90	Above 90
卌 |||	卌 卌		卌 ||||

Count and compare to answer the question. There are 8 scores below 80 and 9 scores above 90.

There are more test scores above 90.

Try It Complete the tally chart to count the marbles. The white marbles are already tallied and crossed off.

White	Black	Dots	Stripes
卌 卌 ||||	1.	2.	3.

144

WHAT IF THE STUDENT CAN'T

Mark Tallies Consistently
- Have students practice writing tallies with a partner. Students can count books on a bookshelf, windows in a classroom, or groups of manipulatives. Reinforce the fact that every fifth line goes diagonally across four vertical tallies.
- Allow students to practice writing tallies for any number and then have a partner count the number of tallies. Partners should check to make sure that each group of tallies contains five lines.

Read Chart Labels
- Review the importance of reading chart labels by reproducing one of the lesson charts on the board, but without the labels. Point out that without labels, you do not know what the information in the chart means. Add the labels and have the student explain how these help in reading the information in the chart.

T144 Grade 3, Activity 89

Name _____

Use the tally chart to answer these questions.

4. How many white marbles are there? _____

5. How many black marbles are there? _____

6. How many marbles with dots are there? _____

7. How many marbles with stripes are there? _____

8. Arrange the marble patterns in order from fewest to most.

_____ _____ _____ _____

Power Practice • Complete the tally chart. Then answer the questions.

This box shows the average temperatures for one month.

72° 71° 68° 75° 65° 68° 72° 77° 78° 80° 82° 81° 81° 79° 78°
75° 72° 69° 68° 70° 71° 74° 76° 80° 81° 82° 71° 69° 74° 73°

60° to 69°	70° to 79°	80° to 89°
9. ⣿⣿	10. ⣿⣿⣿⣿ ⣿⣿	11. ⣿⣿

12. For how many days was the average temperature between 60° and 69°? _____

13. For how many days was the average temperature between 70° and 79°? _____

14. For how many days was the average temperature between 80° and 89°? _____

145

Try It
- Exercises 1-3 help students practice marking tallies and using tallies to keep track. Encourage students to use an organized method so that they do not count any marbles twice and do not leave any out. Suggest that they count one color at a time. First cross off a marble and then add a tally in the correct chart box. Repeat until all marbles are crossed off.

Power Practice
- Have students follow an organized method to complete the tally chart for Exercises 9-14. Encourage them to cross off a number and then mark a tally in the correct chart box. Have volunteers answer the questions in Exercises 12-14 aloud.

WHAT IF THE STUDENT CAN'T

Compare Quantities in Charts
- Point out that the student can use tallies to compare amounts. Help the student recognize why the tally for 8 is clearly greater than the tally for 6. Even without doing an exact count, you can see that one number is greater.

Complete the Power Practice
- As the student completes the exercises, encourage him or her to decide whether or not an exact count is needed to answer the question. For example, in Exercise 13, the student will probably be able to find the highest tally in the chart without counting.

Skill Builder
Blackline Masters

Name _____

Order Numbers

Learn

Use a number line.

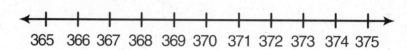

365 366 367 368 369 370 371 372 373 374 375

What Can I Do?
I want to find which numbers come before, after, and between other numbers.

What number comes just **before** 367?

Find 367 on the number line.

Go back 1.

366 comes just **before** 367.

What number comes just **after** 372?

Find 372 on the number line.

Go forward 1.

373 comes just **after** 372.

What number comes **between** 369 and 371?

Find 369 and 371 on the number line.
Find the number that comes just before 371 and just after 369.

370 comes **between** 369 and 371.

Try It • Use the number line to answer each question.

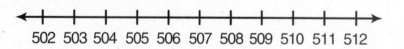

502 503 504 505 506 507 508 509 510 511 512

1. What number comes just *before* 512? _____

2. What number comes just *after* 509? _____

3. What number comes *between* 504 and 506? _____

Name _____

• Write the number that comes just *before*. You may draw a number line to help.

4. _____ 14   **5.** _____ 27   **6.** _____ 60

7. _____ 95   **8.** _____ 132   **9.** _____ 418

10. _____ 521   **11.** _____ 789   **12.** _____ 656

Write the number that comes just *after*. You may draw a number line to help.

13. 17 _____   **14.** 55 _____

15. 113 _____   **16.** 309 _____

17. 667 _____   **18.** 800 _____

Write the number that comes *between*. You may draw a number line to help.

19. 4 _____ 6   **20.** 28 _____ 30

21. 99 _____ 101   **22.** 310 _____ 312

23. 492 _____ 494   **24.** 944 _____ 946

Learn with Partners & Parents

I Spy a Number

• Take turns. One player spies a three-digit number in a store, on a license plate, or on a sign. The player must say, "I spy the number _____," and read the number aloud.

• The second player earns 1 point for telling the number that comes just *before* and another point for telling the number that comes just *after* the spied number.

• Write down all the numbers. The first player to get 25 points is the winner.

Ordering Whole Numbers

Learn

What Can I Do?
I want to order whole numbers from greatest to least.

Use place value.

Look for the greatest number in each place. Start at the left.

hundreds	tens	ones
1	7	5
	9	8
3	5	2
	3	4

↑

Look at the hundreds place. Two numbers have no hundreds. Since 3 is greater than 1, that number is the greatest.

352, 175, _____, _____

Then look at the tens of the other numbers.

↓

hundreds	tens	ones
✓ 1	7̸	5
	9	8
✓ 3	5̸	2
	3	4

Since 9 is greater than 3, that number is next.

352, 175, 98, 34

Try It • Use place value. Order from *greatest* to *least*.

1. 65, 28, 76, 82, 13 _____

2. 116, 193, 127, 188, 100 _____

Power Practice • Order from *greatest* to *least*.

3. 73, 88, 79, 94, 65 _____

4. 315, 195, 327, 255, 97 _____

5. 56, 38, 60, 154, 75 _____

6. 465, 856, 246, 365, 754 _____

7. 38, 47, 42, 29, 37 _____

8. 118, 87, 93, 104, 90 _____

9. 159, 167, 219, 178, 146 _____

10. 68, 73, 69, 61, 75 _____

Name _____

Round to the Nearest Ten

Use a number line.

Find the ten that 12 is closer to.

Circle 12 on the number line.

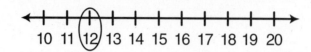

10 11 12 13 14 15 16 17 18 19 20

The number 12 is between two tens on the number line. It is between 10 and 20.

Count the number of spaces from 10 to 12. There are 2 spaces.

Count the number of spaces from 12 to 20. There are 8 spaces.

So, 12 is closer to 10.

What Can I Do?
I want to find the closest ten.

Find the ten that 27 is closer to.

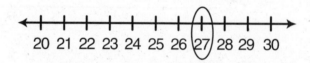

20 21 22 23 24 25 26 27 28 29 30

The number 27 is between the tens 20 and 30.

It is 7 spaces away from 20. It is 3 spaces away from 30.

So, 27 is closer to 30.

Try It • **Choose the closer ten. Circle _a_ or _b_.**

1. Which ten is closer to 19?

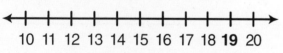

10 11 12 13 14 15 16 17 18 **19** 20

a. 10   **b.** 20

2. Which ten is closer to 43?

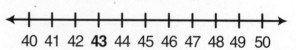

40 41 42 **43** 44 45 46 47 48 49 50

a. 40   **b.** 50

6

Choose the closer ten. Circle *a* or *b*.

3. Which ten is closer to 21?

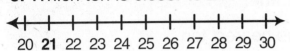

    a. 20   **b.** 30

4. Which ten is closer to 64?

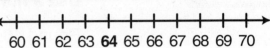

    a. 60   **b.** 70

5. Which ten is closer to 58?

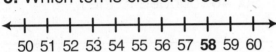

    a. 50   **b.** 60

6. Which ten is closer to 86?

    a. 80   **b.** 90

Power Practice • **Choose the closer ten. Circle *a* or *b*. You may draw a number line to help.**

7. 11

  a. 10   **b.** 20

8. 37

  a. 30   **b.** 40

9. 26

  a. 20   **b.** 30

10. 53

  a. 50   **b.** 60

11. 22

  a. 20   **b.** 30

12. 79

  a. 70   **b.** 80

13. 88

  a. 80   **b.** 90

14. 74

  a. 70   **b.** 80

15. 62

  a. 60   **b.** 70

Round to Tens, Hundreds, and Thousands

Learn

What Can I Do?
I want to round to the nearest ten, hundred, or thousand.

Use a number line.

Round 46 to the nearest ten.

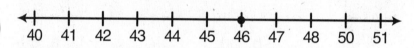

40 41 42 43 44 45 46 47 48 50 51

The number 46 is between 40 and 50. It is closer to 50. So, 46 rounded to the nearest ten is 50.

Round 237 to the nearest hundred.

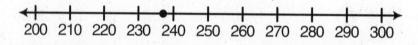

200 210 220 230 240 250 260 270 280 290 300

The number 237 is between 200 and 300. It is closer to 200. So, 237 rounded to the nearest hundred is 200.

Round 3,290 to the nearest thousand without using a number line.

Look at the place to the right of the thousands place.

3,**2**90

If the digit is less than 5, round down.
If the digit is 5 or greater, round up.

2 < 5; so, round 3,290 down to 3,000.

So, 3,290 rounded to the nearest thousand is 3,000.

Try It • **Round to the nearest ten. Use the number line to help.**

1.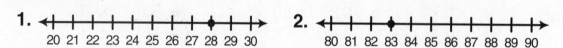
20 21 22 23 24 25 26 27 28 29 30

2.
80 81 82 83 84 85 86 87 88 89 90

28 _____

83 _____

Name_____

Round to the nearest hundred. Use the number line to help.

3.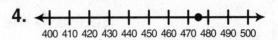
700 710 720 730 740 750 760 770 780 790 800

721 _____

4.
400 410 420 430 440 450 460 470 480 490 500

475 _____

Round to the nearest thousand. Look at the digit to the right of the thousands place to round up or round down.

5. 1,341 _____   **6.** 6,752 _____   **7.** 4,901 _____

Power Practice • **Round to the nearest *ten*.**

8. 12 _____   **9.** 38 _____   **10.** 59 _____

11. 26 _____   **12.** 74 _____   **13.** 63 _____

Round to the nearest *hundred*.

14. 187 _____   **15.** 313 _____   **16.** 578 _____

17. 845 _____   **18.** 529 _____   **19.** 767 _____

Round to the nearest *thousand*.

20. 2,399 _____   **21.** 3,860 _____   **22.** 7,089 _____

23. 8,615 _____   **24.** 5,453 _____   **25.** 6,524 _____

Name_____

Rounding

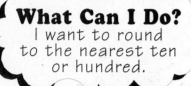
What Can I Do?
I want to round to the nearest ten or hundred.

Round to the given place value.

To round to the nearest **ten,**
use the *ones* digit.

26 rounds to 30.   32 rounds to 30.

To round to the nearest **hundred,**
use the *tens* digit.

257 rounds to 300.   302 rounds to 300.

To round to the nearest **thousand,**
use the *hundreds* digit.

2,901 rounds to 3,000.   3,472 rounds to 3,000.

Try It • Circle the numbers.

1. Circle the numbers that round to 50.

    42 43 44 45 46 47 48 49 50 51 52 53 54 55 56 57 58

2. Circle the numbers that round to 600.

    530 540 550 560 570 580 590 600 610 620 630 640 650 660

Round each number to the nearest *ten*.

3. 76 _____   4. 36 _____   5. 24 _____   6. 57 _____

7. 85 _____   8. 71 _____   9. 91 _____   10. 65 _____

Round each number to the nearest *hundred*.

11. 631 _____   12. 923 _____   13. 349 _____   14. 558 _____

15. 815 _____   16. 128 _____   17. 644 _____   18. 157 _____

© Macmillan/McGraw-Hill

Name_____

Round to the Nearest Ten, Hundred, or Thousand

Learn

What Can I Do?
I want to round to the nearest ten, hundred, or thousand.

Round 6,803 to the nearest thousand.

Step 1
Look at the place to the right of the thousands place.

6,**8**03

Step 2
If the digit is less than 5, round down to 6,000.

If the digit is 5 or greater, round up to 7,000.

8 > 5, so round 6,803 up to 7,000.

So, 6,803 rounded to the nearest thousand is 7,000.

Try It • Round to the nearest ten, hundred, or thousand. Fill in the blanks.

1. Round 29 to the nearest ten.

29 is between _____ and _____.

29 rounds to _____.

2. Round 538 to the nearest hundred.

538 is between _____ and _____.

538 rounds to _____.

Power Practice • Round to the nearest *ten*.

3. 22 _____   **4.** 86 _____   **5.** 45 _____

Round to the nearest *hundred*.

6. 271 _____   **7.** 749 _____   **8.** 615 _____

Round to the nearest *thousand*.

9. 4,672 _____   **10.** 3,333 _____   **11.** 8,501 _____

Name _____

Comparing Numbers

Learn

What Can I Do?
I want to compare two numbers.

Activity **7**

Use a number line.

Which number is greater?

34   43

Find each number on the number line.

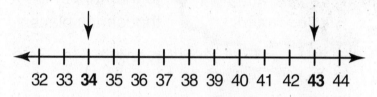

32 33 **34** 35 36 37 38 39 40 41 42 **43** 44

The number to the right on the number line is always the greater number.

43 > 34

Try It . **Use the number line to compare each pair of numbers. Write > or < .**

1.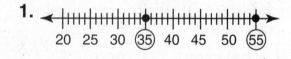

20 25 30 (35) 40 45 50 (55)

35 ◯ 55

2.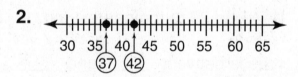

30 35 40 45 50 55 60 65

(37) (42)

42 ◯ 37

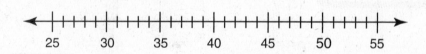

25   30   35   40   45   50   55

3. 41 ◯ 50   **4.** 29 ◯ 39   **5.** 53 ◯ 35

6. 28 ◯ 55   **7.** 47 ◯ 40   **8.** 51 ◯ 52

Name_____

Power Practice
• Use the number lines to compare each pair of numbers. Write > or < .

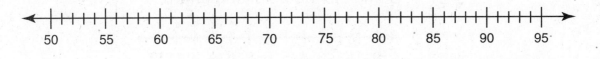

9. 57 ◯ 75   **10.** 66 ◯ 56   **11.** 73 ◯ 83

12. 79 ◯ 59   **13.** 60 ◯ 81   **14.** 77 ◯ 57

15. 82 ◯ 79   **16.** 90 ◯ 59   **17.** 74 ◯ 73

18. 111 ◯ 117

19. 134 ◯ 128

20. 130 ◯ 138

21. 107 ◯ 113

22. 128 ◯ 132

23. 106 ◯ 119

24. 137 ◯ 131

25. 127 ◯ 107

Learn with
Partners & Parents

One More, One Less

Any number of people can play.

• Choose a number from 50 to 59 and write it down. Then look for numbers that are one more than your number and one less than your number. Look in the grocery store, at home, or on license plates and billboards. List where you found the number.

• When you look for numbers, you must find the exact number. If you are looking for 54, then you must find 54. The digits cannot be part of another number, such as 8,542.

• When you find both these numbers, start looking for numbers that are two more and two less than your number. Keep playing until you are looking for zero.

• The person who has found more numbers wins.

© Macmillan/McGraw-Hill

Name _____

Counting On

Learn

Use a number line to count on.

Complete the addition pattern.

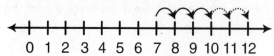

Each number goes up by 1.
Count on by ones. Start at 7.

7, 8, 9, 10, __11__, __12__

Complete the addition pattern.

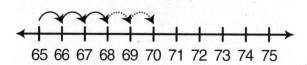

Each number goes up by 1.
Count on by ones. Start at 65.

65, 66, 67, 68, __69__, __70__

What Can I Do?
I want to
complete an
addition pattern.

Try It • Complete each addition pattern.
Use the number line to help.

1.
```
12 13 14 15 16 17 18 19 20 21 22
```

13, 14, 15, 16, _____,_____

2.
```
54 55 56 57 58 59 60 61 62 63 64
```

56, 57, 58, 59, _____,_____

Power Practice • Complete each addition pattern.

3. 2, 3, 4, 5, _____,_____   **4.** 9, 10, 11, 12, _____,_____

5. 38, 39, 40, 41, _____,_____   **6.** 87, 88, 89, 90, _____,_____

7. 110, 111, 112, 113, _____,_____   **8.** 525, 526, 527, 528, _____,_____

Name _____

Skip Counting

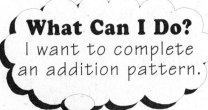

Activity
9

Use a number line to skip count.

Complete the addition pattern.

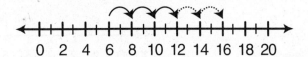

0 2 4 6 8 10 12 14 16 18 20

Skip count by 2s. Start at 6.
6, 8, 10, 12, __14__, __16__

Complete the addition pattern.
Skip count by 5s. Start at 10.
10, 15, 20, 25, __30__, __35__

Complete the addition pattern.
Skip count by 10s. Start at 30.
30, 40, 50, 60, __70__, __80__

What Can I Do?
I want to complete an addition pattern.

Try It • Complete each addition pattern.
Use the number line to help.

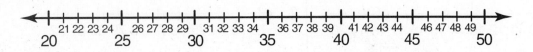

20 21 22 23 24 25 26 27 28 29 30 31 32 33 34 35 36 37 38 39 40 41 42 43 44 45 46 47 48 49 50

1. 32, 34, 36, 38, ____, ____

2. 20, 25, 30, 35, ____, ____

Power Practice • Complete each addition pattern.

3. 3, 6, 9, 12, ____, ____

4. 10, 20, 30, 40, ____, ____

5. 45, 50, 55, 60, ____, ____

6. 56, 58, 60, 62, ____, ____

7. 80, 90, 100, 110, ____, ____

8. 275, 280, 285, 290, ____, ____

© Macmillan/McGraw-Hill

15

Count Back

Learn

What Can I Do?
I want to complete a subtraction pattern.

Use a number line to count back.

Complete each subtraction pattern.

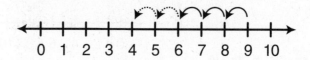

0 1 2 3 4 5 6 7 8 9 10

Count back by ones. Start at 9.

9, 8, 7, 6, __5__, __4__

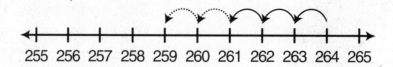

255 256 257 258 259 260 261 262 263 264 265

Count back by ones. Start at 264.

264, 263, 262, 261, _260_, _259_

Try It • Complete each subtraction pattern. Use the number line to help.

1. ←|―|―|―|―|―|―|―|―|―|→
10 11 12 13 14 15 16 17 18 19 20

16, 15, 14, 13, _____, _____

2. ←|―|―|―|―|―|―|―|―|―|―|→
72 73 74 75 76 77 78 79 80 81 82

82, 81, 80, 79, _____, _____

Power Practice • Complete each subtraction pattern.

3. 25, 24, 23, 22, _____, _____

4. 44, 43, 42, 41, _____, _____

5. 587, 586, 585, _____, _____

6. 152, 151, 150, _____, _____

7. 770, 769, 768, _____, _____

8. 803, 802, 801, _____, _____

Skip Count Backward

Learn

What Can I Do?
I want to complete a skip counting pattern.

Use a number line.

Each number in the pattern decreases or goes down by 2.

Skip count backward by 2s. Start at 14.

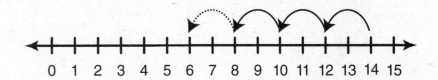

0 1 2 3 4 5 6 7 8 9 10 11 12 13 14 15

Count back 14, 12, 10, 8, 6.

14, 12, 10, 8, __6__

Try It • Complete each skip counting pattern.
Use the number line to help.

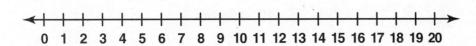
0 1 2 3 4 5 6 7 8 9 10 11 12 13 14 15 16 17 18 19 20

1. 18, 15, 12, 9, _____

2. 20, 16, 12, 8, _____

Power Practice • Write the next number in each skip counting pattern.

3. 30, 25, 20, 15, _____

4. 36, 32, 28, 24, _____

5. 27, 24, 21, 18, _____

6. 60, 54, 48, 42, _____

Skip Count by 5s

Learn

What Can I Do?
I want to complete a pattern.

Skip count to complete the pattern.

Each number in the pattern increases or goes up by 5.

Skip count by 5s. Start at 10.

Count 10, 15, 20, 25, 30, 35.

10, 15, 20, 25, __30__, __35__

Try It • **Skip count by 5s. Write the next number in each pattern.**

1. 5, 10, 15, 20, _____   **2.** 20, 25, 30, 35, _____

3. 15, 20, 25, 30, _____   **4.** 35, 40, 45, 50, _____

Power Practice • Write the next two numbers in each pattern.

5. 25, 30, 35, 40, _____, _____   **6.** 0, 5, 10, 15, _____, _____

7. 35, 40, 45, 50, _____, _____   **8.** 30, 35, 40, 45, _____, _____

9. 45, 50, 55, 60, 65, _____, _____   **10.** 20, 25, 30, 35, _____, _____

11. 60, 65, 70, 75, 80, _____, _____   **12.** 10, 15, 20, 25, _____, _____

Name_____

Ordinal Numbers

Learn

Use ordinal numbers.

In which place is the ?

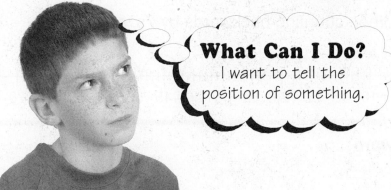

first second third fourth fifth sixth seventh eighth ninth tenth

The is in the seventh place.

What Can I Do?
I want to tell the position of something.

Try It • Write the correct place.

1. In which place is the ? _____

2. In which place is the ? _____

Power Practice • Start from the left. Name the correct place of each shaded object. Circle *a, b, c,* or *d.*

3.

a. first   **b.** second   **c.** third   **d.** fourth

4.

a. seventh   **b.** eighth   **c.** ninth   **d.** tenth

Name_____

Skip Count Backward
by 6 and 7

What Can I Do?
I want to count backwards by 6s and 7s.

Learn

Use number lines.

When counting backwards by 6s, start at 60.

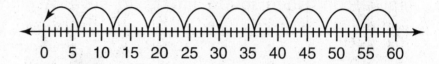

0 5 10 15 20 25 30 35 40 45 50 55 60

When counting backwards by 7s, start at 70.

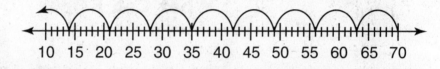

10 15 20 25 30 35 40 45 50 55 60 65 70

Try It • **Count forward.**

1. Count by 6s up to 60.

6, _____, _____, _____, _____, _____, _____, _____, _____, _____

2. Count by 7s up to 70.

7, _____, _____, _____, _____, _____, _____, _____, _____, _____

Power Practice • **Complete each skip counting pattern.**

3. 60, 54, _____, 42, 36, _____   **4.** 70, _____, 56, _____, 42, 35

5. 42, _____, 30, _____, 18, 12   **6.** 48, 42, _____, 30, 24, _____

7. 35, _____, 21, _____, 7, 0   **8.** _____, 24, 18, _____, 6, 0

9. _____, 49, 42, _____, 28, 21   **10.** 63, _____, 49, _____, 35, 28

Skip Count Backward by 8 and 9

What Can I Do?
I want to count backward by 8s and 9s.

Learn

Use number lines.

When counting backward by 8s, start at 80.

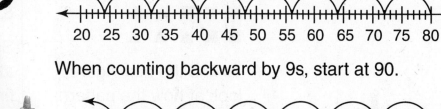

20 25 30 35 40 45 50 55 60 65 70 75 80

When counting backward by 9s, start at 90.

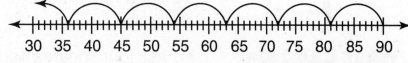

30 35 40 45 50 55 60 65 70 75 80 85 90

Try It • Count backward.

1. Count by 8s starting at 80.

80 _____, _____, _____, _____, _____, _____, _____, _____, _____

2. Count by 9s starting at 90.

90 _____, _____, _____, _____, _____, _____, _____, _____, _____

Power Practice • Complete each skip counting pattern.

3. 80, _____, 64, _____, 48, 40   **4.** _____, 81, 72, _____, 54, 45

5. 40, 32, _____, 16, _____, 0   **6.** 64, _____, 48, 40, _____, 24

7. 54, 45, _____, _____, 18, 9   **8.** 45, 36, _____, 18, 9, _____

9. _____, 48, 40, _____, 24, 16   **10.** 72, 64, _____, 48, _____, 32

Number Patterns

Learn

Look for changes.

What could be the next figure in this pattern?

■ ■ ■ ■ ▲
■ ■ ■ ▲ ▲
■ ■ ▲ ▲ ▲

To find the next figure, look at how the pattern changes.

- First: four squares and one triangle
- Second: three squares and two triangles
- Third: two squares and three triangles

In each figure, there is one more triangle and one less square. So, the next figure will have one square and four triangles.

Look for repeats.

What could be the next number in this pattern?

8, 8, 7, 2, 8, 8, 7, 2, 8, 8, 7

Saying a pattern aloud can help you find how it repeats.

Say "eight, eight, seven, two, eight, eight, seven, two, eight, eight, seven."

The repeated pattern is 8, 8, 7, 2. A 2 comes after every 7. So, the next number is a 2.

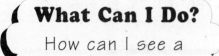

What Can I Do?

How can I see a pattern?

Try It • Circle the letter of the figures that comes next.

1. ▲▲▲▲▲▲▲●
   ▲▲▲▲▲●●
   ▲▲▲▲●●●●

   a. ▲▲▲▲▲▲
   b. ▲●▲●▲●
   c. ▲▲▲●●●●

2. ●●●●
   ●●●■
   ●●●■■

   a. ●●●●
   b. ●●●●■■■
   c. ■■■■●●

3. ●●●●●●▲
   ●●●●●▲▲
   ●●●●▲

   a. ●●●▲
   b. ●●●▲▲
   c. ●●●▲▲▲

Name _____

Write the repeating pattern.

4. 9, 9, 3, 2, 9, 9, 3, 2, 9, 9, 3, 2, 9, 9, 3, 2 ____ ____ ____ ____

5. 6, 7, 1, 5, 6, 7, 1, 5, 6, 7, 1, 5, 6, 7, 1, 5 ____ ____ ____ ____

Power Practice • **Draw the set of figures that come next.**

6. ● ■ ■ ■ ■ ■
　　● ● ■ ■ ■ ■
　　● ● ● ■ ■ ■

_____

7. ▲ ■
　　▲ ■ ■
　　▲ ■ ■ ■

_____

8. ▲ ■ ▲ ■
　　▲ ■ ▲ ■ ▲
　　▲ ■ ▲ ■ ▲ ■

_____

9. ● ● ● ● ● ● ● ●
　　● ● ● ● ● ● ●
　　● ● ● ● ● ●

_____

10. ■ ■ ■ ■ ■ ■ ■ ●
　　■ ■ ■ ■ ■ ● ● ●
　　■ ■ ■ ● ● ● ● ●

_____

11. ■ ● ■ ● ■ ● ■
　　■ ● ■ ● ■ ● ●
　　■ ● ■ ● ■

_____

Write what the next number in each pattern could be.

12. 5, 9, 3, 5, 9, 3, 5, 9, 3, 5, _____

13. 8, 2, 1, 0, 8, 2, 1, 0, 8, 2, 1, _____

14. 3, 3, 4, 9, 3, 3, 4, 9, 3, 3, 4, 9, _____

15. 8, 2, 9, 7, 7, 8, 2, 9, 7, 7, 8, 2, 9, 7, _____

16. 6, 0, 3, 1, 3, 6, 0, 3, 1, 3, 6, 0, 3, _____

17. 1, 1, 2, 2, 3, 3, 4, 4, 5, 5, 6, _____

18. 1, 3, 5, 7, 9, 11, 13, 15, 17, 19, _____

Learn with Partners & Parents

Secret Patterns

One player writes down a secret pattern using these shapes: ▲ ■ ●

The other player asks yes or no questions to guess the pattern. For example: Does the first shape have straight sides? Are there four figures in the pattern?

When you think you know the pattern, write it down. Find out if your guess is correct. Then switch roles and play again.

Name_____

Addition Facts to 20

Learn You can count on, use doubles, or make a ten to add.

Find 7 + 3.

Use the number line to count on.

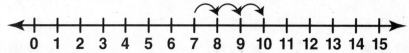

0 1 2 3 4 5 6 7 8 9 10 11 12 13 14 15

Start with the greater number. Start at 7.
Count on 3 spaces. You end at 10.

So, 7 + 3 = 10.

What Can I Do?
I want to add two 1-digit numbers.

Find 6 + 7.

Use doubles to add.

6 + 6 = 12

6 + 7 is 1 more.

So, 6 + 7 = 13.

Find 9 + 5.

Make a ten to add.

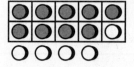

Add 9 + 1 to make a ten.

You made a ten and have 4 left over.

10 + 4 = 14

So, 9 + 5 = 14.

Try It • Count on to add. Draw a number line to help.

1. 4 + 1 = _____   **2.** 2 + 9 = _____   **3.** 5 + 3 = _____

4.   3   **5.**   7   **6.**   2   **7.**   2
     + 6   + 2   + 8   + 5

Use doubles to add.

8. 2 + 3 = _____   **9.** 3 + 4 = _____   **10.** 5 + 6 = _____

11.   7
   + 8
   ‾‾‾

12.   8
   + 9
   ‾‾‾

13.   4
   + 5
   ‾‾‾

14.   7
   + 6
   ‾‾‾

Make a ten to add.

15. 9 + 2 = _____   **16.** 7 + 5 = _____   **17.** 8 + 4 = _____

18.   7
   + 4
   ‾‾‾

19.   5
   + 8
   ‾‾‾

20.   9
   + 6
   ‾‾‾

21.   4
   + 9
   ‾‾‾

Power Practice • Add.

22. 2 + 1 = _____   **23.** 4 + 3 = _____   **24.** 3 + 6 = _____

25. 5 + 4 = _____   **26.** 3 + 3 = _____   **27.** 8 + 3 = _____

28. 6 + 6 = _____   **29.** 5 + 7 = _____   **30.** 9 + 6 = _____

31.   6
   + 4
   ‾‾‾

32.   3
   + 9
   ‾‾‾

33.   8
   + 8
   ‾‾‾

34.   7
   + 4
   ‾‾‾

35.   9
   + 7
   ‾‾‾

36.   5
   + 9
   ‾‾‾

37.   8
   + 9
   ‾‾‾

38.   7
   + 8
   ‾‾‾

Add Two-Digit Numbers

Learn

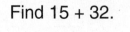

What Can I Do?
I want to add 2-digit numbers.

Use place-value charts and addition facts.

Find 15 + 32.

$$\begin{array}{r} 15 \\ + \ 32 \end{array}$$

Put each addend in a place-value chart.

First add the **ones.**
↓

tens	ones
1	**5**
+ 3	**2**
	7

Then add the **tens.**
↓

tens	ones
1	5
+ **3**	2
4	7

So, 15 + 32 = 47

Try It • Add.

1.

tens	ones
1	1
+ 1	7

2.

tens	ones
2	4
+ 1	3

3.

tens	ones
3	4
+ 2	0

4.

tens	ones
4	1
+	8

5.

tens	ones
4	6
+ 3	1

6.

tens	ones
3	2
+ 5	3

Name_____

7.   18
     + 11

8.   26
     + 12

9.   33
     + 13

10.   15
      + 34

11.   50
      + 17

12.   24
      + 61

13.   38
      + 31

14.   41
      + 52

15.   55
      + 22

16.   11
      + 67

17.   34
      + 53

18.   79
      + 20

19.   94
      + 4

20.   16
      + 82

21.   44
      + 44

22.   43
      + 36

23. 18 + 51 = _____

24. 5 + 52 = _____

25. 33 + 33 = _____

26. 23 + 21 = _____

27. 53 + 32 = _____

28. 26 + 43 = _____

Learn with Partners & Parents

11, 22, 33 Challenge

- Play with a partner. You will need 2 number cubes. Toss one number cube to see who goes first, then take turns.

- The first player tosses both number cubes and makes a two-digit number using the digits shown on the number cubes. The digits can be used in any order.

- The second player chooses another number for the first player to add to the number tossed. That number must be 11, 22, or 33.

- The first player adds the two numbers. You must show the addition on paper. A correct sum earns 5 points. No points are earned for an incorrect sum. The first player to earn 75 points is the winner.

Add 2 or More One- or Two-Digit Numbers

Learn

Use addition facts and place value charts.

Find $3 + 4 + 2 + 5$.

Add two numbers at a time.

Add two numbers.	Add the next number.	Add the next number.
$3 + \mathbf{4} + 2 + 5$	$\underline{3 + 4} + \mathbf{2} + 5$	$\underline{3 + 4 + 2} + \mathbf{5}$
↓	↓ ↓	↓ ↓
7	7 + 2	9 + 5
	↓	↓
	9	14

So, $3 + 4 + 2 + 5 = 14$.

Find $24 + 46 + 12$.

tens	ones
2	4
4	6
+ 1	2

What Can I Do?

I want to add more than two 1- or 2-digit numbers.

First add the ones.
Regroup as needed.

$$
\begin{array}{r}
1 \\
2\,\mathbf{4} \\
4\,\mathbf{6} \\
+\ 1\,\mathbf{2} \\
\hline
\mathbf{2}
\end{array}
$$

$4 + 6 = 10$
$10 + 2 = 12$
12 ones = 1 ten
and 2 ones
Regroup 1 ten.

Then add the tens.

$$
\begin{array}{r}
1 \\
\mathbf{2}\,4 \\
\mathbf{4}\,6 \\
+\ \mathbf{1}\,2 \\
\hline
\mathbf{8}\,2
\end{array}
$$

$1 + 2 = 3$
$3 + 4 = 7$
$7 + 1 = 8$

So, $24 + 46 + 12 = 82$.

Try It • Add.

1. $4 + 5 + 6 =$ ____
Think: $4 + 5 = ?$
$9 + 6 = ?$

2. $7 + 3 + 2 + 8 =$ ____
Think: $7 + 3 = ?$
$10 + 2 = ?$
$12 + 8 = ?$

3. $3 + 2 + 9 + 4 =$ ____
Think: $3 + 2 = ?$
$5 + 9 = ?$
$14 + 4 = ?$

Add.

4.

tens	ones
1	8
1	2
+ 3	4

5.

tens	ones
2	3
1	5
+ 1	7

6.

tens	ones
1	0
3	5
+ 2	5

7. $52 + 12 + 31 =$ _____

8. $14 + 34 + 22 + 8 =$ _____

Power Practice • **Add.**

9. $4 + 6 + 9 + 1 =$ _____

10. $3 + 8 + 1 + 3 =$ _____

11. $5 + 1 + 1 + 6 =$ _____

12. $32 + 46 + 9 =$ _____

13. $14 + 23 + 34 + 17 =$ _____

14. $11 + 12 + 13 + 14 =$ _____

15.
```
   29
   33
 + 24
```

16.
```
   72
   14
  + 9
```

17.
```
   16
   47
   22
  + 4
```

18.
```
   33
   22
  + 9
```

19.
```
   18
   26
   31
 + 10
```

20.
```
   46
   13
   19
  + 7
```

Basic Addition Facts

Learn

What Can I Do?
I want to find the sum of two 1-digit numbers.

Use doubles to add.

Find 7 + 8.

You know that
7 + 7 = 14.
7 + 8 is 1 more.
So, 7 + 8 = 15.

Count on to add.

Find 4 + 3.

Start at 4. Say 5, 6, 7.
So, 4 + 3 = 7.

Make a ten to add.

Find 8 + 6.

Add 8 + 2 to make a ten with 4 left over.

10 + 4 = 14
So, 8 + 6 = 14.

Try It • Count on, use doubles, or make a ten to find each sum.

1. 3 + 2 = _____   **2.** 4 + 5 = _____   **3.** 9 + 4 = _____

4. 8 + 5	**5.** 4 + 7	**6.** 9 + 8	**7.** 6 + 6

Power Practice • Find each sum.

8. 3 + 7 = _____   **9.** 2 + 0 = _____   **10.** 4 + 8 = _____

11. 8 + 3 = _____   **12.** 7 + 7 = _____   **13.** 1 + 9 = _____

14. 7 + 5	**15.** 0 + 9	**16.** 8 + 6	**17.** 9 + 7

Using an Addition Table

Learn

What Can I Do?

I want to use an addition table.

Add.

To find 8 + 7, look across the 8 row until you are under the 7. Answer: 15

Subtract.

To find 13 – 5, look across the 5 row until you find 13. Look in the top row for the answer, 8.

Addition Table

+	0	1	2	3	4	5	6	7	8	9	10
0	0	1	2	3	4	5	6	7	8	9	10
1	1	2	3	4	5	6	7	8	9	10	11
2	2	3	4	5	6	7	8	9	10	11	12
3	3	4	5	6	7	8	9	10	11	12	13
4	4	5	6	7	8	9	10	11	12	13	14
5	5	6	7	8	9	10	11	12	13	14	15
6	6	7	8	9	10	11	12	13	14	15	16
7	7	8	9	10	11	12	13	14	15	16	17
8	8	9	10	11	12	13	14	15	16	17	18
9	9	10	11	12	13	14	15	16	17	18	19
10	10	11	12	13	14	15	16	17	18	19	20

Try It • Use the addition table.

1. Look in the 7 row. Where is the answer to 7 + 6? _____

_____

2. Look in the 4 row. Where is the answer to 12 – 4? _____

_____

Power Practice • Find each sum or difference using the table.

3. 16 – 9 = _____   **4.** 7 + 6 = _____   **5.** 13 – 8 = _____

6. 9 + 5 = _____   **7.** 14 – 8 = _____   **8.** 9 + 6 = _____

9. 13 – 6 = _____   **10.** 8 + 6 = _____   **11.** 15 – 6 = _____

12. 14 – 9 = _____   **13.** 8 + 4 = _____   **14.** 9 + 8 = _____

Name _____

Doubles to Add

Learn

Use addition.

What is the double of 3?

Add 3 to itself to find the double.

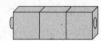

3 + 3 = 6

The double of 3 is 6.

You can use doubles to find other sums.

Find 4 + 5.

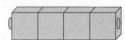 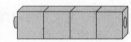

You know that 4 + 4 = 8.

4 + 5 is one more.

 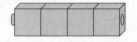

So, 4 + 5 = 9.

What Can I Do?
I want to double a number.

Try It • **Find each double.**

1. Double 2.

2 + 2 = _____

2. Double 5.

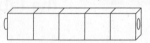 

5 + 5 = _____

Use the double to find the sum.

3. 3 + 3 = _____

3 + 4 = _____

4. 6 + 6 = _____

6 + 7 = _____

32

Power Practice • Find each sum.

5. 4 + 4 = _____   **6.** 6 + 6 = _____   **7.** 9 + 9 = _____

8. 7 + 7 = _____   **9.** 1 + 1 = _____   **10.** 8 + 8 = _____

Use the double to find the sum.

11. 5 + 5 = _____   **12.** 7 + 7 = _____   **13.** 10 + 10 = _____

     5 + 6 = _____   7 + 8 = _____   10 + 11 = _____

14.   8   9   **15.**   6   7
    + 8   + 8   + 6   + 6

16.   7   8   **17.**   9   10
    + 7   + 7   + 9   + 9

Add. Write the double you can use.

18.   7   ☐   **19.**   5   ☐
   + 6 + ☐   + 4 + ☐

20.   8   ☐   **21.**   6   ☐
   + 9 + ☐   + 5 + ☐

22.   8   ☐   **23.**   4   ☐
   + 5 + ☐   + 7 + ☐

24.   7   ☐   **25.**   3   ☐
   + 8 + ☐   + 6 + ☐

Addition Patterns

Learn

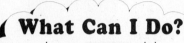

What Can I Do?
I want to add greater numbers mentally.

Use basic facts and patterns to find sums mentally.

Find 700 + 500.

You know the basic fact 7 + 5 = 12.

7 + 5 = 12
Think: 7 ones + 5 ones = 12 ones

70 + **5**0 = **12**0
Think: 7 tens + 5 tens = 12 tens

700 + **5**00 = 1,**2**00
Think: 7 hundreds + 5 hundreds = 12 hundreds

So, 700 + 500 = 1,200.

Try It • Write each sum.

1. 4 + 1 = _____

40 + 10 = _____

400 + 100 = _____

2. 5 + 6 = _____

50 + 60 = _____

500 + 600 = _____

Power Practice • Add. Use mental math.

3. 200 + 600 = _____

4. 30 + 40 = _____

5. 80 + 10 = _____

6. 600 + 600 = _____

7. 800 + 500 = _____

8. 70 + 30 = _____

9. 900 + 600 = _____

10. 500 + 500 = _____

11. 90 + 90 = _____

12. 70 + 80 = _____

Name _____

Addition Patterns

Learn

What Can I Do?
I want to use pictures to add.

Look at the value of each picture, then add.

If ☐ = 2 then

☐ ☐ ☐ ☐ = _____

You know that one ☐ = 2.

☐   ☐   ☐   ☐

Add: 2 + 2 + 2 + 2 = 8

Try It • Complete.

1. If △ = 3 then

△ △ △ = _____

___ + ___ + ___ = _____

2. If ◯ = 5 then

◯ ◯ = _____

___ + ___ = _____

Power Practice • Complete.

3. If ☐ = 5 then

☐ ☐ ☐ ☐ ☐ = _____

4. If ◯ = 10 then

◯ ◯ ◯ ◯ = _____

Commutative Property of Addition

Learn

What Can I Do?
I want to write a different addition sentence using the same addends and sum.

Commutative Property of Addition:

You can change the order of the addends and the sum will be the same.

Use the Commutative Property of Addition to write a different addition sentence for 1 + 4 = 5.

1 + 4 = 5

4 + 1 = 5

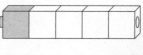

So, 1 + 4 = 4 + 1.

Try It • **Complete.**

1. 2 + 8 = 10 and 8 + 2 = 10

So, 2 + 8 = 8 + _____.

2. 4 + 9 = 13 and 9 + 4 = 13

So, 4 + 9 = _____ + 4.

3. 4 + 7 = 11 and 7 + 4 = 11

So, _____ + 7 = 7 + 4.

4. 6 + 5 = 11 and 5 + 6 = 11

So, 6 + _____ = 5 + 6.

Write a different addition sentence for each.

5.

3 + 4 = 7

_____

6.

1 + 3 = 4

_____

7.

5 + 3 = 8

_____

8.

2 + 1 = 3

_____

Power Practice • Complete.

9. 2 + 6 = 6 + _____

10. 8 + 1 = _____ + 8

11. 4 + _____ = 5 + 4

12. _____ + 3 = 3 + 9

13. 7 + _____ = 8 + 7

14. _____ + 9 = 9 + 5

15. 8 + 4 = _____ + 8

16. 6 + 1 = 1 + _____

17. _____ + 5 = 5 + 2

18. 6 + _____ = 7 + 6

Write a different addition sentence for each.

19. 2 + 7 = 9

_____

20. 3 + 1 = 4

_____

21. 5 + 7 = 12

_____

22. 6 + 9 = 15

_____

23. 8 + 5 = 13

_____

24. 3 + 2 = 5

_____

25. 6 + 3 = 9

_____

26. 9 + 2 = 11

_____

Write two different addition sentences for each model. Use the same addends and sum for each.

27.

_____

28.

_____

Subtraction Facts to 20

Learn

What Can I Do?
I want to find the
difference between
two numbers.

Count back to subtract.

Find 11 – 3.
Start at 11. Count back 3.
Say 10, 9, 8.
So, 11 – 3 = 8.

Use doubles to subtract.

Find 12 – 6.
You know that 6 + 6 = 12.
So, 12 – 6 = 6.

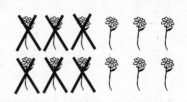

Try It • **Count back or use doubles to subtract.**

1. 6 – 2 = _____

2. 4 – 3 = _____

3. 8 – 4 = _____

4. 18
     – 9

5. 10
     – 5

6. 14
     – 7

7. 16
     – 8

Power Practice • **Subtract.**

8. 3 – 1 = _____

9. 9 – 4 = _____

10. 12 – 5 = _____

11. 12 – 7 = _____

12. 16 – 9 = _____

13. 13 – 4 = _____

14. 11 – 6 = _____

15. 14 – 8 = _____

16. 16 – 7 = _____

17. 6
     – 3

18. 10
     – 8

19. 8
     – 0

20. 17
     – 9

Subtraction

Learn

What Can I Do?
I want to subtract
whole numbers.

Find 53 − 26.

Step 1 Start with
the ones digits.

```
        ones
    5 3
  − 2 6
```

Step 2 Regroup
if you need to.

```
   4 13
    5̶ 3̶
  − 2 6
  ─────
    2 7
```

Try It • Find each difference

1.	71	2.	45	3.	50	4.	82	5.	63
	− 24		− 27		− 16		− 35		− 19
	7		8		4		7		4

Power Practice • Find each difference.

6.	61	7.	80	8.	74	9.	36	10.	58
	− 28		− 64		− 39		− 14		− 29

11.	87	12.	56	13.	73	14.	42	15.	82
	− 28		− 23		− 35		− 27		− 54

16.	62	17.	85	18.	30	19.	91	20.	64
	− 36		− 19		− 14		− 48		− 13

Subtraction

Learn

Use mental math or subtract with regrouping.

Find 12 − 3.

Use mental math for subtraction facts through 20.

So, 12 − 3 = 9.

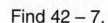

What Can I Do?
I want to subtract a 1-digit number from a 2-digit number.

Find 42 − 7.

Think: 7 ones > 2 ones, so regroup 1 ten for 10 ones.

Regroup to subtract the ones.

$$\begin{array}{r} \overset{3\ 12}{4\,\cancel{2}} \\ -\ 7 \\ \hline 5 \end{array}$$

4 tens 2 ones = 3 tens 12 ones

| Subtract the tens. |

$$\begin{array}{r} \overset{3\ 12}{4\,\cancel{2}} \\ -\ 7 \\ \hline 35 \end{array}$$

So, 42 − 7 = 35.

Try It • Subtract. Use mental math.

1. 9 − 3 = _____

2. 12 − 4 = _____

3. 18 − 9 = _____

4. 17 − 9 = _____

5. 15 − 7 = _____

6. 13 − 8 = _____

Regroup to subtract.

7. 24
− 6

8. 32
− 4

9. 35
− 7

10. 46
− 9

Name _____

11. 8
    − 2

12. 24
    − 4

13. 20
    − 5

14. 27
    − 9

15. 56
    − 7

16. 16
    − 8

17. 36
    − 9

18. 54
    − 6

19. 14 − 7 = _____

20. 42 − 6 = _____

21. 81 − 9 = _____

22. 53 − 8 = _____

23. 75 − 7 = _____

24. 61 − 9 = _____

25. 14 − 6 = _____

26. 40 − 9 = _____

27. 57 − 9 = _____

28. 34 − 5 = _____

29. 22 − 7 = _____

30. 91 − 6 = _____

31. 44 − 5 = _____

32. 60 − 2 = _____

Learn with Partners & Parents

Odd Subtraction

You will need two number cubes and a spinner numbered 0–9. Two or more players can play.

• Players take turns. First toss the number cubes. Use numbers to make a two-digit number. The digits may be in any order.

• Next spin the spinner. Subtract the number on the spinner from the number made with the number cubes.

• If the difference is correct and an even number, the player gets 1 point. If the difference is correct and an odd number, the player gets 2 points. The first player to get 25 points wins.

Subtract Two-Digit Numbers

Learn

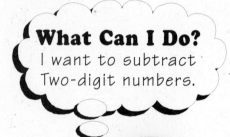

What Can I Do?
I want to subtract
Two-digit numbers.

Use place-value charts and basic subtraction facts.

Find 59 − 24.

$$\begin{array}{r} 59 \\ -\ 24 \\ \hline \end{array}$$

Put each number in a place-value chart.

First subtract the ones.   Then subtract the tens.

tens	ones
5	9
− 2	4
	5

tens	ones
5	9
− 2	4
3	5

So, 59 − 24 = 35.

Try It • Subtract.

1.

tens	ones
2	5
− 1	1

2.

tens	ones
3	7
− 1	4

3.

tens	ones
2	9
−	8

4.

tens	ones
4	2
− 2	0

5.

tens	ones
3	6
− 1	3

6.

tens	ones
3	8
− 2	5

Name_____

7. 19
   − 11

8. 27
   − 12

9. 46
   − 15

10. 48
   − 34

11. 54
   − 24

12. 65
   − 21

13. 34
   − 11

14. 49
   − 24

15. 74
   − 33

16. 66
   − 22

17. 58
   − 46

18. 79
   − 41

19. 94
   − 13

20. 88
   − 17

21. 75
   − 44

22. 99
   − 75

23. 38 − 13 = _____

24. 29 − 6 = _____

25. 45 − 21 = _____

26. 66 − 35 = _____

27. 87 − 34 = _____

28. 76 − 53 = _____

Learn with Partners & Parents

99 Subtraction

Play with a partner. You need four sets of digit cards 0–9, paper, and a pencil.

• Mix the cards well. Place them facedown in the middle of the table. Take turns drawing 2 cards each, but do not show them to the other player.

• Each player makes a number with the two digits on the cards and subtracts that number from 99. The player with the greatest difference gets 2 points. The player with the most points after all the cards are used wins the game.

Name_____

Fact Families

Learn

What Can I Do?
I want to complete a
family of facts.

Use the sum.

If the addition facts are

3 + 5 = 8 and 5 + 3 = 8, then

start each subtraction fact
with the sum which is 8.

Subtract each addend.

8 − 3 = 5
8 − 5 = 3

Each fact uses the same
three numbers 3, 5, and 8.

Try It • **Complete each family of facts.**

1. 8 + 4 = 12

4 + 8 = 12

$\boxed{}$ − 8 = 4

$\boxed{}$ − 4 = 8

2. 6 + 7 = 13

7 + 6 = 13

13 − $\boxed{}$ = 7

13 − 7 = $\boxed{}$

3. 4 + 3 = 7

3 + 4 = 7

7 − 4 = $\boxed{}$

7 − $\boxed{}$ = 4

4. 6 + 3 = 9

3 + 6 = 9

$\boxed{}$ − 6 = 3

$\boxed{}$ − 3 = 6

5. 3 + 9 = 12

9 + 3 = 12

12 − $\boxed{}$ = 9

12 − 9 = $\boxed{}$

6. 3 + 8 = 11

8 + 3 = 11

11 − 3 = $\boxed{}$

11 − $\boxed{}$ = 3

Power Practice • Write the pair of related subtraction facts for each pair of addition facts.

7. $9 + 7 = 16$

$7 + 9 = 16$

_____

_____

8. $9 + 1 = 10$

$1 + 9 = 10$

_____

_____

9. $6 + 8 = 14$

$8 + 6 = 14$

_____

_____

10. $4 + 6 = 10$

$6 + 4 = 10$

_____

_____

11. $7 + 4 = 11$

$4 + 7 = 11$

_____

_____

12. $9 + 4 = 13$

$4 + 9 = 13$

_____

_____

13. $6 + 2 = 8$

$2 + 6 = 8$

_____

_____

14. $8 + 9 = 17$

$9 + 8 = 17$

_____

_____

15. $7 + 5 = 12$

$5 + 7 = 12$

_____

_____

16. $8 + 5 = 13$

$5 + 8 = 13$

_____

_____

Learn with Partners & Parents

Fact Family Roll

You will need two 1–6 number cubes.

- Toss the cubes to get two numbers to add. If the numbers are the same, toss again.

- The first player to write two addition and two subtraction facts gets one point.

- Play the game until one player has 7 points.

Addition and Subtraction Facts

Learn

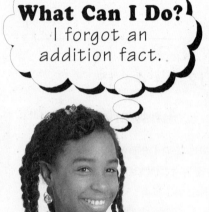

What Can I Do?
I forgot an addition fact.

Count On

Think: 3 + 8 = ?

Remember that 3 + 8 is the same as 8 + 3.

You can count on from the greater number.

Think: 8, 9, 10, 11
8 + 3 = 11

Fact with 10

Think: 9 + 8 = ?

You might remember that 10 + 8 = 18. You know that 9 + 8 will be 1 less,
so 9 + 8 = 17

Count Back

Think: 12 − 3 = ?

You can't rearrange subtraction facts. Count back to find the difference.

Think: 12, 11, 10, 9
12 − 3 = 9

Related Facts

Think: 13 − 5 = ?

You may remember that 5 + 8 = 13. Then you can find 13 − 5 = 8. Use related addition facts to help solve subtraction.

Try It • Rearrange and add.

1. 3 + 9

9 + ____ = ____

2. 4 + 7

____ + ____ = ____

3. 2 + 9

____ + ____ = ____

Count back to subtract.

4. 11 − 3 = ____

5. 9 − 2 = ____

6. 11 − 2 = ____

Use a fact with 10 to help you add or subtract.

7. 9 + 6 = ?
10 + 6 = 16

So, 9 + 6 = ____.

8. 17 − 9 = ?
17 − 10 = 7

So, 17 − 9 = ____.

9. 18 − 9 = ?
18 − 8 = 10

So, 18 − 9 = ____.

Add or subtract. Then check your answer.

10. 8 + 7 = _____   **11.** 14 − 8 = _____   **12.** 12 + 6 = _____

_____ − 7 = 8   _____ + 8 = 14   _____ − 6 = 12

Power Practice • **Add or subtract**

13. 6 + 9 = _____   **14.** 15 − 8 = _____

15. 9 + 7 = _____   **16.** 19 − 9 = _____

17. 16 − 7 = _____   **18.** 13 − 5 = _____

19. 9 + 3 = _____   **20.** 11 − 9 = _____

21. 12 − 5 = _____   **22.** 14 − 6 = _____

23. 4 + 8 = _____   **24.** 8 + 3 = _____

25. 8 + 1 = _____   **26.** 16 − 9 = _____

27. 17 − 9 = _____   **28.** 14 − 8 = _____

29. 12 + 7 = _____   **30.** 18 − 6 = _____

Learn with
Partners & Parents

The Answer Is. . .

This game can help you remember addition and subtraction facts. Try this game with 2 to 4 players.

• Write the numbers 10 to 20 on index cards and mix them.

• Turn one card over. Players take turns writing addition or subtraction problems that have the answer shown.

• If a player writes an incorrect problem or cannot think of another problem to add to the list, he or she is out for the round.

• Keep playing until no one can add another problem. The last player to add a problem gets to keep the card.

• Turn the next card over to begin the next round. The player with the most cards at the end of the game is the winner.

Add 3 or More Numbers

Learn

What Can I Do?
I want to add 3 or more numbers.

Use the Associative Property to add two numbers at a time.

Find $4 + 2 + 8$.

Group the numbers to make addition easier.

$4 + (2 + 8) =$
$\downarrow$

$4 + \quad 10 \quad = 14$ Make a ten. Add mentally.

So, $4 + 2 + 8 = 14$.

Try It

Add. Show how you grouped the numbers.

1. $3 + 2 + 9 =$ _____

2. $5 + 5 + 6 =$ _____

Power Practice

Add.

3. $7 + 1 + 2 =$ _____

4. $5 + 3 + 4 =$ _____

5. $2 + 2 + 5 + 3 =$ _____

6. $4 + 6 + 6 =$ _____

Learn with Partners & Parents

Number Cube Roll

You need four 1–6 number cubes.

• The first player tosses the four cubes.

• The second player writes a number sentence to add the four numbers tossed.

• The first player then writes a number sentence in which the numbers are grouped differently.

• Each player checks the other's number sentence. If both players agree, both get a point for the round, and the second player tosses. If a player misses a sentence, that player loses a point, and the other player tosses.

• Play until one or both players have earned 10 points.

Repeated Addition

Learn

What Can I Do?
I want to add the same number many times.

Use skip counting.

Find 4 + 4 + 4 + 4 + 4.

Look at the number of 4s. There are five 4s.

Skip count by 4s five times.

4 + 4 + 4 + 4 + 4

4,   8,   12,   16,   20

So, 4 + 4 + 4 + 4 + 4 = 20

Try It • **Find each sum. Skip count to help.**

1. 2 + 2 + 2 + 2 = _____

Skip count by 2s.

_____, _____, _____, _____

2. 5 + 5 + 5 = _____

Skip count by 5s.

_____, _____, _____

Power Practice • **Find each sum.**

3. 3 + 3 + 3 + 3 + 3 = _____

4. 6 + 6 + 6 = _____

5. 4 + 4 + 4 + 4 = _____

6. 5 + 5 + 5 + 5 + 5 + 5 = _____

7. 7 + 7 + 7 + 7 = _____

8. 8 + 8 + 8 + 8 = _____

9. 2 + 2 + 2 + 2 + 2 + 2 = _____

10. 9 + 9 + 9 + 9 + 9 + 9 = _____

Name _____

Add 3 or More Addends

Learn

Use basic facts and regrouping.

Find 13 + 25 + 18.

Step 1 Add the ones. Regroup if you need to.

$$
\begin{array}{r}
1 \\
13 \\
25 \\
+\ 18 \\
\hline
6
\end{array}
$$

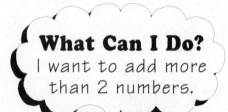
What Can I Do?
I want to add more
than 2 numbers.

Step 2 Then add the tens. Remember to add
the number of tens you regrouped.

$$
\begin{array}{r}
1 \\
13 \\
25 \\
+\ 18 \\
\hline
56
\end{array}
$$

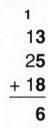

Try It . **Use basic facts and regrouping. Complete to find
each sum.**

1.
$$
\begin{array}{r}
1 \\
24 \\
16 \\
+\ 13 \\
\hline
3
\end{array}
$$

2.
$$
\begin{array}{r}
1 \\
16 \\
44 \\
+\ 12 \\
\hline
2
\end{array}
$$

3.
$$
\begin{array}{r}
12 \\
51 \\
+\ 25 \\
\hline
8
\end{array}
$$

4.
$$
\begin{array}{r}
34 \\
22 \\
+\ 45 \\
\hline
1
\end{array}
$$

Name _____

5. 15
         15
       + 15

6. 12
         24
       + 36

7. 34
         26
       + 31

8. 23
         33
       + 43

9. 44
         55
       + 66

10. 27
          23
        + 38

11. 84
          23
        + 16

12. 123
          123
        + 123

13. 200
          500
        + 300

14. 34
          34
        + 34

15. 47
          48
        + 49

16. 400
          300
        + 700

17. 25 + 42 + 19 = _____

18. 113 + 243 + 115 = _____

19. 19 + 19 + 19 = _____

20. 300 + 400 + 200 = _____

21. 18 + 52 + 18 + 52 = _____

22. 900 + 800 + 700 = _____

23. 400 + 600 + 300 = _____

24. 24 + 35 + 46 + 57 = _____

Learn with Partners & Parents

Exercise Exchange

• Working by yourself, write six exercises. Three of the exercises should involve adding four two-digit numbers. The other exercises should involve adding four three-digit numbers.

• Create an answer key for your exercises.

• Then exchange exercises with your partner. Find the answers to your partner's exercises.

• For any answers that disagree, work with your partner to determine the correct sum.

Column Addition

Learn

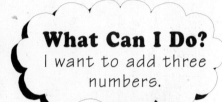

What Can I Do?
I want to add three numbers.

Step 1 Line up digits.

Write the numbers in a column. Line up the digits.

```
  1 4 6
    2 7
+ 5 3 2
```

Step 2 Start with the ones.

Start at the top. Say the sums to yourself as you add.

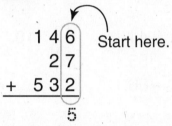

```
  1 4 6    Start here.
    2 7
+ 5 3 2
      5
```

Think: 6 plus 7 is 13.
13 plus 2 is 15.

Now add the tens.
Then add the hundreds.

Try It • Find each sum.

1.
```
  8
  4
+ 2
```

2.
```
  7
  1
+ 6
```

3.
```
  5
  9
+ 3
```

4.
```
  4
  2
+ 7
```

5.
```
  6
  5
+ 2
```

6.
```
  5
  3
+ 1
```

7.
```
  4
  6
+ 8
```

8.
```
  9
  3
+ 4
```

9.
```
  5
  2
+ 8
```

10.
```
  6
  7
+ 3
```

11.
```
  8
  5
+ 7
```

12.
```
  9
  4
+ 6
```

Name _____

Find each sum.

13.	14.	15.	16.
25 83 + 32	59 43 + 72	87 63 + 54	29 93 + 38

17.	18.	19.	20.
56 17 + 4	38 6 + 81	6 52 + 48	15 87 + 6

Power Practice • **Find each sum.**

21.	22.
58 9 + 72	63 147 + 41

23.	24.
368 210 + 512	413 67 + 529

25.	26.
2,158 1,749 + 5,321	6,215 4,670 + 1,912

27.	28.
802 157 + 4,016	5,106 853 + 29

Learn with Partners & Parents

Three Number Addition

Two or three players can play.

• Take turns. Each player names a three-digit or a four-digit number until three numbers are named.

• Write down each number as it is named. Add the three numbers.

• The first player to get the correct sum wins one point.

• Play until one player has 11 points.

Name _____

Adding Money

Learn

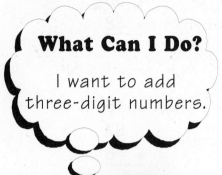

Rewrite the problem.

What is $5.78 + $0.98?

Write this problem by stacking the numbers. Remember to stack the numbers so that the ones are above the ones.

To add, start with the ones.

Think: 8 + 8 = 16
Write the 6 and regroup the 10 ones as 1 ten.

Think: 1 ten + 7 tens + 9 tens = 17 tens.
Write the 7 and rename 10 tens as 1 hundred.

Think: 1 hundred + 5 hundreds = 6 hundreds.
Write the 6.

$$
\begin{array}{r} \$5.78 \\ + 0.98 \\ \hline \end{array}
\qquad
\begin{array}{r} \overset{1}{\$5.78} \\ + 0.98 \\ \hline 6 \end{array}
\qquad
\begin{array}{r} \overset{1}{\$}\overset{1}{5}.78 \\ + 0.98 \\ \hline 76 \end{array}
\qquad
\begin{array}{r} \overset{1}{\$}\overset{1}{5}.78 \\ + 0.98 \\ \hline \$6.76 \end{array}
$$

So, $5.78 + $0.98 = $6.76.

Estimate before you add.

What is $3.85 + $5.17?

Round each amount to the nearest dollar.

Think: $3.85 is close to $4.
$5.17 is close to $5.

So, the answer will be close to $4 + $5, or $9.

Rewrite the problem to add.

$$
\begin{array}{r} \$3.85 \\ + 5.17 \\ \hline \$9.02 \end{array}
$$

The answer is $9.02. It is close to your estimate of $9.

Name _____

1. $2.26 + $3.67   **2.** $7.35 + $1.19   **3.** $8.20 + $4.51

$____.____ ____ $____.____ ____ $____.____ ____

+$____.____ ____   +____.____ ____   +$____.____ ____
_____   _____   _____

$____.____ ____ $____.____ ____ $____.____ ____

Estimate. Then find the exact sum. Use your estimate to check your answer.

4. $6.08 + $5.89   **5.** $7.17 + $8.25

$6.08 is close to _____. $7.17 is close to _____.

$5.89 is close to _____. $8.25 is close to _____.

The answer will be close to _____.   The answer will be close to _____.

Exact sum = _____   Exact sum = _____

Power Practice • Find each sum.

6. $4.84   **7.** $7.04   **8.** $9.32
     + 2.73   + 6.09   + 5.12

9. $3.89   **10.** $6.49   **11.** $8.02
     + 8.02   + 8.86   2.20
                                               + 0.79

12. $5.32 + $1.26 = _____   **13.** $6.25 + $1.04 = _____

14. $5.12 + $2.95 = _____   **15.** $4.10 + $3.27 = _____

16. $7.42 + $3.27 = _____   **17.** $3.89 + $3.99 = _____

Subtracting Money

Learn

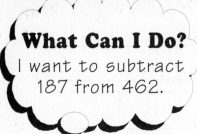

What Can I Do?
I want to subtract
187 from 462.

Regroup tens and hundreds.

Write the subtraction problem.

$4.62   Think: I can't subtract 7 from 2
− 1.87   because 7 is greater than 2.
           I need to regroup.

Look at the tens column.

The 6 in the tens column equals 6 tens.
It can also equal 5 tens plus 10 ones by
regrouping 1 ten as 10 ones.

$$\begin{array}{r} \overset{5\ 12}{\$4.\cancel{6}\cancel{2}} \\ -\ 1.87 \\ \hline 5 \end{array}$$ Think: 12 − 7 = 5

Now look at the tens.
You can't subtract 8 tens from 5 tens.
Look at the hundreds column.

The 4 in the hundreds column
equals 4 hundreds. It can also equal
3 hundreds and 10 tens by
regrouping 1 hundred as 10 tens.

Finally, subtract 100 from 300.

$$\begin{array}{r} \overset{15}{\overset{3\ \$12}{\$4.\cancel{6}\cancel{2}}} \\ -\ 1.87 \\ \hline \$2.75 \end{array}$$

Check your answer with addition.

$2.75 + $1.87 = $4.62

$$\begin{array}{r} \overset{15}{\overset{3\ \$12}{\$4.\cancel{6}\cancel{2}}} \\ -\ 1.87 \\ \hline \$0.75 \end{array}$$ Think:
15 tens − 8 tens = 7 tens

Name _____

1.　　685
　　− 222 _____

2.　　712
　　− 431 _____

3.　　$2.99
　　− 1.57 _____

4.　　902
　　− 374 _____

5.　　843
　　− 255 _____

6.　　$1.28
　　− 0.97 _____

Complete.

7. 8 tens = 7 tens and _____ ones

8. 6 hundreds = 5 hundreds and _____ tens

9. 9 tens = _____ tens and 10 ones

10. 4 hundreds = _____ hundreds and 10 tens

Power Practice • Find each difference.

11.　　$9.57
　　− 7.23

12.　　843
　　− 757

13.　　736
　　− 98

14.　　406
　　− 389

15.　　600
　　− 217

16.　　$7.04
　　− 0.88

17. 837 − 225 = _____

18. 756 − 657 = _____

19. $5.62 − $3.79 = _____

20. 336 − 63 = _____

21. 400 − 282 = _____

22. $772 − $108 = _____

23. $7.83 − $6.94 = _____

24. 405 − 317 = _____

Equal Groups

Learn

Use pictures and count.

There are 3 plates with 2 crackers on each plate.

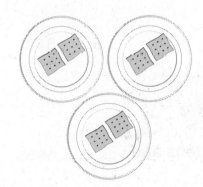

What Can I Do?
I want to describe
equal groups.

How many groups of crackers are there?
How many in each group?

Step 1

Count the number
of plates.

There are 3 groups.

Step 2

Count the number of
crackers on each plate.

There are 2 in
each group.

So, there are 3 groups of 2.

Try It • Write the number of groups.

1.

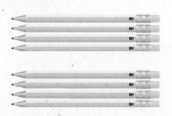

_____ groups of 4

2.

_____ groups of 3

Name _____

• **Write the number in each group.**

3.

5 groups of _____

4.

3 groups of _____

Power Practice • **Complete.**

5.

_____ groups of 2

6.

4 groups of _____

7.

_____ groups of _____

8.

_____ groups of _____

9.

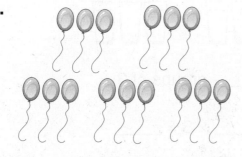

_____ groups of _____

10.

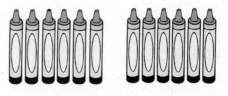

_____ groups of _____

© Macmillan/McGraw-Hill

59

Equal Groups

Learn

What Can I Do?
I want to write a number sentence to describe a picture.

Write a multiplication sentence.

Megan gave 5 apples to each of 4 friends.

There are 4 groups of 5.

Number of groups		Number in each group		Total
↓		↓		↓
4	×	5	=	20

Try It • **Complete.**

1.

2 groups of _____

2 × _____ = _____

2.

_____ groups of 3

_____ × 3 = _____

Name _____

Complete.

3.

_____ groups of _____

_____ × _____ = _____

4.

_____ groups of _____

_____ × _____ = _____

Power Practice

Write the multiplication sentence that each picture shows.

5.

_____ × _____ = _____

6.

_____ × _____ = _____

© Macmillan/McGraw-Hill

Learn with Partners & Parents

Spinning Groups

- You will need a spinner numbered 1 to 8, and many counters, pennies, or beans in a paper bag.

- Take turns. The first player spins the spinner, and takes a handful of counters from the bag without looking.

- Make equal groups using the counters. Each group should have the number of counters shown on the spinner. (If there are any left over counters, put them back in the bag.)

- Players get 2 points for each equal group. For instance, if you make 5 equal groups of 3 counters each, you get 10 points.

- Each player gets 10 turns. The player with the most points after 10 turns wins the game.

Equal Groups

Learn

What Can I Do?
I want to find the total number of items in a problem with groups of items.

Draw a picture.

José has 4 boxes of 6 pencils. How many pencils does he have in all?

Think: There are 4 groups of 6 pencils.

Draw a picture to solve.

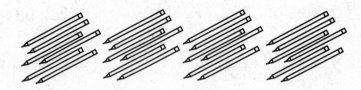

There are 24 pencils in all.

Try It • **Finish drawing each picture.**
Then write the total amount.

1. Draw 3 groups of 2 triangles.

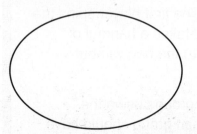

Total = _____ triangles

---

2. Draw 2 groups of 5 squares.

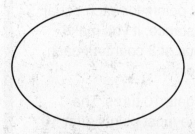

Total = _____ squares

Name _____

Power Practice • Draw each picture.
Then write the total amount.

3. 5 groups of 5 rectangles

Total = _____ rectangles

4. 4 groups of 7 rectangles

Total = _____ rectangles

5. 2 groups of 9 circles

Total = _____ circles

6. 6 groups of 3 triangles

Total = _____ triangles

7. 7 groups of 8 squares

Total = _____ squares

8. 9 groups of 4 circles

Total = _____ circles

Use Arrays to Multiply

Learn

What Can I Do?

I want to write a number sentence for an array.

Write a multiplication sentence for the picture.

row 1 ○○○○

row 2 ○○○○

row 3 ○○○○

There are 3 rows of 4.

Number of rows	Number in each row	Total
↓	↓	↓
3	× 4	= 12

Try It • Complete.

1. ○ ○ ○
   ○ ○ ○

   2 rows of _____

   $2 \times$ _____ = _____

2. ○ ○ ○ ○ ○
   ○ ○ ○ ○ ○
   ○ ○ ○ ○ ○
   ○ ○ ○ ○ ○

   _____ rows of 5

   _____ $\times 5 =$ _____

3. ○ ○ ○ ○ ○ ○ ○
   ○ ○ ○ ○ ○ ○ ○
   ○ ○ ○ ○ ○ ○ ○
   ○ ○ ○ ○ ○ ○ ○

   _____ rows of _____

   _____ $\times 7 =$ _____

Complete.

4.

_____ rows of _____

_____ × _____ = _____

5.

_____ rows of _____

_____ × _____ = _____

Power Practice • Write the multiplication sentence that each array shows.

6.

_____ × _____ = _____

7.

_____ × _____ = _____

8.

_____ × _____ = _____

9.

_____ × _____ = _____

Multiplication Facts Through 5

Learn

What Can I Do?
I want to practice multiplication facts through 5.

Skip count on a number line.

Find 5×4.

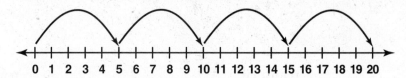

0 1 2 3 4 5 6 7 8 9 10 11 12 13 14 15 16 17 18 19 20

Skip count by 5s four times.

5, 10, 15, 20

So, $5 \times 4 = 20$.

Try It • Use the number line to help you multiply.

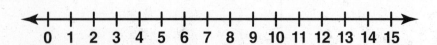

0 1 2 3 4 5 6 7 8 9 10 11 12 13 14 15

1. $3 \times 5 =$ _____   **2.** $2 \times 6 =$ _____

Power Practice • Multiply.

3. $4 \times 6 =$ _____   **4.** $5 \times 1 =$ _____   **5.** $3 \times 9 =$ _____

6. 8
   $\times 2$

7. 7
   $\times 5$

8. 8
   $\times 4$

Multiplication Facts Through 8

Learn

Use equal groups.

Find 6×5.

Draw 6 groups of 5 circles.

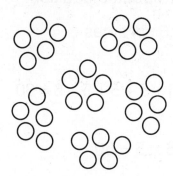

There are 30 circles in all.

So, $6 \times 5 = 30$.

What Can I Do?
I want to practice multiplication facts through 8.

Use doubling.

Find 8×8.

You can double a 4s fact to find an 8s fact.

$4 \times 8 = 32$

Double the product.

$32 + 32 = 64$

So, $8 \times 8 = 64$.

Try It • Use equal groups or doubling to multiply.

1. $8 \times 5 =$ _____

2. $7 \times 6 =$ _____

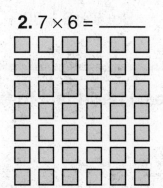

Power Practice • Multiply.

3. $8 \times 2 =$ _____

4. $7 \times 5 =$ _____

5. $6 \times 8 =$ _____

6. $7 \times 3 =$ _____

7. $7 \times 7 =$ _____

8. $6 \times 9 =$ _____

Name _____

Multiplication Facts Through 9

Learn

What Can I Do?
I want to multiply
two numbers.

Use any multiplication strategy.

Find 6×5.

Double a known fact.	Use repeated addition.
Double 3×5 to find 6×5.	Add 5 six times.
$3 \times 5 = 15$ $15 + 15 = 30$	$5 + 5 + 5 + 5 + 5 + 5 = 30$
So, $6 \times 5 = 30$.	So, $6 \times 5 = 30$.

Skip count on a number line.

Skip count by 5s six times.

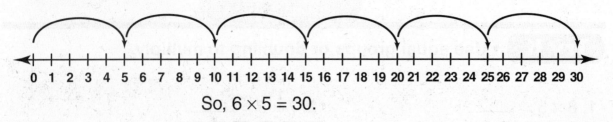

So, $6 \times 5 = 30$.

Try It • Double a known fact to find each product.

1. $4 \times 9 = $ _____

Double 2×9

2. $8 \times 5 = $ _____

Double 4×5

3. $6 \times 5 = $ _____

Double 3×5.

4. $10 \times 7 = $ _____

Double 5×7

Use repeated addition to find each product.

5. $3 \times 7 =$ _____ **6.** $5 \times 5 =$ _____

Add: _____ Add: _____

Skip count to find each product.

7. $5 \times 3 =$ _____ **8.** $4 \times 6 =$ _____

Count: _____ Count: _____

Power Practice • Find each product. Use any method.

9. $2 \times 6 =$ _____ **10.** $4 \times 4 =$ _____ **11.** $5 \times 7 =$ _____

12. $6 \times 7 =$ _____ **13.** $3 \times 8 =$ _____ **14.** $9 \times 3 =$ _____

15. $7 \times 4 =$ _____ **16.** $8 \times 6 =$ _____ **17.** $5 \times 8 =$ _____

18. $\begin{array}{r} 8 \\ \times\,2 \\ \hline \end{array}$ **19.** $\begin{array}{r} 3 \\ \times\,6 \\ \hline \end{array}$ **20.** $\begin{array}{r} 7 \\ \times\,7 \\ \hline \end{array}$ **21.** $\begin{array}{r} 9 \\ \times\,3 \\ \hline \end{array}$

22. $\begin{array}{r} 6 \\ \times\,6 \\ \hline \end{array}$ **23.** $\begin{array}{r} 9 \\ \times\,8 \\ \hline \end{array}$ **24.** $\begin{array}{r} 8 \\ \times\,4 \\ \hline \end{array}$ **25.** $\begin{array}{r} 6 \\ \times\,9 \\ \hline \end{array}$

26. $\begin{array}{r} 9 \\ \times\,4 \\ \hline \end{array}$ **27.** $\begin{array}{r} 7 \\ \times\,8 \\ \hline \end{array}$ **28.** $\begin{array}{r} 7 \\ \times\,9 \\ \hline \end{array}$ **29.** $\begin{array}{r} 9 \\ \times\,9 \\ \hline \end{array}$

Multiplication Facts

Learn

Use a Multiplication Table.

Example: To find 7 times 8, look across the
7 row until you are under the 8. The product is 56.

What Can I Do?

I want to multiply
two numbers.

×	0	1	2	3	4	5	6	7	8	9	10
0	0	0	0	0	0	0	0	0	0	0	0
1	0	1	2	3	4	5	6	7	8	9	10
2	0	2	4	6	8	10	12	14	16	18	20
3	0	3	6	9	12	15	18	21	24	27	30
4	0	4	8	12	16	20	24	28	32	36	40
5	0	5	10	15	20	25	30	35	40	45	50
6	0	6	12	18	24	30	36	42	48	54	60
row → 7	0	7	14	21	28	35	42	49	56	63	70
8	0	8	16	24	32	40	48	56	64	72	80
9	0	9	18	27	36	45	54	63	72	81	90
10	0	10	20	30	40	50	60	70	80	90	100

Try It • Adding can help you multiply. Complete each pair of
problems to see how.

1. $5 + 5 + 5 =$ _____

$3 \times 5 =$ _____

2. $9 + 9 =$ _____

$2 \times 9 =$ _____

3. $2 + 2 + 2 + 2 =$ _____

$4 \times 2 =$ _____

4. $6 + 6 + 6 + 6 =$ _____

$4 \times 6 =$ _____

5. $7 + 7 + 7 =$ _____

$3 \times 7 =$ _____

6. $8 + 8 =$ _____

$2 \times 8 =$ _____

Power Practice • Multiply.

7. $6 \times 9 =$ _____

8. $7 \times 7 =$ _____

9. $8 \times 6 =$ _____

10. $8 \times 9 =$ _____

11. $4 \times 5 =$ _____

12. $4 \times 6 =$ _____

13. $4 \times 9 =$ _____

14. $7 \times 5 =$ _____

Patterns

Learn

What Can I Do?
I want to complete a
multiplication pattern.

Find the factor.

In this kind of pattern, the numbers 1, 2, 3, and so on are multiplied by the same factor. Find the factor.

60	120	180	240	?
↑	↑	↑	↑	↑
1×60	2×60	3×60	4×60	5×60

The factor is 60.
Since $5 \times 60 = 300$, the ? equals 300.

Try It • **Make a pattern starting with each number.
Multiply it by 2, 3, 4, 5.**

1. 40, _____, _____, _____, _____   **2.** 90, _____, _____, _____, _____

3. 800; _____; _____; _____; _____

Power Practice • **Complete each multiplication pattern.**

4. 700; 1,400; 2,100; 2,800; _____   **5.** 30, 60, 90, 120, _____

6. 900; 1,800; 2,700; 3,600; _____   **7.** 200, 400, 600, 800, _____

8. 400; 800; 1,200; 1,600; _____   **9.** 20, 40, 60, 80, _____

Multiply with 0 and 1

Learn

Identity Property of Multiplication: The product of 1 and any number is that number.

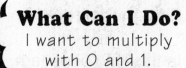

What Can I Do?
I want to multiply with 0 and 1.

Zero Property of Multiplication: The product of 0 and any number is 0.

Use the Identity Property of Multiplication.

Find 1×4.

So, $1 \times 4 = 4$

Use the Zero Property of Multiplication.

Find 7×0.

So, $7 \times 0 = 0$

Try It • **Multiply. Circle the property you used.**

1. $3 \times 1 =$ _____

Identity Property

Zero Property

2. $0 \times 2 =$ _____

Identity Property

Zero Property

3. $\begin{array}{r} 0 \\ \times\, 4 \\ \hline \end{array}$

Identity Property

Zero Property

4. $\begin{array}{r} 5 \\ \times\, 1 \\ \hline \end{array}$

Identity Property

Zero Property

Name _____

5. $2 \times 0 =$ _____   **6.** $1 \times 6 =$ _____   **7.** $8 \times 1 =$ _____

8. $4 \times 0 =$ _____   **9.** $1 \times 5 =$ _____   **10.** $9 \times 0 =$ _____

11. $7 \times 1 =$ _____   **12.** $2 \times 1 =$ _____   **13.** $0 \times 8 =$ _____

14.	0	**15.**	6	**16.**	4	**17.**	8
	$\times 3$		$\times 1$		$\times 1$		$\times 0$

18.	1	**19.**	3	**20.**	0	**21.**	9
	$\times 2$		$\times 0$		$\times 5$		$\times 1$

22.	0	**23.**	1	**24.**	0	**25.**	0
	$\times 6$		$\times 8$		$\times 7$		$\times 9$

26.	0	**27.**	0	**28.**	1	**29.**	5
	$\times 0$		$\times 1$		$\times 1$		$\times 0$

30.	6	**31.**	1	**32.**	1	**33.**	1
	$\times 0$		$\times 1$		$\times 7$		$\times 0$

Use a Multiplication Table

Learn

What Can I Do?
I want to find patterns in a multiplication table.

Look at the rows and the columns.

What pattern do you see in the 2s row and the 4s row?

↓**Columns**

x	0	1	2	3	4	5	6	7	8	9	
0	0	0	0	0	0	0	0	0	0	0	
1	0	1	2	3	4	5	6	7	8	9	
2	0	2	4	6	8	10	12	14	16	18	←2s row
3	0	3	6	9	12	15	18	21	24	27	
4	0	4	8	12	16	20	24	28	32	36	←4s row
5	0	5	10	15	20	25	30	35	40	45	

Rows →

The numbers in the 4s row are double the numbers in the 2s row.

Try It • Complete. Write *odd*, *even*, or *odd and even*.

1. The numbers in the 3s **row** are _____.

2. The numbers in the 6s **column** are _____.

Power Practice • Use the multiplication table.

3. Which **rows** have only even numbers? _____

4. Which **columns** have both odd and even numbers? _____

_____

5. What do you notice about the first six numbers in the 5s **row** and

the 5s **column?** _____

_____

Multiplication Patterns

Learn

What Can I Do?
I want to multiply by
10; 100; or 1,000.

Look for a pattern.

The number of zeros in the product
is the same as in the power of ten.

1 zero	→	$4 \times \mathbf{10} = 40$
2 zeros	→	$4 \times \mathbf{100} = 400$
3 zeros	→	$4 \times \mathbf{1,000} = 4,000$

Try It • Complete each pattern.

1. $7 \times 10 =$ _____

$7 \times 100 =$ _____

$7 \times 1,000 =$ _____

2. $2 \times 10 =$ _____

$2 \times 100 =$ _____

$2 \times 1,000 =$ _____

3. $9 \times 10 =$ _____

$9 \times 100 =$ _____

$9 \times 1,000 =$ _____

4. $3 \times 10 =$ _____

$3 \times 100 =$ _____

$3 \times 1,000 =$ _____

5. $8 \times 10 =$ _____

$8 \times 100 =$ _____

$8 \times 1,000 =$ _____

6. $5 \times 10 =$ _____

$5 \times 100 =$ _____

$5 \times 1,000 =$ _____

Power Practice • Find each product.

7. $9 \times 100 =$ _____

8. $3 \times 1,000 =$ _____

9. $7 \times 10 =$ _____

10. $6 \times 10 =$ _____

11. $5 \times 100 =$ _____

12. $3 \times 1,000 =$ _____

13. $8 \times 1,000 =$ _____

14. $4 \times 10 =$ _____

15. $8 \times 10 =$ _____

16. $4 \times 100 =$ _____

17. $6 \times 1,000 =$ _____

18. $2 \times 100 =$ _____

Associative Property of Addition

Learn

What Can I Do?
I want to add
3 numbers.

Associative Property of Addition: The grouping of the addends does not change the sum.

Use the Associative Property of Addition to find
$5 + 1 + 9$.

Group the numbers to make addition easier.
Use parentheses.

$5 + (1 + 9) =$ ___?___

$5 + 10 = 15$

So, $5 + 1 + 9 = 15$.

> Look for a ten
> or a double

Try It • **Find each sum. Add the grouped addends first.**

1. $(8 + 2) + 3$

_____ $+ 3 =$ _____

2. $7 + (2 + 2)$

$7 +$ _____ $=$ _____

Power Practice • **Find each sum.**

3. $6 + 9 + 1 =$ _____

4. $3 + 7 + 3 =$ _____

5. $9 + 5 + 4 =$ _____

6. $3 + 2 + 7 =$ _____

7. $5 + 8 + 2 =$ _____

8. $4 + 6 + 5 =$ _____

9. $8 + 4 + 6 =$ _____

10. $9 + 3 + 7 =$ _____

Multiplication Properties

Learn

What Can I Do?
I want to use properties of multiplication.

Property	What It Tells You
Commutative	You can multiply two numbers in either order.
Zero	Any number times zero is zero.
Distributive	You can break a product into the sum of two other products.

Try It • Use the Distributive Property to fill in the blanks.

1. $5 \times 43 = (5 \times 40) + (5 \times$ _____ $)$ **2.** $4 \times 31 = (4 \times 30) + ($ _____ $\times 1)$

3. $9 \times 27 = (9 \times$ _____ $) + (9 \times 7)$ **4.** $8 \times 62 = ($ _____ $\times 60) + (8 \times 2)$

Power Practice • Complete by writing the missing number. Tell which property you used.

5. $5 \times 0 =$ _____   _____ Property

6. $3 \times 26 = (3 \times$ _____ $) + ($ _____ $\times 6)$ _____ Property

7. $6 \times 7 = 7 \times$ _____   _____ Property

8. $7 \times 18 = (7 \times$ _____ $) + (7 \times$ _____ $)$ _____ Property

Multiplying with Multiples of 10, 100, or 1,000

Activity **52**

Learn

What Can I Do?
I want to multiply with tens, hundreds, and thousands.

Use place value.

$5 \times 4,000 = 5 \times 4$ thousands

Use the basic fact.

5×4 thousands $= 20$ thousands $= 20,000$

Think :
$5 \times 4 = 20$

Try It • Write each number in standard form.

1. 24 tens = _____

2. 56 hundreds = _____

3. 63 thousands = _____

4. 18 tens = _____

5. 30 hundreds = _____

6. 12 thousands = _____

7. 35 tens = _____

8. 14 hundreds = _____

9. 45 thousands = _____

Complete the steps to find each product.

10. 3×80

= 3 × _____ tens

= _____ tens

= _____

11. 7×400

= 7 × _____ hundreds

= _____ hundreds

= _____

12. $6 \times 3,000$

= 6 × _____ thousands

= _____ thousands

= _____

Use the basic fact to write each product.

13. $4 \times 6 = 24$

$4 \times 60 =$ _____

14. $7 \times 9 = 63$

$7 \times 900 =$ _____

15. $5 \times 8 = 40$

$5 \times 8{,}000 =$ _____

16. $3 \times 9 = 27$

$3 \times 90 =$ _____

17. $6 \times 5 = 30$

$6 \times 500 =$ _____

18. $2 \times 6 = 12$

$2 \times 6{,}000 =$ _____

19. $6 \times 7 =$ _____

$6 \times 70 =$ _____

20. $8 \times 3 =$ _____

$8 \times 300 =$ _____

21. $4 \times 5 =$ _____

$4 \times 5{,}000 =$ _____

22. $5 \times 3 =$ _____

$5 \times 30 =$ _____

23. $9 \times 2 =$ _____

$9 \times 200 =$ _____

24. $8 \times 8 =$ _____

$8 \times 8{,}000 =$ _____

Power Practice • Find each product.

25.   800
        $\times\ 9$

26.   70
         $\times\ 7$

27. 4,000
        $\times\ \ 3$

28.   60
         $\times\ 8$

29.   50
         $\times\ 4$

30. 8,000
        $\times\ \ 4$

31.   600
        $\times\ \ 6$

32. 2,000
        $\times\ \ 6$

33. 900
       $\times\ 5$

34.   30
         $\times\ 4$

35. 7,000
        $\times\ \ 8$

36.   90
         $\times\ 7$

37. 7,000
        $\times\ \ 6$

38. 900
       $\times\ 9$

39.   50
         $\times\ 2$

40. 500
       $\times\ 6$

Multiplying a Two-Digit Number by a One-Digit Number

Learn

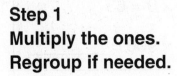

What Can I Do?
I want to multiply a one-digit number times a two-digit number.

Step 1
Multiply the ones.
Regroup if needed.

```
  4
 2⑦
×⑥
───
  2
```

Think: 6 x 7 = 42

Step 2
Multiply the tens.
Add.

```
  4
 ②7
×⑥
───
162
```

Think: 6 x 2 = 12
Then add. 12 + 4 = 16

Try It • Finish each problem.

```
      4
1. 38
  × 5
  ────
     0
```

```
      1
2. 76
  × 3
  ────
     8
```

```
      2
3. 54
  × 7
  ────
     8
```

```
      6
4. 27
  × 9
  ────
     3
```

```
      1
5. 84
  × 4
  ────
     6
```

```
      7
6. 38
  × 9
  ────
     2
```

```
      2
7. 54
  × 6
  ────
     4
```

```
      1
8. 37
  × 2
  ────
     4
```

```
      4
9. 46
  × 8
  ────
     8
```

```
       2
10. 68
   × 3
   ────
      4
```

```
       5
11. 59
   × 6
   ────
      4
```

```
       3
12. 65
   × 7
   ────
      5
```

Name _____

Find each product.

13. 32 × 1	**14.** 73 × 3	**15.** 53 × 7	**16.** 43 × 2
17. 91 × 5	**18.** 62 × 5	**19.** 78 × 3	**20.** 34 × 2

Power Practice • **Find each product.**

21. 32 × 6	**22.** 68 × 2	**23.** 24 × 7	**24.** 69 × 4
25. 24 × 9	**26.** 53 × 7	**27.** 78 × 3	**28.** 46 × 8
29. 88 × 3	**30.** 39 × 5		
31. 26 × 8	**32.** 57 × 6		
33. 47 × 2	**34.** 83 × 4		
35. 65 × 5	**36.** 45 × 9		

Learn with
Partners & Parents

Greatest Product Game

You will need one set of 0 to 9 digit cards.

• Turn the cards over and mix them up. Each player draws three cards.

• Make a problem like this:

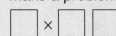

Find your product.

• The player with the greater product gets one point. Play until one player has 7 points.

Name _____

Multiplying a Three-Digit Number by a One-Digit Number

Learn

What Can I Do?
I want to multiply three-digit numbers.

1. Multiply ones.	2. Multiply tens. Add.	3. Multiply hundreds. Add.
2 45③ × ⑦ ‾‾‾‾ 1	3 2 4⑤3 × ⑦ ‾‾‾‾ 7 1	3 2 ④53 × ⑦ ‾‾‾‾‾ 3 , 1 7 1
Think: 7 x 3 = 21	Think: 7 x 5 = 35 Then add. 35 + 2 = 37.	Think: 7 x 4 = 28 Then add. 28 + 3 = 31.

Try It • Find each product. These problems have no regrouping.

1. 302
× 4

2. 643
× 2

3. 512
× 3

4. 714
× 2

Finish each problem.

5. ⁴⁵ 179
× 6
‾‾‾‾
74

6. ¹³ 624
× 8
‾‾‾‾
92

7. ³¹ 273
× 5
‾‾‾‾
65

8. ⁴⁵ 458
× 7
‾‾‾‾
06

9. ⁶ 717
× 9
‾‾‾‾
3

10. ³ 528
× 4
‾‾‾‾
2

11. ⁵ 638
× 7
‾‾‾‾
6

12. ¹ 425
× 3
‾‾‾‾
5

Name _____

Find each product. Use a dollar sign and decimal point in each answer.

13. $3.52
    ×   6

14. $1.76
    ×   5

15. $8.04
    ×   8

16. $4.63
    ×   2

Power Practice • Find each product.

17. 314
    ×   7

18. 261
    ×   3

19. 585
    ×   4

20. 193
    ×   7

21. 426
    ×   2

22. 619
    ×   9

23. 758
    ×   5

24. 294
    ×   8

25. $7.24
    ×   5

26. $5.81
    ×   6

27. $2.90
    ×   4

28. $6.35
    ×   2

29. $8 \times 341 =$ _____

30. $3 \times 826 =$ _____

31. $7 \times 684 =$ _____

32. $9 \times 256 =$ _____

33. $5 \times 489 =$ _____

34. $9 \times 327 =$ _____

35. $8 \times 295 =$ _____

36. $6 \times 372 =$ _____

37. $3 \times 898 =$ _____

38. $5 \times \$2.43 =$ _____

39. $9 \times \$7.56 =$ _____

40. $6 \times \$4.07 =$ _____

41. $6 \times \$7.15 =$ _____

42. $5 \times \$9.49 =$ _____

43. $8 \times \$3.89 =$ _____

44. $7 \times \$4.78 =$ _____

45. $9 \times \$6.85 =$ _____

46. $4 \times \$7.79 =$ _____

Function Tables

Learn

What Can I Do?

I want to find missing numbers in a function table.

Look for the rule.

Look at the number going in, the input. Then look at the number coming out, the output. What number would make this true?.

3 x <u>?</u> = 15

Input	Output
③	⑮
4	20
6	30
9	?

Think: 3 times 5 is 15.

The rule is "times 5."

So, 9 x 5 = 45

Try It • **Use the rules to complete the tables.**

1. Rule: × 6

Input	Output
3	18
4	24
7	

2. Rule: × 3

Input	Output
2	6
6	18
9	

3. Rule: × 4

Input	Output
1	4
5	20
8	

4. Rule: × 8

Input	Output
3	24
6	48
	56

5. Rule: × 2

Input	Output
4	8
6	12
	16

6. Rule: × 7

Input	Output
2	14
4	28
	35

Power Practice • Complete each table.
Then identify the rule.

7. Rule: _____

Input	Output
3	21
5	35
7	49
9	

8. Rule: _____

Input	Output
1	3
3	9
6	18
7	

9. Rule: _____

Input	Output
4	24
5	30
7	42
8	

10. Rule: _____

Input	Output
3	12
5	20
6	24
8	

11. Rule: _____

Input	Output
4	20
6	30
7	35
9	

12. Rule: _____

Input	Output
2	18
4	36
5	45
7	

13. Rule: _____

Input	Output
3	24
5	40
7	56
	64

14. Rule: _____

Input	Output
2	4
4	8
6	12
	18

15. Rule: _____

Input	Output
1	6
3	18
4	24
	36

16. Rule: _____

Input	Output
4	16
6	24
8	32
	40

17. Rule: _____

Input	Output
2	10
4	20
8	40
10	

18. Rule: _____

Input	Output
3	18
5	30
7	42
	54

Missing Factors

Learn

Use basic multiplication facts.

Write the missing factor.

$2 \times$ __?__ $= 10$

Think: 2 times what number is equal to 10?

Find the multiplication fact for 2 with a product of 10.

What Can I Do?
I want to find a missing factor.

$2 \times 1 = 2$
$2 \times 2 = 4$
$2 \times 3 = 6$
$2 \times 4 = 8$
$2 \times 5 = 10$

So, 5 is the missing factor.

Try It • **Write each product. Then write each missing factor.**

1. $3 \times 4 =$ _____

$3 \times$ _____ $= 12$

2. $4 \times 5 =$ _____

$4 \times$ _____ $= 20$

Power Practice • **Write each missing factor.**

3. $2 \times$ _____ $= 14$

4. $5 \times$ _____ $= 15$

5. $4 \times$ _____ $= 16$

6. $3 \times$ _____ $= 24$

7. $6 \times$ _____ $= 24$

8. $4 \times$ _____ $= 36$

9. $7 \times$ _____ $= 63$

10. $5 \times$ _____ $= 20$

Closest Multiple

Learn

What Can I Do?
I want to find multiples close to a given number.

Use a list of multiples.

Example: What multiple of 5 is closest to 27?

Multiples of 5: 5, 10, 15, 20, 25, 30, 35, 40, 45, 50

Answer: 25

Try It • List the first ten multiples of each number.

1. 6 _____

2. 7 _____

3. 8 _____

Power Practice • Write a multiple *less than* each number.

What multiple of 6 is closest to each number?

4. 55 _____ **5.** 20 _____ **6.** 39 _____ **7.** 51 _____ **8.** 25 _____

What multiple of 7 is closest to each number?

9. 45 _____ **10.** 30 _____ **11.** 59 _____ **12.** 23 _____ **13.** 50 _____

What multiple of 8 is closest to each number?

14. 43 _____ **15.** 66 _____ **16.** 73 _____ **17.** 20 _____ **18.** 35 _____

Closest (Three–Digit) Multiple

Learn

What Can I Do?

I want to use closest multiples to help me estimate quotients.

Use multiplication facts to estimate quotients.

To estimate the quotient of 255 ÷ 8 look for the closest multiple of 8 and 10 that is less than 255.

Think:

8 × 1 = 8, so 8 × 10 = 80	80 is less than 255.
8 × 2 = 16, so 8 × 20 = 160	160 is less than 255.
8 × 3 = 24, so 8 × **30 = 240**	240 is less than 255.
8 × 4 = 32, so 8 × 40 = 320	320 is too great.

So, 240 is the closest multiple of 8 and 10 that is less than 255.

Since 8 × 30 = 240, the quotient of 255 ÷ 8 is about 30.

Try It • **Complete.**

1. To estimate the quotient of 235 ÷ 6, find the closest multiple of _____ and 10 that is less than _____.

2. 6 × 1 = 6, so 6 × 10 = _____

   6 × 2 = 12, so 6 × 20 = _____

   6 × 3 = 18, so 6 × 30 = _____

   6 × 4 = 24, so 6 × 40 = _____

   6 × 5 = 30, so 6 × 50 = _____

   6 × 6 = 36, so 6 × 60 = _____

   6 × 7 = 42, so 6 × 70 = _____

3. The closest multiple of 6 and 10 that is less than 235 is 6 × 30, or _____.

4. So, the quotient of 235 ÷ 6 is about _____.

Continue the list of multiples. Circle the closest multiple less than the number.

5. 255

Multiples of 7 and 10: 7 × 10 = 70, 7 × 20 = _____, 7 × 30 = _____,

7 × 40 = _____, 7 × 50 = _____, 7 × 60 = _____,

7 × 70 = _____, 7 × 80= _____, 7 × 90 = _____

6. 338

Multiples of 8 and 10: 8 × 10 = 80, 8 × 20 = _____, 8 × 30 = _____,

8 × 40 = _____, 8 × 50 = _____, 8 × 60 = _____,

8 × 70 = _____, 8 × 80= _____ , 8 × 90 = _____

Power Practice • Find the closest multiples that are less than each number. Complete.

Find the closest multiple of 6 and 10 that is less than each number.

7. 554 _____ So the quotient of 554 ÷ 6 is about _____.
8. 207 _____ So the quotient of 207 ÷ 6 is about _____.

Find the closest multiple of 5 and 10 that is less than each number.

9. 354 _____ So the quotient of 354 ÷ 5 is about _____.
10. 337 _____ So the quotient of 337 ÷ 5 is about _____.

Find the closest multiple of 7 and 10 that is less than each number.

11. 451 _____ So the quotient of 451 ÷ 7 is about _____.
12. 207 _____ So the quotient of 207 ÷ 7 is about _____.

Find the closest multiple of 9 and 10 that is less than each number.

13. 387 _____ So the quotient of 387 ÷ 9 is about _____.
14. 472 _____ So the quotient of 472 ÷ 9 is about _____.

Find the closest multiple of 8 and 10 that is less than each number.

15. 432 _____ So the quotient of 432 ÷ 8 is about _____.
16. 665 _____ So the quotient of 665 ÷ 8 is about _____.

Meaning of Division

Learn

What Can I Do?

I want to draw pictures for division problems.

Put the same number in each group.	**Make equal groups.**
12 stars 4 stars in each group	18 circles 3 equal groups of circles

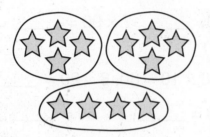

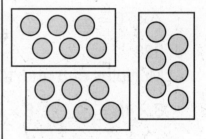

Count the groups. 3 groups of stars	Count the number in each group. 6 circles in each group

Try It • **Use counters or small objects.**

1. Use 20 counters. Put 4 counters in each group.
   How many groups do you get?

   _____ groups of counters

2. Use 18 counters. Make 2 equal groups.
   How many counters are there in each group?

   _____ counters in each group

3. Use 15 counters. Put 3 counters in each group.
   How many groups do you get?

   _____ groups of counters

4. Use 24 counters. Make 4 equal groups.
   How many counters are there in each group?

   _____ counters in each group

Power Practice . Draw each picture. Then tell how many equal groups, or how many are in each group.

5. 8 squares

4 squares in each group

_____ groups of squares

6. 10 triangles

2 equal groups of triangles

_____ triangles in each group

7. 6 stars

3 stars in each group

_____ groups of stars

8. 9 circles

3 equal groups of circles

_____ circles in each group

9. 16 triangles

8 triangles in each group

_____ groups of triangles

10. 12 squares

3 equal groups of squares

_____ squares in each group

Division Facts Through 9

Learn

What Can I Do?
I want to divide one number by another number.

Use any division strategy.

Find 24 ÷ 6.

A. Use a related multiplication fact. Think: How many 6s make 24?

$4 \times 6 = 24$, so $24 \div 6 = 4$

B. Use an array.

You can make 4 equal groups of 6.
So, $24 \div 6 = 4$.

C. Use repeated subtraction.

Subtract 6 four times.

$24 - 6 = 18$
$18 - 6 = 12$
$12 - 6 = 6$
$6 - 6 = 0$

So, $24 \div 6 = 4$.

D. Skip count backward on a number line.

Skip count backward by 6 four times.

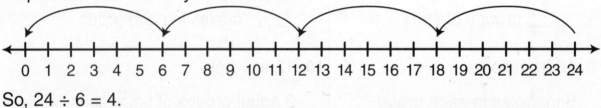

So, $24 \div 6 = 4$.

Try It • Find each double.

A. Use a related multiplication fact to find the quotient.

1. _____ $\times 7 = 28$, so $28 \div 7 =$ _____

2. _____ $\times 6 = 30$, so $30 \div 6 =$ _____

Name _____

A. Use an array to find each quotient.

3. 27 ÷ 9 = _____

4. 15 ÷ 3 = _____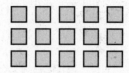

B. Use repeated subtraction to find each quotient.

5. 9 ÷ 3 = _____

Subtract: _____

_____

6. 30 ÷ 5 = _____

Subtract: _____

_____

_____

C. Skip count backward to find each quotient.

7. 45 ÷ 5 = _____

Count backward: _____

_____

8. 42 ÷ 6 = _____

Count backward: _____

_____

Power Practice • **Find each quotient. Use any method.**

9. 8 ÷ 4 = _____

10. 20 ÷ 4 = _____

11. 48 ÷ 8 = _____

12. 35 ÷ 5 = _____

13. 36 ÷ 6 = _____

14. 40 ÷ 5 = _____

15. 28 ÷ 4 = _____

16. 12 ÷ 6 = _____

17. 49 ÷ 7 = _____

18. 8)64

19. 9)81

20. 7)21

21. 4)16

22. 4)24

23. 7)42

24. 8)32

25. 4)36

Division Facts

Learn

Use a related multiplication fact.

To find 56 ÷ 8, think:
What number times 8 equals 56?

Since 7 × 8 is 56, 56 ÷ 8 = 7.

Use a Multiplication Table.

What Can I Do?
I want to practice the division facts.

×	0	1	2	3	4	5	6	7	8	9	10
0	0	0	0	0	0	0	0	0	0	0	0
1	0	1	2	3	4	5	6	7	8	9	10
2	0	2	4	6	8	10	12	14	16	18	20
3	0	3	6	9	12	15	18	21	24	27	30
4	0	4	8	12	16	20	24	28	32	36	40
5	0	5	10	15	20	25	30	35	40	45	50
6	0	6	12	18	24	30	36	42	48	54	60
7	0	7	14	21	28	35	42	49	56	63	70
row → 8	0	8	16	24	32	40	48	56	64	72	80
9	0	9	18	27	36	45	54	63	72	81	90
10	0	10	20	30	40	50	60	70	80	90	100

Example: To find 56 ÷ 8, look across the 8 row until you get to 56. The answer, 7, is directly above the 56.

Try It • Use the related multiplication fact to write each quotient.

1. 6 × 8 = 48

48 ÷ 6 = _____

2. 6 × 9 = 54

54 ÷ 9 = _____

3. 7 × 7 = 49

49 ÷ 7 = _____

4. 4 × 8 = 32

32 ÷ 8 = _____

5. 9 × 8 = 72

72 ÷ 8 = _____

6. 5 × 9 = 45

45 ÷ 5 = _____

7. 7 × 9 = 63

63 ÷ 7 = _____

8. 5 × 7 = 35

35 ÷ 5 = _____

9. 8 × 8 = 64

64 ÷ 8 = _____

Name _____

Use the multiplication table if you need help.
Practice dividing by 7.

10. $49 \div 7 =$ _____   **11.** $35 \div 7 =$ _____   **12.** $28 \div 7 =$ _____

13. $14 \div 7 =$ _____   **14.** $70 \div 7 =$ _____   **15.** $56 \div 7 =$ _____

16. $63 \div 7 =$ _____   **17.** $21 \div 7 =$ _____   **18.** $42 \div 7 =$ _____

Practice dividing by 8.

19. $72 \div 8 =$ _____   **20.** $32 \div 8 =$ _____   **21.** $16 \div 8 =$ _____

22. $40 \div 8 =$ _____   **23.** $24 \div 8 =$ _____   **24.** $56 \div 8 =$ _____

25. $8 \div 8 =$ _____   **26.** $64 \div 8 =$ _____   **27.** $48 \div 8 =$ _____

Practice dividing by 9.

28. $45 \div 9 =$ _____   **29.** $18 \div 9 =$ _____   **30.** $63 \div 9 =$ _____

31. $27 \div 9 =$ _____   **32.** $90 \div 9 =$ _____   **33.** $72 \div 9 =$ _____

34. $81 \div 9 =$ _____   **35.** $54 \div 9 =$ _____   **36.** $36 \div 9 =$ _____

Power Practice • **Find each quotient.**

37. $64 \div 8 =$ _____   **38.** $56 \div 7 =$ _____   **39.** $24 \div 4 =$ _____

40. $35 \div 5 =$ _____   **41.** $32 \div 8 =$ _____   **42.** $63 \div 7 =$ _____

43. $21 \div 7 =$ _____   **44.** $8 \div 1 =$ _____   **45.** $48 \div 8 =$ _____

46. $72 \div 9 =$ _____   **47.** $28 \div 4 =$ _____   **48.** $24 \div 6 =$ _____

49. $16 \div 2 =$ _____   **50.** $36 \div 9 =$ _____   **51.** $81 \div 9 =$ _____

Name _____

Division with Remainders

Learn

What Can I Do?
I want to divide by a one-digit number.

Find the greatest possible quotient.

⑦ ←— **quotient**
6)45

Make sure the remainder is less than the divisor.

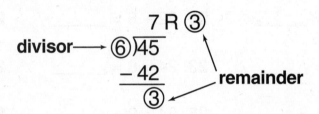

divisor —→ ⑥)45 7 R ③
      − 42
        ③ —→ **remainder**

Try It • Finish each problem. Find each quotient and remainder.

1. 4)38
    − 36

2. 5)47
    − 45

3. 8)50
    − 48

4. 6)28
    − 24

5. 6)37
    − 36

6. 8)61
    − 56

7. 2)15
    − 14

8. 7)43
    − 42

9. 9)75
    − 72

10. 5)22
    − 20

11. 7)25
    − 21

12. 3)17
    − 15

Name _____

Power Practice • Write the remainder and the quotient.

13. 37 ÷ 7 = _____ R _____   **14.** 26 ÷ 3 = _____ R _____

15. 34 ÷ 5 = _____ R _____   **16.** 62 ÷ 9 = _____ R _____

17. 11 ÷ 2 = _____ R _____

Learn with Partners & Parents

Division Roll

You will need three 1–6 number cubes.

18. 40 ÷ 6 = _____ R _____

- Toss the cubes. Use the numbers to make two different division problems like this:

19. 44 ÷ 8 = _____ R _____

- Find the quotient and remainder for each problem you make.

- Toss again. Find the problems with the greatest and least quotients.

20. 29 ÷ 4 = _____ R _____

- Toss to get three different digits. Write all six division problems you can make with these digits.

Multiplication and Division Facts

Learn

Use counters.

What Can I Do?
I forgot some multiplication and division facts.

Make an array to show the multiplication fact.	Make an array to show the division fact.
4×6	$24 \div 8$
Show 4 rows of 6 counters each. Then count to find the product.	Use 24 counters in all. Show groups of 8. Then count the number of groups to find the quotient.

There are 24 counters.

$4 \times 6 = 24$

There are 3 groups of 8.

$24 \div 8 = 3$

Try It • Use counters. Multiply or divide.

1. $\begin{array}{r} 7 \\ \times 5 \\ \hline \end{array}$

2. $\begin{array}{r} 8 \\ \times 4 \\ \hline \end{array}$

3. $\begin{array}{r} 6 \\ \times 3 \\ \hline \end{array}$

4. $5\overline{)15}$

5. $7\overline{)28}$

6. $6\overline{)18}$

Name_____

7. 3
   ×2

8. 4
   ×6

9. 2
   ×7

10. 0
    ×4

11. 6)30

12. 3)27

13. 7)42

14. 9)36

15. 9
    ×4

16. 8
    ×8

17. 7
    ×5

18. 2
    ×9

19. 5)40

20. 1)6

21. 4)8

22. 7)56

23. 8
    ×0

24. 7
    ×9

25. 4
    ×4

26. 7
    ×2

27. 8)72

28. 9)54

29. 9)72

30. 5)20

31. 9
    ×9

32. 1
    ×3

33. 7
    ×8

34. 9
    ×3

35. 8)48

36. 2)16

37. 5)45

38. 4)32

Multiply and Divide by 10, 100, and 1,000

Activity 64

Learn

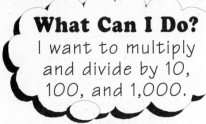

What Can I Do?
I want to multiply and divide by 10, 100, and 1,000.

Use basic facts.

To multiply by 10, 100, or 1,000, use basic facts to write the first digit.

$7 \times 10 = ?$
$7 \times 100 = ?$
$7 \times 1,000 = ?$

Use the basic fact $7 \times 1 = 7$.

Then count the number of zeros in 10, 100, or 1,000. Write the number of zeros in the product.

10 has 1 zero, so $7 \times \mathbf{10} = \mathbf{70}$.
100 has 2 zeros, so $7 \times \mathbf{100} = \mathbf{700}$.
1,000 has 3 zeros, so $7 \times \mathbf{1,000} = \mathbf{7,000}$.

Use multiplication to divide.

To divide by 10, 100, or 1,000, use what you know about multiplication.

You know that multiplication and division are related operations.

$60 \div 10 = ?$ ⟶ $6 \times 10 = 60$, so $60 \div 10 = 6$.

$600 \div 100 = ?$ ⟶ $6 \times 100 = 600$, so $600 \div 100 = 6$.

$6,000 \div 1,000 = ?$ ⟶ $6 \times 1,000 = 6,000$, so $6,000 \div 1,000 = 6$.

Name_____

1. $10 \times 9 =$ _____   **2.** $8 \times 100 =$ _____   **3.** $4 \times 1,000 =$ _____

Use multiplication to complete each division sentence.

4. $4 \times 100 = 400$ so $400 \div 100 =$ _____

5. $1,000 \times 8 = 8,000$ so $8,000 \div 1,000 =$ _____

6. $7 \times 10 = 70$ so $70 \div 10 =$ _____

Power Practice • Find each product or quotient.

7. $1,000 \times 5 =$ _____   **8.** $400 \div 100 =$ _____

9. $7,000 \div 1,000 =$ _____   **10.** $2 \times 100 =$ _____

11. $30 \div 10 =$ _____   **12.** $100 \times 8 =$ _____

13. $\begin{array}{r} 1,000 \\ \times\ \ 2 \\ \hline \end{array}$ **14.** $100\overline{)800}$ **15.** $\begin{array}{r} 100 \\ \times 3 \\ \hline \end{array}$ **16.** $1,000\overline{)9,000}$

17. $\begin{array}{r} 1,000 \\ \times\ \ 3 \\ \hline \end{array}$ **18.** $1,000\overline{)4,000}$ **19.** $\begin{array}{r} 1,000 \\ \times\ \ 5 \\ \hline \end{array}$ **20.** $10\overline{)90}$

21. $1,000 \times 3 =$ _____   **22.** $6,000 \div 1,000 =$ _____

23. $50 \div 10 =$ _____   **24.** $100 \times 4 =$ _____

25. $1,000 \times 8 =$ _____   **26.** $40 \div 10 =$ _____

Name _____

Meaning of Fractions

Look at the parts of the fraction.

Every fraction has **two** parts.

numerator→ $\dfrac{7}{8}$ ← denominator

The **denominator** is the number below the line. It tells how many parts in the whole.

The **numerator** is the number above the line. It tells how many parts in the fraction.

Think: $\frac{7}{8}$ means 7 out of 8 parts.

I should color 7 out of 8 parts to show $\frac{7}{8}$.

This picture shows $\frac{7}{8}$.

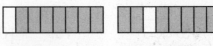

Notice that there are many ways to show $\frac{7}{8}$.

These drawings also show $\frac{7}{8}$.

What Can I Do?

I want to show $\frac{7}{8}$ of this rectangle.

 Try It • **Complete each sentence. Then color to show the fraction.**

1. Color $\frac{4}{5}$ of the circle.

I will color _____ out of _____ parts.

2. Color $\frac{1}{4}$ of the rectangle.

I will color _____ out of _____ parts.

3. Color $\frac{5}{12}$ of the square.

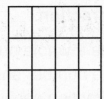

I will color ____ out of ____ parts.

4. Color $\frac{3}{10}$ of the rectangle.

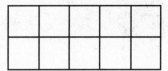

I will color ____ out of ____ parts.

Power Practice • Show the fraction.

5. Color $\frac{5}{6}$ of the rectangle.

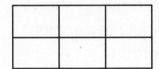

6. Color $\frac{7}{10}$ of the circle.

7. Color $\frac{1}{8}$ of the square.

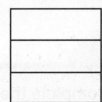

8. Color $\frac{2}{3}$ of the square.

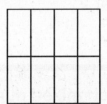

9. Color $\frac{3}{16}$ of the rectangle.

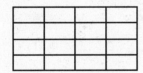

10. Color $\frac{1}{2}$ of the circle.

11. Color $\frac{11}{12}$ of the circle.

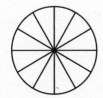

12. Color $\frac{7}{20}$ of the rectangle.

Name _____

Mixed Numbers

Learn

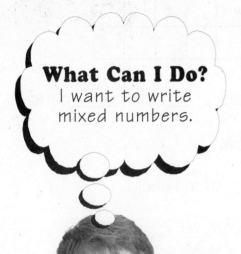

What Can I Do?
I want to write mixed numbers.

Write a number and a fraction.

A mixed number includes a whole number and a fraction. The whole number shows the number of wholes. The fraction shows the number of remaining parts.

To write the mixed number, write the whole number and the fraction together. Write the whole number first.

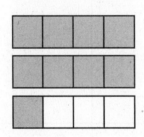

This drawing shows 2 whole rectangles colored. It also shows $\frac{1}{4}$ rectangle colored. All together, the drawing shows the mixed number $2\frac{1}{4}$.

Try It • Complete the sentences. Then write each mixed number.

1.

There are _____ wholes.

The fraction is _____ .

The mixed number is _____ .

2.

There is _____ whole.

The fraction is _____ .

The mixed number is _____ .

3.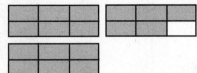

There are ____ wholes.

The fraction is _____ .

The mixed number is _____ .

4.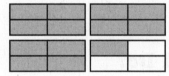

There are ____ wholes.

The fraction is _____ .

The mixed number is _____ .

Power Practice • Write each mixed number.

5.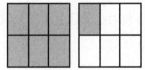

_____

6.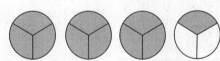

_____

7.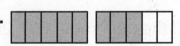

_____

8.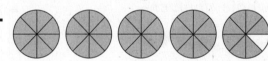

_____

9.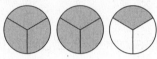

_____

10.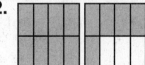

_____

11.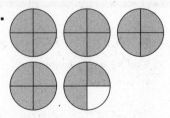

_____

12.

_____

105

Hundreds, Tens, and Ones

Learn

Use place-value models.

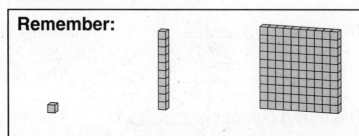

Remember:

1 one = 1   **1 ten = 10**   **1 hundred = 100**

How many **ones** are in 7?

 Count the ones. 1,2,3,4,5,6,7
So 7 = 7 ones

How many **tens** are in 50?

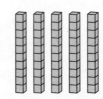 Count the tens. 10,20,30,40,50
So 50 = 5 tens

What Can I Do?
I want to find the number of ones, tens, and hundreds in whole numbers.

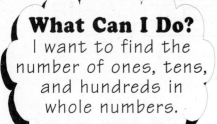

How many **hundreds** are in 200?

 Count the hundreds. 100, 200
So 200 = 2 hundreds

Try It • **Write the number of ones.**

1. ▱▱▱

3 = _____ ones

2. ▱▱▱▱▱▱▱▱▱

9 = _____ ones

3. ▱▱▱▱▱▱

6 = _____ ones

Name _____

Write the number of tens.

4.

5.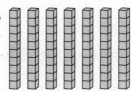

6.

40 = _____ tens   70 = _____ tens   30 = _____ tens

Write the number of hundreds.

7.

8.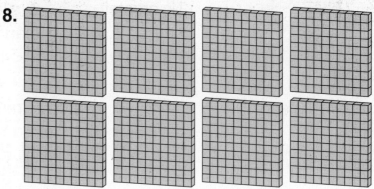

100 = _____ hundred   800 = _____ hundreds

Power Practice • Write each missing number.

9.   2 = _____ ones   10.   50 = _____ tens

11. 300 = _____ hundreds   12.   60 = _____ tens

13. 500 = _____ hundreds   14.   80 = _____ tens

15. 900 = _____ hundreds   16.   20 = _____ tens

17.   5 = _____ ones   18.   90 = _____ tens

19. 400 = _____ hundreds   20.   10 = _____ ten

Name _____

Compare Numbers

Learn

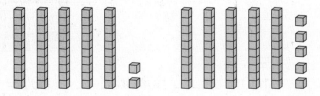

What Can I Do?
I want to compare two numbers.

Use place-value models to compare numbers.

Remember: You can compare numbers using >, <, and =.

> means **greater than**	< means **less than**	= means **equal to**
3 is greater than 1.	2 is less than 4.	5 is equal to 5.
3 > 1	2 < 4	5 = 5

Compare 23 and 19.

Compare the tens first.
If the tens are the same, compare the ones.

2 tens are greater than 1 ten.
2 tens > 1 ten
So, 23 > 19

Compare 52 and 55.

Compare the tens first.
If the tens are the same, compare the ones.

5 tens = 5 tens, so compare the ones.
2 ones < 5 ones
So, 52 < 55

Try It . Compare. Write >, <, or =.
Use place-value models to help.

1.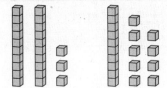

8 ◯ 7

2.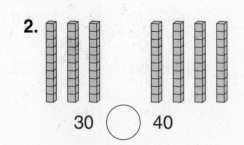

30 ◯ 40

Name _____

Compare. Write >, <, or =. Use place-value models to help.

3.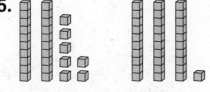

18 ◯ 18

4.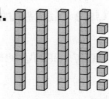

45 ◯ 26

5.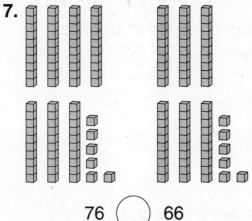

27 ◯ 31

6.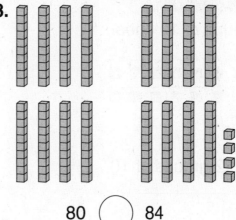

53 ◯ 53

7.

76 ◯ 66

8.

80 ◯ 84

Power Practice • Compare. Write >, <, or =.

9. 9 ◯ 5   **10.** 12 ◯ 17   **11.** 20 ◯ 40

12. 22 ◯ 22   **13.** 14 ◯ 32   **14.** 18 ◯ 16

15. 45 ◯ 34   **16.** 59 ◯ 62   **17.** 67 ◯ 37

18. 23 ◯ 32   **19.** 71 ◯ 76   **20.** 98 ◯ 98

Regroup Ones

Learn

What Can I Do?
I want to regroup ones
as tens and ones.

Use place-value models.

How many tens and ones are in 25 ones?

25 ones = _____ tens _____ ones

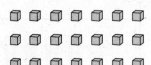

25 ones

Make groups of 10 ones.

There are 2 groups of 10.

Trade each group of 10 ones
for 1 ten.

There are 2 tens and 5 ones.

So, 25 ones = 2 tens 5 ones.

Try It • **Write the number of tens and ones. Use the place-value models to help.**

1.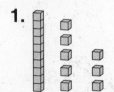

    18 = _____ ten _____ ones

2.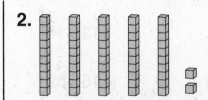

    52 = _____ tens _____ ones

Circle groups of 10 ones.
Write the number of tens and ones.

3. ⬛ ⬛ ⬛ ⬛ ⬛ ⬛ ⬛ ⬛ ⬛

⬛ ⬛ ⬛ ⬛ ⬛ ⬛ ⬛

16 ones = ___ ten ___ ones

4. ⬛ ⬛ ⬛ ⬛ ⬛ ⬛ ⬛ ⬛ ⬛ ⬛ ⬛ ⬛ ⬛

⬛ ⬛ ⬛ ⬛ ⬛ ⬛ ⬛ ⬛ ⬛ ⬛ ⬛ ⬛ ⬛

⬛ ⬛ ⬛ ⬛ ⬛

31 ones = ___ tens ___ one

5. ⬛ ⬛ ⬛ ⬛ ⬛ ⬛ ⬛ ⬛ ⬛ ⬛ ⬛

⬛ ⬛ ⬛ ⬛ ⬛ ⬛ ⬛ ⬛ ⬛ ⬛ ⬛

⬛ ⬛ ⬛ ⬛ ⬛ ⬛ ⬛

29 ones = ___ tens ___ ones

6. ⬛ ⬛ ⬛ ⬛ ⬛ ⬛ ⬛ ⬛ ⬛ ⬛ ⬛ ⬛ ⬛ ⬛

⬛ ⬛ ⬛ ⬛ ⬛ ⬛ ⬛ ⬛ ⬛ ⬛ ⬛ ⬛ ⬛ ⬛

⬛ ⬛ ⬛ ⬛

43 ones = ___ tens ___ ones

Power Practice • **Write the number of tens and ones.**

7. 11 = _____ ten _____ one

8. 17 = _____ ten _____ ones

9. 34 = _____ tens _____ ones

10. 55 = _____ tens _____ ones

11. 67 = _____ tens _____ ones

12. 82 = _____ tens _____ ones

13. 78 = _____ tens _____ ones

14. 96 = _____ tens _____ ones

15. 23 = _____ tens _____ ones

16. 19 = _____ ten _____ ones

17. 41 = _____ tens _____ one

18. 92 = _____ tens _____ ones

Name_____

Hundreds and Tens

Learn

What Can I Do?

I want to write whole numbers for hundreds and tens.

Use a place-value chart.

Write the number.

7 tens = _____

7 tens is the same as 70.

So, 7 tens = 70.

hundreds	tens	ones
	7	0

3 hundreds = _____

3 hundreds is the same as 300.

So, 3 hundreds = 300.

hundreds	tens	ones
3	0	0

Try It • Fill in the place-value chart. Write each number.

1. | hundreds | tens | ones |
   |----------|------|------|
   | | | |

   2 tens = _____

2. | hundreds | tens | ones |
   |----------|------|------|
   | | | |

   5 hundreds = _____

3. | hundreds | tens | ones |
   |----------|------|------|
   | | | |

   6 hundreds = _____

4. | hundreds | tens | ones |
   |----------|------|------|
   | | | |

   6 tens = _____

5. | hundreds | tens | ones |
   |----------|------|------|
   | | | |

   4 tens = _____

6. | hundreds | tens | ones |
   |----------|------|------|
   | | | |

   9 hundreds = _____

Name_____

Fill in the place-value chart. Write the number of tens or hundreds.

7.
hundreds	tens	ones

_____ hundreds = 300

8.
hundreds	tens	ones

_____ tens = 80

9.
hundreds	tens	ones

_____ tens = 20

10.
hundreds	tens	ones

_____ hundreds = 700

11.
hundreds	tens	ones

_____ hundreds = 800

12.
hundreds	tens	ones

_____ tens = 70

Power Practice • **Write each number.**

13. 4 tens = _____

14. 2 hundreds = _____

15. 3 tens = _____

16. 1 hundred = _____

17. 6 hundreds = _____

18. 9 tens = _____

19. 8 tens = _____

20. 8 hundreds = _____

21. 5 tens = _____

22. 4 hundreds = _____

23. 7 hundreds = _____

24. 6 tens = _____

25. _____ tens = 50

26. _____ hundreds = 900

27. _____ hundreds = 400

28. _____ ten = 10

29. _____ tens = 80

30. _____ hundreds = 500

Ten Thousands, Thousands, and Hundreds

Learn

What Can I Do?
I want to write whole numbers for ten thousands, thousands, and hundreds.

Use a place-value chart.

Write the number.

4 ten thousands = _____

ten-thousands	thousands	,	hundreds	tens	ones
4	0		0	0	0

4 ten thousands is the same as 40,000.
↑

Always write a comma between the thousands and hundreds places.

So, 4 ten thousands = 40,000.

---

8 thousands = _____

ten-thousands	thousands	,	hundreds	tens	ones
	8		0	0	0

8 thousands is the same as 8,000.

So, 8 thousands = 8,000.

---

2 hundreds = _____

ten-thousands	thousands	,	hundreds	tens	ones
			2	0	0

2 hundreds is the same as 200.

So, 2 hundreds = 200.

Try It • **Fill in the place-value chart. Write each number.**

1.

ten-thousands	thousands	,	hundreds	tens	ones

   5 ten thousands = _____

2.

ten-thousands	thousands	,	hundreds	tens	ones

   6 thousands = _____

3.

ten-thousands	thousands	,	hundreds	tens	ones

   4 hundreds = _____

4.

ten-thousands	thousands	,	hundreds	tens	ones

   8 ten thousands = _____

Power Practice • **Write each number.**

5. 2 thousands = _____   **6.** 6 hundreds = _____

7. 3 ten thousands = _____   **8.** 1 ten thousand = _____

9. 5 thousands = _____   **10.** 7 hundreds = _____

11. 9 ten thousands = _____   **12.** 2 ten thousands = _____

13. 7 thousands = _____   **14.** 9 hundreds = _____

15. 8 hundreds = _____   **16.** 2 thousands = _____

17. 5 ten thousands = _____   **18.** 1 hundred = _____

Place Value

Learn

Activity
72

What Can I Do?

I want to find the number of tens.

Use place-value models.

How many tens are in 30?

Show 30 ones.	Make groups of 10.	Trade each 10 ones for 1 ten.

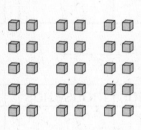 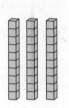

So, there are 3 tens in 30.

Try It • Complete. Use the place-value models to help.

1.

20 = _____ tens

2.

70 = _____ tens

Power Practice • Complete.

3. 60 = _____ tens

4. 50 = _____ tens

5. 80 = _____ tens

6. 10 = _____ ten

7. 90 = _____ tens

8. 40 = _____ tens

9. 70 = _____ tens

10. 20 = _____ tens

11. 30 = _____ tens

Name_____

Expanded Notation or Expanded Form **Learn**

What Can I Do?
I want to show the expanded form for a number.

Use a place-value chart.

thousands	hundreds	tens	ones
6	3	0	7

Write the value of each digit.

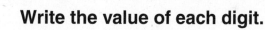

$6{,}307 = \quad 6{,}000 \quad + \quad 300 \quad + \; 0 \; + \; 7$
thousands   hundreds   tens   ones

Try It • Write each number in expanded notation.

1. $1{,}208 = $ _____ + _____ + _____ + _____
thousands   hundreds   tens   ones

2. $9{,}422 = $ _____ + _____ + _____ + _____
thousands   hundreds   tens   ones

3. $7{,}320 = $ _____ + 300 + 20 + _____

Power Practice • Write each number in expanded notation.

4. $8{,}437 = $ _____ + _____ + _____ + _____

5. $2{,}954 = $ _____ + _____ + _____ + _____

6. $6{,}015 = $ _____ + _____ + _____ + _____

Rename Tens and Ones

Learn

What Can I Do?
I want to rename tens and ones as ones.

Use place-value models.

Show 34.

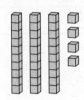

Trade one ten for 10 ones.

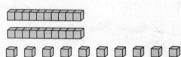

Now there are 2 tens 14 ones.

Try It
• Trade one ten for 10 ones. Use the place-value models to help.

1.

1 ten 6 ones = _____ tens _____ ones

2.

6 tens 3 ones = _____ tens _____ ones

Power Practice
• Write each missing number.

3. 2 tens 9 ones = _____ ones

4. 1 ten 1 one = _____ ones

5. 4 tens 2 ones = _____ ones

6. 3 tens 0 ones = _____ ones

7. 7 tens 7 ones = _____ ones

8. 5 tens 6 ones = _____ ones

9. 6 tens 5 ones = _____ ones

10. 9 tens 8 ones = _____ ones

Name_____

Place Value

What Can I Do?
I want to write numbers for place-value models.

Learn

Count tens and ones.

3 tens 4 ones

tens	ones
3	4

3 tens 4 ones = 34

Try It • **Write the tens and ones for each picture.**

1.

____ tens ____ ones

2.

____ ten ____ ones

3.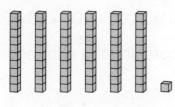

____ tens ____ one

4.

____ tens ____ ones

5.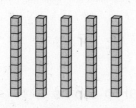

____ tens ____ ones

6.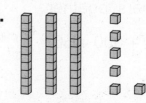

____ tens ____ ones

© Macmillan/McGraw-Hill

Equivalent Names

Learn

What Can I Do?
I get confused when I try to rename a number.

Use a place-value chart.

Is 5,428 equal to 5 thousands, 4 hundreds, 2 tens, and 8 ones? Write 5,428 in a place-value chart.

thousands	hundreds	tens	ones
5	4	2	8

Read the numbers and their place value.

5 thousands 4 hundreds 2 tens 8 ones

Yes, 5,428 is equal to 5 thousands, 4 hundreds, 2 tens, and 8 ones.

Is 5,428 equal to 54 hundreds, 2 tens, and 8 ones? Read the place-value chart.

Think: 5 thousands 4 hundreds is the same as 54 hundreds.

So 5,428 is also equal to 54 hundreds, 2 tens, and 8 ones.

Write a number in expanded notation or expanded form.

Write 9,366 in expanded notation.

First, write the thousands. 9,000
Write the hundreds. 300
Write the tens. 60
Write the ones. 6

Add the numbers together.

$9,366 = 9,000 + 300 + 60 + 6$

Is 5,612 equal to $5,000 + 100 + 60 + 2$?

To answer, combine the expanded number.

$$\begin{array}{r} 5,000 \\ 100 \\ 60 \\ +\quad 2 \\ \hline 5,162 \end{array}$$

5,162 is **not** equal to 5,612.

5,612 is equal to
$5,000 + 600 + 10 + 2$.

Name _____

 • **Use the place-value chart to help you answer each question.**

1. Is 6,938 equal to 6 thousands, 3 hundreds, 9 tens, and 8 ones?

thousands	hundreds	tens	ones

_____

Complete each expanded notation.

2. 1,502 = _____ + 500 + _____

3. 9,911 = 9,000 + _____ + _____ + _____

4. 8,067 = _____ + _____ + _____

5. 2,821 = _____ + _____ + _____ + _____

Power Practice • **Circle the numbers in each row that are equal.**

6. 668   6 hundreds 6 tens 8 ones   600 + 80 + 6

7. 7,283   7 thousands 2 tens 3 ones   7,000 + 200 + 80 + 3

8. 6,594   65 hundreds 9 tens 4 ones   6,000 + 5,000 + 9,000 + 4,000

Write the number in the box that is equal to each number below.

628	6,208	6,882

9. 600 + 20 + 8   **10.** 6,000 + 800 + 80 + 2   **11.** 62 hundreds 8 ones

_____   _____   _____

Counting Coins

Learn

What Can I Do?
I want to find the value of a set of coins.

You can skip count and count on to count coins.

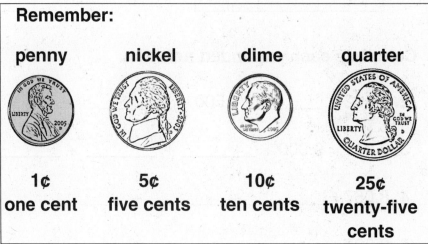

Remember:

penny	nickel	dime	quarter
1¢ one cent	5¢ five cents	10¢ ten cents	25¢ twenty-five cents

Find the total amount.

Start with the coins that have the greatest value.

Start at 25¢. Skip count by 5s and say, 25¢, 30¢, 35¢, 40¢.

Then count on and say, 41¢, 42¢, 43¢.

25¢,   30¢,   35¢,   40¢,   41¢,   42¢,   43¢

So, the total amount is 43¢.

Name _____

Try It • Skip count or count on to fill in the blanks. Then write each amount.

1.

_____¢ _____¢ _____¢ _____¢ _____¢

Total amount: _____¢

2.

_____¢ _____¢ _____¢ _____¢ _____¢ _____¢

Total amount: _____¢

3.

_____¢ _____¢ _____¢ _____¢ _____¢ _____¢

Total amount: _____¢

Power Practice • Write each amount.

4.

_____¢

5.

_____¢

6.

_____¢

7.

_____¢

8.

_____¢

© Macmillan/McGraw-Hill

123

Name_____

Time to the Hour, Half Hour, and Quarter Hour

Learn

Look at the hour hand and the minute hand.

The **hour hand** is the *short* hand.
The **minute hand** is the *long* hand.

What Can I Do?
I want to tell time on a clock.

Read:
five o'clock

Write:
5:00

Read:
ten-thirty

Write:
10:30

Read:
seven-fifteen

Write:
7:15

Try It • **Complete. Write each time.**

1.

The **hour hand** is on the _____.

The **minute hand** is on the _____.

The time is ___:___.

2.

The hour hand is on the _____.

The minute hand is on the _____.

The time is ___:___.

Name_____

Complete. Write each time.

3.

The hour hand is past the _____.

The minute hand is on the _____.

The time is ___:___.

4.

The hour hand is past the _____.

The minute hand is on the _____.

The time is ___:___.

Power Practice

Write each time.

5.

___:___

6.

___:___

7.

___:___

8.

___:___

Learn with Partners & Parents

How Long?

You need one set of alphabet cards, paper, and pencils.

• Each player marks a paper with 3 columns titled *15 Minutes, Half Hour,* and *Hour.*

• Shuffle the cards and place them facedown. One player turns over the top card and lets every player see the letter.

• All players have 5 minutes to think of as many activities as they can for each column. Each activity must start with the letter that was drawn. For example, for the letter G, the player might write "Go to the store" in the hour column.

• The player with the most activities wins 5 points.

Measuring Length

Learn

Use counting.

Line up the paper clips with the left end of the object.

What Can I Do?
I want to measure an object using paper clips.

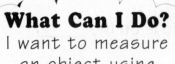

Add more paper clips until you reach the right end of the object.

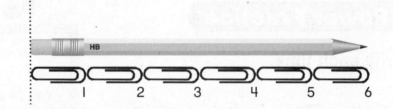

Count the paper clips you used.
This pencil is about 6 paper clips long.

Try It • **Use counting. How many paper clips long is each object?**

1.

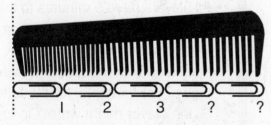

_____ paper clips

2.

_____ paper clips

3.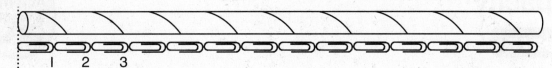

1 2 3

—— paper clips

Power Practice · How many paper clips long is each object?

4.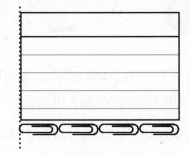

_____ paper clips

5.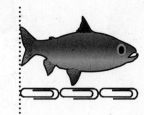

_____ paper clips

6.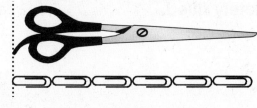

_____ paper clips

7.

_____ paper clips

8.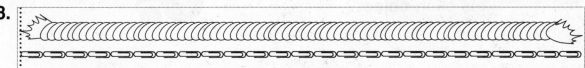

_____ paper clips

9.

_____ paper clips

10.

_____ paper clips

Capacity

Learn

What Can I Do?
I want to tell which object holds more liquid.

Use comparison.

Think about the size of each object in real life.

Which one is larger? The larger object will hold more liquid when completely filled.

The pool is larger than the glass in real life, so the pool has a greater capacity.

Try It • Use comparison. Underline the object that holds more liquid when completely filled.

1.

CIDER

1 Gallon

2.

Name_____

Power Practice • Underline the object that holds more liquid when completely filled.

3.

4.

5.

6.

7.

8.

9.

10.

Name _____

Classify Polygons

Learn

Count how many sides.
Count how many angles.

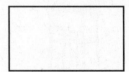

Each shape has 4 sides.
Each shape has 4 angles.

What Can I Do?
I want to tell what
a group of shapes
has in common.

Count how many sides.
Count how many angles.

Each shape has 3 sides.
Each shape has 3 angles.

Try It • Circle the shape that does *not* belong.

1.   2.

_____   _____

Name _____

3.

 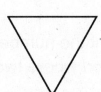 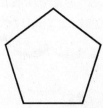

4.

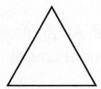

5.

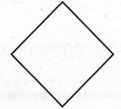 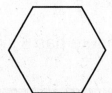 

6.

  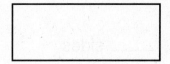

Identify Sides and Angles

Learn

Use counting.

Count the number of sides of the figure.
A side is a straight line segment.

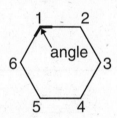

Count the number of angles. An angle is
formed where two line segments meet.

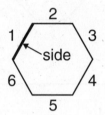

This figure has 6 sides and 6 angles.

What Can I Do?
I want to tell the
number of sides and
angles of a figure.

Try It • Continue numbering sides and angles.
Write the number of sides and angles for each figure.

1.

_____ sides

_____ angles

2.

_____ sides

_____ angles

Name_____

Power Practice • Write the number of sides and angles for each figure.

3.

_____ sides

_____ angles

4.

_____ sides

_____ angles

5.

_____ sides

_____ angles

6.

_____ sides

_____ angles

7.

_____ sides

_____ angles

8.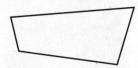

_____ sides

_____ angles

9.

_____ sides

_____ angles

10.

_____ sides

_____ angles

11.

_____ sides

_____ angles

12.

_____ sides

_____ angles

13.

_____ sides

_____ angles

14.

_____ sides

_____ angles

Name _____

Comparing Angles

Activity
83

Learn

What Can I Do?
I want to tell which of two angles is greater.

Look for the greater opening.

Look at the open end of the angles. Which has the greater opening between the lines of the angle?

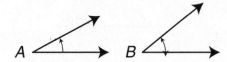

The angle with the greater opening between the lines is the greater angle.

Angle *B* has a greater opening, so angle *B* > angle *A*.

Try It • Circle the angle with the greater opening.

1.

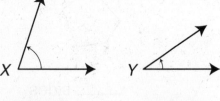

angle *X*   angle *Y*

2.

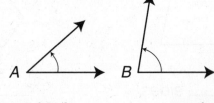

angle *A*   angle *B*

3.

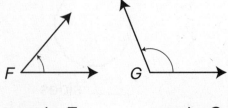

angle *F*   angle *G*

4.

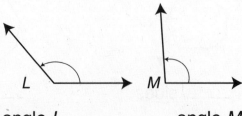

angle *L*   angle *M*

Compare each pair of angles. Circle the angle with the greater opening. Write > or <.

5.

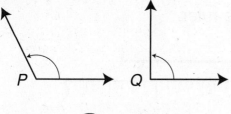

angle P ◯ angle Q

6.

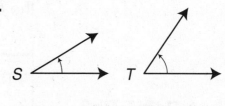

angle S ◯ angle T

Power Practice • **Compare each set of angles. Write > or <.**

7.

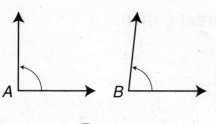

angle J ◯ angle K

8.

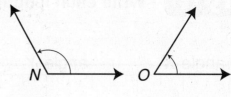

angle C ◯ angle D

9.

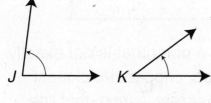

angle A ◯ angle B

10.

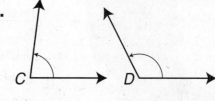

angle N ◯ angle O

11.

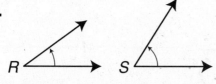

angle R ◯ angle S

12.

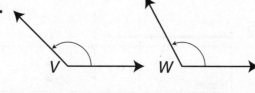

angle V ◯ angle W

Measuring Line Segments

Learn

Use a ruler.

Line up the left end of the line segment with the edge of the ruler.

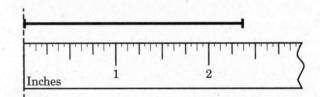

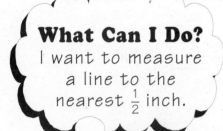

What Can I Do?
I want to measure a line to the nearest $\frac{1}{2}$ inch.

Read the ruler where the line segment ends at the right.

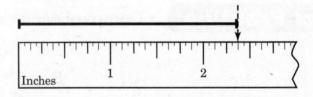

If the line ends at a point that is not exactly a whole or half inch, choose the closest measure. To the nearest $\frac{1}{2}$ inch, this line is about $2\frac{1}{2}$ inches long.

Try It • Write each length to the nearest $\frac{1}{2}$ inch.

1.

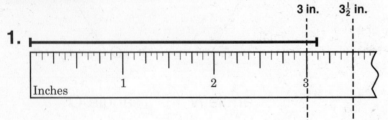

_____

2.

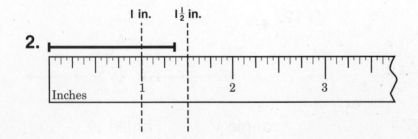

_____

Power Practice • Use an inch ruler. Measure the length of each line segment to the nearest $\frac{1}{2}$ inch.

3. |——————————————| _____

4. |————————————————————| _____

5. |————————————————————| _____

6. |——————————————| _____

7. |————————| _____

8. |————————————| _____

9. |——————————————————| _____

10. |——————————————| _____

11. |——————————| _____

Identify Equal Parts

Learn

What Can I Do?

How can I tell if the parts are equal?

Compare sizes of the parts.

Which circle shows equal parts?

Look at the first circle. The three parts do not have the same shape and size. They are not equal.

Look at the second circle. The four parts have the same shape and size. They are equal.

The second circle shows equal parts.

Use a mental picture.

Does this square show equal parts?

Think about cutting the square along the lines. You can cut it into these four parts.

Imagine stacking the parts. You can see they have the same size and shape. These four parts are equal.

So, the square shows equal parts.

Name _____

Tell whether or not each rectangle shows equal parts.
• Write *equal* or *not equal*. Use the drawings to help you compare parts.

1.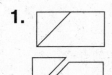

_____

2.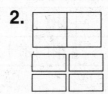

_____

3.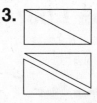

_____

Power Practice • Tell whether or not each shape shows equal parts. Write *equal* or *not equal*.

4.

_____

5.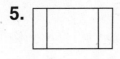

_____

6.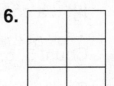

_____

7.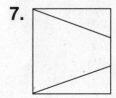

_____

8.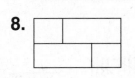

_____

9.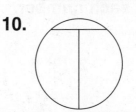

_____

10.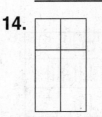

_____

11.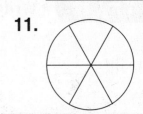

_____

12.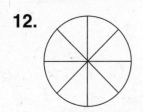

_____

13.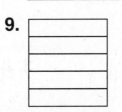

_____

14.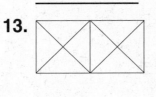

_____

15.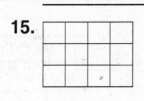

_____

16.

_____

17.

_____

18.

_____

19.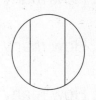

_____

Name_____

Tally Marks and Charts

Learn

What Can I Do?
I want to read a tally chart.

Count the tallies.

Fruit in a Box	
Oranges	卌 |||
Pears	卌 卌	

How many oranges are in the box?

Count the tally marks for oranges.

| = a count of 1

卌 = a count of 5

Count 5, 6, 7, 8.

So, there are 8 oranges in the box.

Try It • **Write each number.**

1. |||| _____

2. 卌 || _____

3. 卌 卌 卌 _____

Power Practice • **Use the tally chart.**

Mr. Quintero's Class	
boys	卌 卌 ||||
girls	卌 卌

4. How many boys are in the class? _____

5. How many girls are in the class? _____

6. How many total students are in the class? _____

Name_____

Read Pictographs

Learn

What Can I Do?
I want to compare information in a pictograph.

Use the key and count the symbols.

Books Read	
Jessie	
Eric	
Anna	

Key: = 3 books

Who read the most books?

Use the key to find how many books each student read.

Jessie: 3 + 3 + 3 = 9 books

Eric: 3 + 3 = 6 books

Anna: 3 + 3 + 3 + 3 + 3 = 15 books

15 books > 9 books > 6 books

So, Anna read the most books.

Try It • **Use the pictograph above.**

1. Who read the least number of books? _____

2. How many more books did Anna read than Jessie? _____

3. How many books did Eric and Anna read? _____

4. How many books did the students read in all? _____

Name_____

Read Bar Graphs

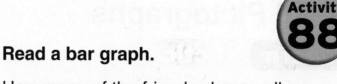

Learn

What Can I Do?
I want to compare information.

Read a bar graph.

How many of the friends chose yellow as their favorite color?

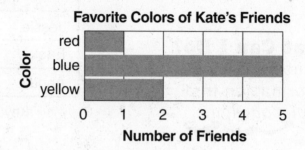

Favorite Colors of Kate's Friends

Look at the bar for yellow.
The bar ends at 2.
So, 2 friends chose yellow.

Try It • Use the bar graph above.

1. How many friends chose red? _____

2. How many friends chose blue? _____

3. Does the graph show that the friends liked

   blue or yellow better? _____

4. How many more friends chose blue than

   chose yellow? _____

5. Which color do the friends like least? _____

6. How many more friends chose yellow than red? _____

Name_____

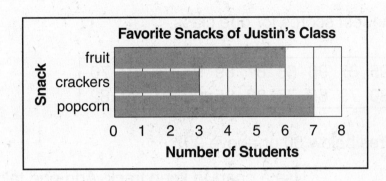

7. What is the title of the bar graph? _____

_____

8. Which snack is the class favorite? _____

9. How many students chose fruit as their

favorite snack?_____

10. How many more students like popcorn better than

crackers? _____

11. How many students voted in all? _____

12. Which was the least favorite snack? _____

13. How many more students voted for
popcorn over fruit? _____

Frequency Tables

Learn

Make a Tally Chart

This box shows the test scores for one class.

87	76	91	92	95	87	96	68	87	89	97	76	69	70
82	93	65	91	80	79	86	75	82	95	90	91	89	82

Are more test scores below 80 or above 90?

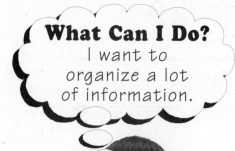

What Can I Do?
I want to organize a lot of information.

Use a chart to keep track. Add one tally mark for each test score. Cross off the scores you have tallied.

Below 80	80 to 90	Above 90
卌 |||	卌 卌		卌 ||||

Count and compare to answer the question. There are 8 scores below 80 and 9 scores above 90.

There are more test scores above 90.

Try It . Complete the tally chart to count the marbles. The white marbles are already tallied and crossed off.

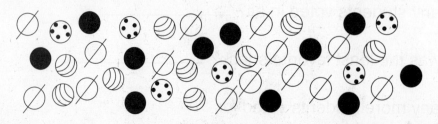

White	Black	Dots	Stripes
卌 卌 ||||	**1.**	**2.**	**3.**

Name _____

Use the tally chart to answer these questions.

4. How many white marbles are there? _____

5. How many black marbles are there? _____

6. How many marbles with dots are there? _____

7. How many marbles with stripes are there? _____

8. Arrange the marble patterns in order from fewest to most.

_____ _____ _____ _____

Power Practice • **Complete the tally chart. Then answer the questions.**

This box shows the average temperatures for one month.

72° 71° 68° 75° 65° 68° 72° 77° 78° 80° 82° 81° 81° 79° 78°
75° 72° 69° 68° 70° 71° 74° 76° 80° 81° 82° 71° 69° 74° 73°

60° to 69°	70° to 79°	80° to 89°
9. ‖‖ ‖	**10.** ‖‖ ‖‖ ‖‖ ‖‖ ‖	**11.** ‖‖ ‖‖

12. For how many days was the average temperature between 60° and 69°? _____

13. For how many days was the average temperature between 70° and 79°? _____

14. For how many days was the average temperature between 80° and 89°? _____